THE ENCYCLOPEDIA OF
REPTILES
AMPHIBIANS & INVERTEBRATES

A Complete Visual Guide

THE ENCYCLOPEDIA OF

REPTILES

AMPHIBIANS & INVERTEBRATES

CHIEF CONSULTANTS

Dr Noel Tait
Consultant in Invertebrate Biology
Sydney, Australia

Dr Richard C. Vogt
Curator of Herpetology and Professor
National Institute for Amazon Research
Manaus, Amazonas, Brazil

CONSULTANT

Dr Hugh Dingle
Professor Emeritus
University of California, Davis, USA

FOG CITY PRESS

A Complete Visual Guide

Conceived and produced by Weldon Owen Pty Ltd
59 Victoria Street, McMahons Point
Sydney NSW 2060, Australia
Copyright © 2006 Weldon Owen Inc.

Chief Executive Officer John Owen
President Terry Newell
Publisher Sheena Coupe
Creative Director Sue Burk
Vice President International Sales Stuart Laurence
Administrator International Sales Kristine Ravn

Project Editors Stephanie Goodwin, Angela Handley, Jennifer Losco
Designers Clare Forte, Heather Menzies, Jacqueline Richards,
Karen Robertson
Cover Design Heather Menzies, Juliana Titin
Picture Research Annette Crueger, Jennifer Losco, Heather Menzies
Text Jenni Bruce, Karen McGhee, Richard C. Vogt

Species Gallery Illustrations MagicGroup s.r.o. (Czech Republic) —
www.magicgroup.cz
Feature Illustrations Guy Troughton
Maps Andrew Davies Creative Communication, Map Illustrations
Information Graphics Andrew Davies Creative Communication
Index Sarah Plant/Puddingburn Publishing Services

Editorial Coordinators Helen Flint, Irene Mickaiel
Production Director Chris Hemesath
Production Coordinator Charles Mathews

ISBN-13: 978-1-74089-353-4
ISBN-10: 1-74089-353-0

Color reproduction by Chroma Graphics (Overseas) Pte Ltd
Printed by SNP Leefung Printers Ltd.
Printed in China

A Weldon Owen Production

10 9 8 7 6 5 4 3

CONTENTS

FOREWORD

This lavishly illustrated book is an introduction to the natural history of three groups of animals: reptiles, amphibians, and invertebrates. The diversity of living reptiles and amphibians is amazing—there are more than 8,000 species of reptiles and 5,400 species of amphibians. Despite the constraints of their limited body forms, they have a remarkable array of behavioral patterns and survival strategies. Frogs, for example, exploit two very different niches—as tadpoles they are herbivores, as adults they become predators. The 3,000 species of snakes range from tiny burrowing blind snakes to huge constrictors more than 33 feet (10 m) long. Their habitats encompass the subterranean, the arboreal, and the aquatic. The ways in which reptiles and amphibians move and reproduce are equally varied—their courtship, parental care, territorial defense, and migration can rival those of mammals and birds.

Invertebrates, with more than 1.3 million species, constitute over 95 percent of all known animal species, and countless more are yet to be discovered. They are unified and distinguished by what they lack: they have no backbone, no bones, and no cartilage. In form, they are as diverse as brightly colored butterflies, venomous spiders, floating jellyfishes, porous sponges, and a multitude of bugs and beetles. They are at home in the air, on land, and in the seas. They swim, burrow, creep, run, and fly. Yet, despite their impressive numbers, the behavior and ecology of most of these animals have never been studied. In this volume we provide an overview of representative species in each major group.

Habitat destruction, environmental degradation, pollution, illegal collecting, and the introduction of alien species threaten the existence of many reptiles, amphibians, and invertebrates. If we are to ensure the survival of these creatures, we must control the impact of our own species on the environments in which they live. At the present time 80 percent of the turtles and 30 percent of the known species of frogs and toads are listed in the IUCN Red List of Threatened Species. If nothing is done, their status will have to be revised, as they slip from rare and threatened to endangered or extinct in the ponds they once inhabited. Without international cooperation among governments and the public will to preserve creatures such as these, life on our planet will become less diverse. Bleak will be the spring when there are no frogs singing.

DR RICHARD C. VOGT
Curator of Herpetology and Professor,
National Institute for Amazon Research, Manaus, Amazonas, Brazil

HOW TO USE THIS BOOK

This book is divided into three taxonomic parts, namely Reptiles, Amphibians, and Invertebrates. Each part begins with an overview of the characteristics of the group, its evolution, classification, biology, behavior, habitats, adaptations, and conservation status. Then follow the species sections, which are broken down into chapters devoted to particular subgroups. The structure of these sections reflects the taxonomy of each of the featured groups. The section on Invertebrates, for example, profiles a larger taxonomic group than Reptiles or Amphibians to ensure that the diversity of Invertebrates is adequately conveyed. The book concludes with a comprehensive glossary and index.

HABITAT ICONS

The 19 habitat icons below indicate at a glance the various habitats in which a species or group can be found. It should be noted that the icons are used in the same order throughout the book, rather than in their order of significance. More detailed profiles of these habitats can be found at the beginning of each taxonomic part.

- Tropical rain forest
- Tropical monsoon forest
- Temperate forest
- Coniferous forest
- Moorlands and heath
- Open habitat, including savanna, grassland, fields, pampas, and steppes
- Desert and semidesert
- Mountains and highlands
- Tundra
- Polar regions
- Seas and oceans
- Coral reefs
- Mangrove swamps
- Coastal areas, including beaches, oceanic cliffs, sand dunes, intertidal rock pools, and/or coastal waters (as applicable to group)
- Rivers and streams, including river and stream banks
- Wetlands, including swamps, marshes, fens, floodplains, deltas, and bogs
- Lakes and ponds
- Urban areas
- Parasitic

Group global distribution
A map shows the worldwide distribution of the group being profiled, followed by text that discusses the distribution of particular groups in more detail.

Section and chapter
This indicates the group of animals under discussion.

TORTOISES AND TURTLES

Classification box
This shows the taxonomic groups to which the animals belong in the animal kingdom.

CLASS	Reptilia
ORDER	Testudines
FAMILIES	14
GENERA	99
SPECIES	293

Turtles and tortoises are the only vertebrates that house the pelvic and pectoral girdles within a shell made of ribs fused with bone. The first fossils to show this trait appeared 220 million years ago in the Triassic period, when dinosaurs roamed the earth. The shell design has since undergone various modifications. The African pancake tortoise has a flexible flat shell allowing it to wedge into crevices; it then inflates, after which it is impossible to pull out. Softshell turtles lack a hard shell; instead, the bones are covered with a smooth leathery shell, giving them more speed. There is still controversy as to whether turtles are derived from a different lineage to other reptiles.

Distribution Turtles are found on all continents except Antarctica, and in all oceans. 241 species of turtles have adapted to freshwater rivers, lakes, and ponds; 45 tortoises are terrestrial; only seven species live in the oceans.

Lavish photographs
Taken by leading wildlife photographers, these portray the habits and habitats of different species.

Saddleback giant The Galápagos tortoise (above) has a saddleback carapace. This condition is more often seen in adult male tortoises, due to enhanced mating success, from populations on the drier and more barren islands of the Galápagos.

Turtle skeleton A turtle's shell has an outer layer of epidermal scutes (usually 38 on the carapace and 16 on the plastron). Under these, a shell of fused ribs (the plastron) supports the body. The vertebrae are joined to the inside of the carapace.

Detailed diagram
Where appropriate, diagrams are included to illustrate points about anatomy or adaptation.

retracting neck

claws   scute   carapace   plastron

Baby leatherback Leatherback turtles lay up to six nests of up to 200 eggs a year for decades. This hatchling has passed the first hurdle: 2 months incubating in the sand with predators digging around it. It now has to face the many threats in the sea.

EVOLUTION SHELLED OUT
In addition to the shell, turtles and tortoises have evolved many unique features. Turtle muscles are able to withstand high levels of lactic acid, so they do not tire after swimming rapidly. They also fill their large urinary bladders with water for ballast to maintain buoyancy.

Turtles and tortoises occupy niches as predators, grazers, croppers, and scavengers. Some have gut flora to digest plant cells; others are seed dispersers. Wood turtles stomp on the ground with their front feet, then eat the earthworms that come out of the ground.

Some sea turtles and freshwater turtles nest within a few days in tremendous numbers on the same nesting beach. These mass nestings, known as arribadas, evolved to swamp local predators—it would be impossible for them to eat all of the eggs or kill all of the females. The success of these adaptations has helped turtles to survive over millions of years; now, as a result of human intervention, two-thirds of all turtle species are being carefully monitored by the IUCN.

Swimming sea turtle The forelimbs of sea turtles have been modified into flipper-shaped paddles that move synchronously, resembling aquatic flying rather than swimming. Sea turtles are so adept in the water that they rarely leave it except to nest. Freshwater turtles swim using all four limbs in turn.

CONSERVATION INFORMATION

Within the fact files, each profiled species is allocated a conservation status, using IUCN and other conservation categories, as follows:

✝ Indicates that a species is listed under the following categories:
Extinct (IUCN) It is beyond reasonable doubt that the last individual of a given species has died.
Extinct in the wild (IUCN) Only known to survive in captivity or as a naturalized population outside its former range.

⚡ Indicates that a species is listed under the following categories:
Critically endangered (IUCN) Facing a very high and immediate risk of extinction in the wild.
Endangered (IUCN) Facing a very high risk of extinction in the wild in the near future.

The following categories are also used:
Vulnerable (IUCN) Facing a high risk of extinction in the wild in the foreseeable future.
Near threatened (IUCN) Likely to qualify for one of the above categories in the near future.
Conservation dependent (IUCN) Dependent upon species- or habitat-specific conservation programs to keep it out of one of the above threatened categories.

Data deficient (IUCN) Inadequate information available to make an assessment of its risk.
Not known Not evaluated or little studied.
Common Widespread and abundant.
Locally common Widespread and abundant within its range.
Uncommon Occurs widely in low numbers in preferred habitat(s).
Rare Occurs in only some of preferred habitat or in small restricted areas.

Conservation watch box
This provides information about the status of a particular species or group of animals. These boxes may also outline factors that threaten the animal's survival.

⚡ CONSERVATION WATCH

Arachnid alert The conservation movement has paid little attention to arachnids. Only 18 species have been assessed by the IUCN, but all of these are on the Red List. Further research is needed, but arachnid diversity is no doubt threatened by habitat loss, pollution, pesticide use, and invasive exotic species.

Snippets
These highlight distinguishing aspects or characteristics of the species, such as color variations, behavior, habitat, size, and anatomical features.

Name labels
Labels provide the common and scientific names, as well as the species' family, order, or class, where appropriate.

TORTOISES AND TURTLES **REPTILES**   25

Matamata characterized its long snorkel nose, which allows it to lie in shallow water and reach the surface to respire without frightening its prey

Matamata
Chelus fimbriatus

Twist-necked turtle
Platemys platycephala

Common snake-necked turtle
Chelodina longicollis

Twist-necked turtle is the only species of turtle known to have triploid chromosomes in some populations

Helmeted turtle
Pelomedusa subrufa

Giant Amazon river turtle
Podocnemis expansa

Chelidae Fitzroy turtle
Rheodytes leukops

Serrated turtle
Pelusios sinuatus

Hilaire's toadhead turtle
Phrynops hilarii

Victoria short-necked turtle
Emydura victoriae

FACT FILE

Matamata The matamata, relying on its camouflage, lies waiting for small fishes to pass. With lightning speed, it opens its mouth and thrusts out its neck simultaneously, creating a sucking force that pulls fishes into its mouth.

Up to 18 in (46 cm)
Aquatic
♀♂ Unknown
12–28
Common

Amazonia (N. South America)

Giant Amazon river turtle Selection for fast incubation was influenced by the unpredictability of rising river levels. The eggs hatch in 45 days, and nest temperatures often reach 104°F (40°C), the highest known for any turtle.

Up to 42 in (107 cm)
Aquatic
♀♂ TSD
60–150
Conserv. dependent

Amazon & Orinoco basins (N. South America)

BEGINNING OF LIFE
Sea turtles lay their eggs on the same beaches that their ancestors have used for millennia. Once the nest has been covered with sand, the eggs are left to chance to go undetected by predators. Hatchlings must race to the sea, running the risk of predation by hungry mammals and birds, to the dubious safety of waters filled with even more predators. Survival rates for some species may be as low as 1 in 50,000.

Hatchling flatback turtles
Hatchling turtles are on their own.
Their only chance of survival is to
scamper to the sea in a large group.

Fact file
This profiles several of the illustrated species or groups, with information about their characteristics and behavior.

Distribution map
This shows the species' or group's range (and former range, where appropriate). A world or regional map is used according to distribution.

Habitat icons
The icons indicate the various habitats in which the profiled animal(s) can be found. A full list is on the opposite page.

Panel feature box
Illustrations and text provide information about an interesting aspect of a species or group of species.

FACT FILE STATISTICS
Important or interesting facts about a species or group use the following icons and information. All measurements are maximums.

Length
⚡ Reptiles: snakes and lizards: snout to vent; other reptiles: head and body including tail
🐢 Turtles: length of carapace
🦎 Amphibians: head and body, including tail

Weight/Mass
⚖ Body weight

Reproduction: Reptiles
● Number of eggs

Habit: Reptiles and Amphibians
◯ Terrestrial
◯ Aquatic
◯ Burrowing
◯ Arboreal
◯ Varies between the above

Breeding season: Amphibians
⇗ When breeding occurs, e.g. spring

Breeding: Reptiles
◢ Viviparous (producing live young)
◯ Oviparous (producing eggs that develop outside the maternal body)
◉ Ovoviviparous (producing eggs that develop within the maternal body)

Sex: Reptiles
♀♂ Indicates whether a species is temperature sex determined (TSD) or genetically sex determined (GSD);

Number of genera and species: Reptiles and Invertebrates
The number of genera and species in the relevant taxonomic group

REPTILES

REPTILES

PHYLUM	Chordata
CLASS	Reptilia
ORDERS	4
FAMILIES	60
GENERA	1,012
SPECIES	8,163

Modern reptiles are not simply relics from the age of the dinosaurs, now dwarfed in the shadow of their evolutionary heyday. Reptiles, like all other major animal groups, are continuously adapting to their environments. Today's species are the product of 300 million years of evolution that began with some of the earliest creatures to walk on land. They gave rise to two evolutionary lineages: one leading to mammals (Synapsida) and the other to birds and reptiles (Diapsida). Turtles were once thought to belong to the Anapsida, a sister group to the Diapsida. New biochemical studies suggest, however, that they are diapsids, and that the anapsids evolved later.

MODERN DIVERSITY

The diapsid reptiles diverged during the Triassic (248–206 million years ago) into two main groups: the Lepidosaura (scaly reptiles, such as lizards, snakes, amphisbaenians, and tuataras); and the Archosauria (ruling reptiles, including crocodiles, pterosaurs, dinosaurs, and ancestral birds). Turtles appear in the fossil record from 210 million years ago.

There were once as many as 16 major reptile orders; now there are just four. Squamata—the snakes, lizards, and worm lizards—is by far the most diverse and widespread of the modern groups. It is also the group that displays the widest range of body size and form, from the largest lizard—Indonesia's Komodo dragon, up to 10 feet (3 m) long, to tiny geckos no longer than an inch (2.5 cm). Crocodilia includes the crocodiles, alligators, and gharials, all of which have protective bony plates in their skin, short limbs, skulls with long snouts, and long tails with deep sides adapted for swimming. Testudines contains the tortoises and turtles, most of which live in freshwater or terrestrial habitats. Seven species live in marine habitats and some tortoises exist in desert regions. Order Rhynchocephalia contains just two species of tuatara, both of which occur only on islands off New Zealand.

Reptiles, like amphibians and fishes, are ectothermic—they have a limited capability to generate their own body heat internally through metabolic activity. Instead, they are dependent on warmth from the external environment. Sea turtles, particularly the giant leatherback turtle that ventures into the Arctic Sea, can raise their body temperature above that of the water through their metabolic activity when swimming. Unlike mammals, reptiles are not able to control their internal temperature by sweating. To avoid excessive daytime heat, many desert species of snakes and lizards are nocturnal.

Lizard life Madagascar's panther chameleon relies on acute vision and lightning-sharp reflexes to capture prey—mostly insects, but also other reptiles and small birds. To heat their bodies, chameleons can darken their skin color to better absorb and retain the Sun's warmth.

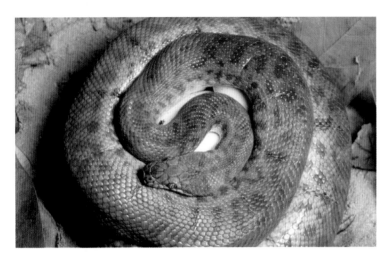

LAND INVADERS

Several key physiological developments freed reptiles from their aquatic beginnings. The evolution of the cleidoic—or waterproof—egg was pivotal, not only for reptiles but for vertebrates in general. A closed-system egg, in which water, nutrients, and waste are stored until hatching, allowed reptiles to move away from water to reproduce. Still, the eggs of some modern species must be buried in a moist place to survive. Other species have developed thick shells to avoid dehydration. Although all turtles and crocodiles lay their eggs,

Devoted parent The mothers of many snake species stay with or near their eggs to deter predators. Most female pythons, including Australia's children's python, also coil their bodies around their brood, generating warmth by muscle twitching to hasten development of the embryos within the eggs. During the entire incubation time, which may take months, the female remains with her eggs and does not feed.

Misplaced survivor The Seychelles giant tortoise was believed extinct for at least 120 years until scientists rediscovered it in the late 1990s. Individuals from this species, including museum specimens and animals in zoos, were previously thought to have belonged to another giant tortoise species. Modern DNA analysis was needed to crack this case of mistaken identity.

Crocodile call Reptiles produce eggs within which the embryo develops and hatches (or is born, in the case of live-bearing species). A series of fluid-filled sacs cushion the developing embryo within a calcareous shell that is permeable to gases, such as oxygen and carbon dioxide, but which restricts water loss. While still in their eggs in an underground nest, Nile crocodiles call to their mothers when they are ready to hatch.

some snakes and lizards retain theirs internally to give birth to live young. Other snakes and lizards are viviparous—they nurture their developing embryos through blood vessels connected to the mother.

Impermeable skin gave reptiles the chance to live permanently out of water without dehydrating. Salt glands on the side of the nose of some turtles, snakes, and lizards also help to reduce water loss. These excrete unwanted salts to reduce the amount of water required in the urine. Snakes and lizards excrete urine as a near-solid waste, composed mainly of uric acid crystals. This is another key adaptation for water conservation.

Internal fertilization has also helped free reptiles from an aquatic life. Females have a combined urinogenital opening. In tuataras, males also have a similar vent that they bring up against that of the female to transfer sperm in a "cloacal kiss." Male crocodiles and turtles have a penis, while lizards and snakes have two functional hemipenes. This is somewhat like having two penises, although they use only one at a time. Reptiles such as snakes and lizards can remain bound together in copulation for hours. The intricate hemipenes are valuable identification structures in the taxonomy of snakes.

Skin replacement Most vertebrates lose skin cells continuously but snakes shed, or slough, their entire outer layer all at once at various times throughout the year. Snakes are particularly vulnerable to predators until their new skin layer, which is secreted beneath the old one, fully hardens. They will even shed their translucent eye caps. Timing is related to both internal and environmental cues.

REPTILES THROUGH THE AGES

The ancestral reptile group, the Captorhinomorpha, which gave rise to all reptiles, had probably appeared by about 315 million years ago. This group of rather small and agile lizard-like animals is known from fossils found in ancient tree stumps from the late Carboniferous, as well as in subsequent Permian sediments. These ancient predators did not have the powerful snapping bite of the early amphibians from which they probably arose. Instead, their crunching bite was better suited to deal with the chitinous armor of their insect prey. The Archosauromorpha—the ruling reptiles from which dinosaurs and crocodiles ultimately arose—was, and remains, the most diverse reptile group ever. Early representatives were the rhyncosaurs—herbivores which, along with synapsids (mammal-like reptiles), were the dominant land animals for about 60 million years until the rise of the dinosaurs. They did not take to the air until the late Permian, when *Coelurosauravus*, with a 12-inch (30-cm) wing span, took flight.

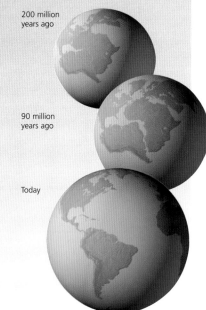

CONTINENTAL DRIFT

Extensive geological, paleontological, and biological evidence suggests ancient connections between continents and indicates that these land masses are still drifting inches apart annually. It is thought that about 300 million years ago, all today's continents were joined in one large supercontinent known as Pangea. This huge land mass began separating about 200 million years ago to create two great continents. Biological similarities between past species preserved in the fossil record and present species support evidence that Australia, India, Africa, South America, and Antarctica were once part of a southern supercontinent known as Gondwana. Similarly, Asia, North America, and Europe were once joined in a northern land mass, known as Laurasia.

200 million years ago

90 million years ago

Today

Pteranodon, *a pterosaur from the late Cretaceous, fed on fish like a pelican.*

Coelurosauravus, *from the Permian, could glide from tree to tree like a flying lizard today.*

Pachyachis, *from the Cretaceous, may be related to the ancestor of modern snakes.*

Stegosaurus, *from the Jurassic, was a dinosaur that ate plants.*

Dimetrodon, *from the Permian, was related to the ancestors of mammals.*

Hylonomus, *from the Carboniferous, is known only from fossils found trapped in fossilized tree trunks.*

Proganochelys, *from the Triassic, had much in common with living tortoises.*

Planocephalosaurus

Deinosuchus, *from the Cretaceous, could be the largest crocodile ever to have lived.*

Archelon

Ichthyosaurus, *from the Jurassic, was streamlined and ate fish like a modern dolphin.*

Early reptiles
Reptiles were at their most diverse during the Cretaceous, 165–144 million years ago.

Elasmosaurus, *from the Cretaceous, had the longest neck of any marine reptile.*

DINOSAURS RULE

The earliest dinosaurs appeared around the same time as the lineage that led to modern reptiles. They were small, bipedal, and carnivorous but the group diversified quickly. By the end of the Triassic, 206 million years ago, many herbivorous forms had appeared, including some that had begun approaching the massive sizes for which dinosaurs are renowned. The radiation of dinosaurs across Earth's terrestrial habitats coincided with the appearance and global spread of coniferous trees, the main source of food for the largest of these creatures.

Dinosaurs dominated the planet for 150 million years, reaching their peak diversity during the Jurassic. The last dinosaurs disappeared some 65 million years ago as part of the mass extinction at the end of the Cretaceous. Thought to have been caused by a catastrophic event, such as a meteor hitting Earth, this extinction also saw the demise of almost all other large reptiles. Two important exceptions were turtles and crocodiles. Lower temperatures may have exterminated the dinosaurs if they had temperature-controlled sex determination. Crocodiles and turtles may have survived as they produce females at both low and high temperatures, and males at medium temperatures.

CLASSIFICATION

As well as having discovered, described, and given names to some 1.7 million modern species of animals, biologists include extinct species in their classification system. This is particularly significant for reptiles because current reptilian diversity is a mere shadow of what it has been during Earth's history. The classification process does two things: it provides a unique name for each animal, both extinct and living; and it sorts them into a hierarchy of increasingly inclusive groups, known as taxa, based on evolutionary relationships. In this way, all animals can be unequivocally recognized and associated with other species having a common ancestry. Much of the new taxonomy relies on biochemical studies of DNA to determine common ancestry and species divergence.

Naming rights Biologists use a system known as Linnaean classification to sort and organize living organisms. Its principal feature is that it assigns a unique two-part name to every organism, such as *Crocodylus intermedius*. The first part indicates the genus to which an organism belongs. The second part, combined with the first, is the species. Only one organism within any genus will ever be assigned this name.

Living fossils Two species of tuatara, *Sphenodon punctatus* and *S. guntheri*, are the only survivors of a large reptile group that was widespread more than 225 million years ago. Fossil evidence reveals the relict species, which are now confined to small islands off New Zealand, have changed little since their evolution. Tuataras were once threatened but now, through strict conservation measures, more than 60,000 thrive on 30 islands.

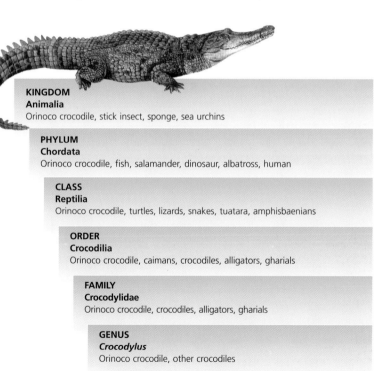

KINGDOM
Animalia
Orinoco crocodile, stick insect, sponge, sea urchins

PHYLUM
Chordata
Orinoco crocodile, fish, salamander, dinosaur, albatross, human

CLASS
Reptilia
Orinoco crocodile, turtles, lizards, snakes, tuatara, amphisbaenians

ORDER
Crocodilia
Orinoco crocodile, caimans, crocodiles, alligators, gharials

FAMILY
Crocodylidae
Orinoco crocodile, crocodiles, alligators, gharials

GENUS
Crocodylus
Orinoco crocodile, other crocodiles

SPECIES
Crocodylus intermedius
Orinoco crocodile

GROWING GROUP

So far, more than 8,000 reptile species have been described. Although some of the largest and most spectacular—such as the Komodo dragon, leatherback turtle, and saltwater crocodile—are very distinctive, many closely related forms are characterized by only subtle differences. Sometimes, such intangible areas as vocalizations and behavior can yield features of value in classifying reptiles. Internal attributes, including aspects of the skeleton and even tissues and organs, are also often used to differentiate between groups. Most often, though, attributes involving external appearance and structure are the keys to classifying reptiles. These include shape, size, body proportions, and coloration. For example, differences in the number, shape, and structure of scales can be of great significance in snake and lizard identification and classification.

Because many modern reptiles are small and secretive, occur only across a localized range, or inhabit unexplored regions, as many as 25 new species are still being discovered and described each year. Most of these new species are from the vast, uncharted regions of the Amazon rain forest.

REPTILES

Class Reptilia

Order Testudines
Tortoises and turtles

Order Crocodilia
Crocodilians

Order Rhyncocephalia
Tuatara

Order Squamata
Lizards and snakes

Suborder Amphisbaenia
Worm lizards

Order Testudines, page 24

BIOLOGY AND BEHAVIOR

Because reptiles have internal fertilization, species recognition is vital. In order to get together to mate, individuals need to be able to communicate clearly with others of their own kind. Some reptilian communication is visual, as occurs with displaying iguanid lizards. Most snakes employ a form of olfactory communication, which includes the use of chemical substances called pheromones. Crocodiles, alligators, and some lizards use calls, grunts, and other vocalizations to communicate with prospective mates. Signals provide information, not only for species identity, but also about the gender and reproductive fitness of individuals. The loudness and deepness of the crocodile's bellow is an indicator of its size and prowess.

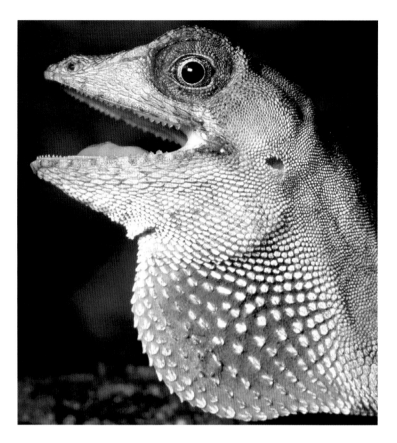

TERRITORIALITY

Most male lizards both advertise and defend their territory with ritualized displays. Among the Iguanidae and Agamidae, this posturing emphasizes body coloration and patterns. Displays can be reinforced by "push-ups," head-bobbing, or other movements. Territoriality is uncommon in snakes. However some, such as the vipers and pit vipers, have elaborate male combat rituals that may establish reproductive rights. Sparring male rattlesnakes, for example, raise their heads and bodies high, and twist against opponents, trying to topple them. Some male tortoises butt shells in strength tests to establish reproductive superiority. Larger aquatic turtles maintain their preferred basking positions on logs by aggressive behavior.

COURTSHIP

In snake courtship, the male usually crawls repeatedly over the female to orient their heads in the same position, while also aligning his tail with hers. Some males hold females in place using a biting grip to the head or neck. Sometimes male lizards do the same, while bringing their tails into a mating position. Many turtles have well-defined rituals. Male false map turtles, for example, court females by vibrating the sides of their faces with long fingernails. A male identifies a female by head markings and then convinces her that he is the correct species by the speed of the vibrating and the number of vibrations per second. The gopher turtle circles his mate on land, sometimes butting her shell to induce passivity so he can mount her.

Colorful display Chameleons (below) are renowned for their ability to rapidly change their skin color, a skill used more in communication than camouflage. Color change can convey emotion and sexual status to prospective mates and is also used by males in defending territories. Sexual excitement can cause an explosion of color.

Ready to mate New World anole lizards (above) are noted for displays of their colorful, sail-like dewlaps. Although both sexes have dewlaps, those of the males are usually bigger and more brightly colored, and are used to advertise territory ownership. Mature males also use a back crest in breeding and territorial displays.

Mating ritual A male adder of the species *Vipera berus* will begin courting a receptive female with tongue flicks across her body. The pair's tails, and sometimes also their bodies, vibrate in unison. If another male approaches, the first will vigorously defend his mating rights. The two males will thrash about entwined in a dance-like duel.

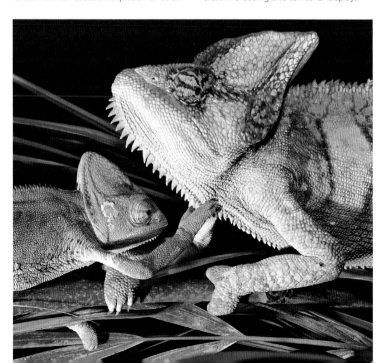

MIGRATION

Reptiles are not normally noted for their migratory skills. Sea turtles are among the most spectacular exceptions, with all species swimming great distances between feeding grounds and nesting sites. Some populations of the green sea turtle migrate from the coast of Brazil to nesting beaches 3,000 miles (5,000 km) away on Ascension Island in the mid-Atlantic Ocean. Other, less spectacular, reptile migrators include prairie rattlesnakes, which can travel up to 9 miles (15 km) from their hibernation den in the spring and return in the fall. Marine iguanas of the Galapagos Islands migrate hundreds of miles between lava reefs where they feed on algae, to nesting beaches where they lay their eggs.

Sophisticated travelers To reach their nesting beaches, sea turtles routinely migrate thousands of miles across open ocean. This involves sophisticated guidance mechanisms that are not yet fully understood by scientists. One popular theory suggests they may be able to detect and use Earth's geomagnetic fields, as some birds do. Celestial cues may also be important.

PARENTAL CARE

Female reptiles typically deposit eggs in nests dug in the sand or humus, or in burrows, leaving them to hatch unattended. Some female snakes and lizards retain embryos within the oviducts and bear live young. Parental care is rare, although there are some notable exceptions. Female North American skinks stay with their eggs, keeping them moist and protecting them from fungus and predators. When they hatch, the mother licks the young clean and they go on their way. Rattlesnakes stay with their newborn young for a week or more, and Indian cobras guard their nests from predators until the eggs hatch.

Precious mouthful Many species of crocodilians have extended parental care. As well as guarding their nests when the eggs hatch and their young start peeping, females open their nests and carry their young in their mouth to the water. Once in the water the group of hatchling crocs, called a pod, often stay with their mother for their first six weeks. This extended parental care helps crocodile populations rebound rapidly if hunting pressure is decreased.

Scare tactics The bearded dragons and frilled-neck lizards of Australia have elaborate throat fans which they greatly enlarge when confronted by a potential threat. They can make themselves appear even more intimidating by opening their mouth and rising on their hindlegs. If none of that works, they will flee at speed, running on their hindlegs.

DEFENSE

Biting, the most common reptilian defense, is well developed in many snake families, especially the true vipers, pit vipers, and elapids such as cobras and their relatives, all of which produce venom. The only venom-producing lizards are the bearded lizards of the Americas.

Body structure and habitat affect the way reptiles express aggression. Many lizards flatten the body while raising it high, making them seem larger to would-be predators. Snakes often inflate or enlarge their neck in a threatening manner, as most cobras do, while other snakes flash a bright color on the underside of the tail to startle and confuse predators.

CATCHING FOOD

Most reptiles are predators. Smaller species tend to exploit insects and other invertebrates. Larger reptiles commonly feed on mammals, fishes, and birds. The primary function of the venom of poisonous snakes is to immobilize prey so it can be consumed. Non-venomous snakes use other methods such as constriction with body coils, as boas and rat snakes do. Some reptiles actively hunt prey. Others adopt a sit-and-wait strategy, striking out only when a potential meal nears. Some even use lures to draw prey close. Australia's death adder, for example, has a modified scale at the end of its tail which it waves from side to side, simulating an insect.

Open threat Many snakes and lizards threaten potential predators by gaping their mouths widely. This display is intended to convey aggression but also makes snakes such as the parrot snake (below) appear larger.

Cryptic coloration Like many other reptiles, this short-horned lizard (below) avoids detection by being so well camouflaged it blends in with its rocky surrounds. Remaining still completes the deception.

Methodical predators The slow-moving gopher snake (bottom) hunts mainly by smell, flicking its forked tongue into rocky burrows and crevices in search of prey such as small rodents, lizards, birds, and sometimes even other snakes.

HABITATS AND ADAPTATIONS

Being ectothermic makes reptiles largely intolerant of colder climates. As a result, species numbers in all groups decrease toward higher latitudes and elevations, until eventually they drop out altogether. Just one hardy snake and one lizard species occur above the Arctic Circle, in Scandinavia. On some mountains, lizards scurry around snow banks on their daily activities. Such examples, however, are unusual. There are two kinds of places where reptiles really excel. They are abundant in the tropics and they form a conspicuous part of the desert fauna. Turtles and crocodilians are mainly aquatic, whereas most lizards and snakes are terrestrial or arboreal. There are, as always, interesting exceptions: some tortoises not only live away from water but they do so in desert regions; and some sea snakes live a totally aquatic existence.

TERRESTRIAL REPTILES

The limbs of reptiles are highly adapted to the kind of environment in which they live. Fast-running terrestrial lizards usually have relatively long legs and well-developed toes and claws to help push against the ground. Some lizards with exceptionally long limbs increase their speed by rearing up and running on their hindlegs. These lizards have extremely long tails that work as a counterbalance during bipedal running.

Being limbless, terrestrial snakes have a different suite of adaptations. They are able to move across the ground by bending the body and pushing backward against surface irregularities. The large transverse scales on the underside are firmly attached in front, but have a free edge behind where they overlap the following scale. These free edges catch against the ground to prevent the snake from slipping backward. In order to move over surfaces such as loose sand and soft mud, snakes adopt a method known as sidewinding. The snake uses a point of contact with the ground as purchase, then lifts its trunk clear of the ground to secure another point of contact. In sea snakes, which no longer need to grip on the ground, the belly scales are reduced and, in some cases, are no different in size and shape from the dorsal ones. Many terrestrial snakes are long and narrow with relatively long tails, attributes associated with rapid movement across the ground.

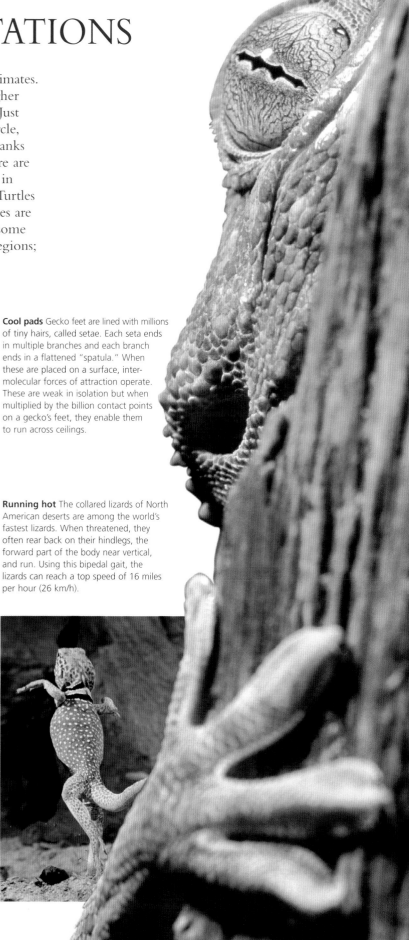

Cool pads Gecko feet are lined with millions of tiny hairs, called setae. Each seta ends in multiple branches and each branch ends in a flattened "spatula." When these are placed on a surface, inter-molecular forces of attraction operate. These are weak in isolation but when multiplied by the billion contact points on a gecko's feet, they enable them to run across ceilings.

Running hot The collared lizards of North American deserts are among the world's fastest lizards. When threatened, they often rear back on their hindlegs, the forward part of the body near vertical, and run. Using this bipedal gait, the lizards can reach a top speed of 16 miles per hour (26 km/h).

ARBOREAL REPTILES

Many tree-climbing lizards have sharp claws to grasp bark. Geckos grip, even on near-smooth surfaces, using expanded toe pads of ripple-like lamellae. Chameleons have opposable toes that can grasp twigs and a prehensile tail to curl, monkey-style, around branches.

Despite being limbless, many arboreal snakes are amazing climbers: some ascend vertical tree trunks without coiling, instead using crevices in tree bark for purchase. Other arboreal snakes are triangular shaped in cross-section. This provides greater strength and rigidity when the body is extended without support during climbing. Tree-dwelling requires the ability to judge distances. Most arboreal lizards and snakes have forward-directed eyes that can be focused in front to achieve stereovision.

Perhaps the most unusual adaptation of arboreal reptiles is the ability to glide. A genus of Asian lizards (*Draco*) has extended ribs which support the normally loose flank skin to form gliding "wings." If disturbed, these "flying lizards" will escape out of their tree and glide long distances, either to the ground or to another tree trunk. At least one Asian "flying" snake (*Chrysopelea*) leaps from trees and, by flattening its body, can glide and break its fall. No modern reptiles, however, match the soaring capabilities of the long-extinct pterodactyls.

AQUATIC REPTILES

Females of most aquatic reptile species must come to land to lay their eggs. Only some marine snakes give birth to live young in water and never emerge on land. All reptiles must rise to the surface to breathe periodically but some have evolved capabilities for prolonged diving. Nostril-closing valves, a tight-fitting mouth, and permeable skin that absorbs oxygen and releases bends-causing nitrogen bubbles, enable some sea snakes to remain submerged for up to two hours and dive to 330 feet (100 m).

Aquatic reptiles with limbs have evolved webbed feet or, in the sea turtles, flippers. Sea snakes have a flattened, paddle-shaped tail, as do crocodilians and some semi-aquatic lizards. Reptilian kidneys cannot cope with high salinities, and life in the sea is possible for marine reptiles only by virtue of special salt-excreting glands. For example, sea turtles have a modified tear gland that excretes brine from the eye, and the saltwater crocodile has small salt glands scattered over the surface of its tongue.

Floating predator The nostrils and eyes of crocodilians and aquatic snakes are located high on the dorsal surface. This allows an animal to remain low in the water without obstructing either breathing or vision.

SUBTERRANEAN REPTILES

In a dark burrow where the head is in direct contact with the soil, eyes are of no use. Not surprisingly, some burrowing snakes and lizards have only rudimentary eyes. Most truly underground-dwelling reptiles have also lost their limbs. Although these can be useful for digging, they increase friction within a burrow and take up space. The skull bones of many burrowing lizards and snakes are fused into a solid compact structure to form a battering ram. Blindsnakes (family Typhlopidae) have a sharp point on the tail that provides an anchor as they push their smooth, highly polished body through the soil. Amphisbaenians have grooves around their bodies to provide traction so they can inch forward in their burrows.

The limblessness of snakes is probably explained by their ancestry. It is thought they arose from burrowing lizards with reduced limbs. Supposedly, they arose several times. That snakes did have legs at one time is attested for by the vestigial legs, or spurs, found in modern boas and pythons.

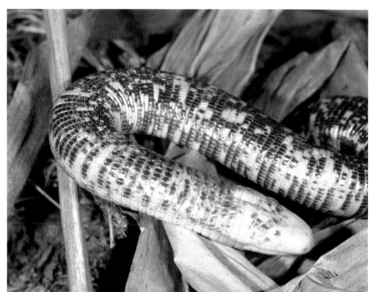

Tunnel life The worm lizards, or amphisbaenians, are among the very few completely subterranean and self-tunneling reptiles. None of the 150-plus species has hindlimbs and only a few have rudimentary forelimbs.

REPTILES ON ISLANDS

Many lizards live in and under driftwood that eventually washes out to sea and onto distant shores, carrying adults or eggs in crevices. Some geckos have salt-tolerant eggs that are sticky when laid but become firmly fixed to surfaces when dry. Dispersal by rafting is a relatively rare phenomenon, and a second member of the species may not arrive during the life-span of an individual reptile. Most arriving species would die out with the death of the colonizing reptile unless both sexes were present.

Parthenogenesis, where females can lay eggs without insemination by a male, is one solution. Some gecko species characteristic of remote islands are parthenogenic and have few or no males. A colony could be established if just one individual or egg washed up on an island. A widely distributed Pacific blindsnake is also parthenogenic. Some of the parthenogenic whiptail lizards (*Cnemidophorus*) need courtship and pseudo-copulation from other females to stimulate the ovulation of their eggs.

Distant travelers The only relatives of the iguanas of Fiji and neighboring Pacific islands are in South and Central America. Their ancestors rafted across the Pacific Ocean, and once isolated, evolved into the species of today.

REPTILES IN DANGER

Reptilian biodiversity, like that of most animal groups, is being eroded at an unprecedented rate. Many scientists believe reptile species are disappearing in higher numbers and more quickly than ever before. The last great reptile extinction occurred 65 million years ago, took the last of the dinosaurs, and was caused by a natural event. This time, blame is leveled at the human species and its rapid and massive population growth during recent centuries. Just over 60 percent of all known reptile species are now included on the IUCN Red List of Threatened Species.

IMAGE PROBLEMS

The major causes of reptile decline are the same as for other animal groups: habitat clearing and fragmentation; poaching, hunting, and overexploitation; and pollution. Reptiles, however, tend to suffer more indifference to their plight than groups with more "cuddly" appeal. Giant pandas, Bengal tigers, and humpback whales are all held up as flagship species to draw attention to the plight of disappearing mammals. Among reptiles there is no equivalent pin-up species embraced by the wider conservation movement. Reptiles often gain protection or attention as a by-product of attempts to save other species. Reptilian conservation is also hampered by the fear many people seem to have for these creatures. Only through grass roots educational programs will we appreciate the role of reptiles in the ecosystem.

Stop the traffic Trafficking in wild reptiles is a multimillion-dollar business. It feeds the demand for exotic creatures as pets, food, and as material for decorative objects. Most die in transit. China has become the major importer of turtles, placing nearly all of the turtles in Southeast Asia on the IUCN Red List. Authorities intercepted the traffic of 1,500 live turtles (above) bound for China in 2002.

Snake losses Weak economies in several South American countries are contributing to anaconda declines. They are suffering habitat destruction to make way for unsustainable and badly planned forestry, agricultural, and urban developments aimed at quick financial returns. Anacondas are also poached for their skins. Commercial farming could be a long-term solution.

TORTOISES AND TURTLES

CLASS	Reptilia
ORDER	Testudines
FAMILIES	14
GENERA	99
SPECIES	293

Turtles and tortoises are the only vertebrates that house the pelvic and pectoral girdles within a shell made of ribs fused with bone. The first fossils to show this trait appeared 220 million years ago in the Triassic period, when dinosaurs roamed the earth. The shell design has since undergone various modifications. The African pancake tortoise has a flexible flat shell allowing it to wedge into crevices; it then inflates, after which it is impossible to pull out. Softshell turtles lack a hard shell; instead, the bones are covered with a smooth leathery shell, giving them more speed. There is still controversy as to whether turtles are derived from a different lineage to other reptiles.

Distribution Turtles are found on all continents except Antarctica, and in all oceans: 241 species of turtles have adapted to freshwater rivers, lakes, and ponds; 45 tortoises are terrestrial; only seven species live in the oceans.

Baby leatherback Leatherback turtles lay up to six nests of up to 200 eggs a year for decades. This hatchling has passed the first hurdle: 2 months incubating in the sand with predators digging around it. It now has to face the many threats in the sea.

EVOLUTION SHELLED OUT

In addition to the shell, turtles and tortoises have evolved many unique features. Turtle muscles are able to withstand high levels of lactic acid, so they do not tire after swimming rapidly. They also fill their large urinary bladders with water for ballast to maintain buoyancy.

Turtles and tortoises occupy niches as predators, grazers, croppers, and scavengers. Some have gut flora to digest plant cells; others are seed dispersers. Wood turtles stomp on the ground with their front feet, then eat the earthworms that come out of the ground.

Some sea turtles and freshwater turtles nest within a few days in tremendous numbers on the same nesting beach. These mass nestings, known as arribadas, evolved to swamp local predators—it would be impossible for them to eat all of the eggs or kill all of the females. The success of these adaptations has helped turtles to survive over millions of years; now, as a result of human intervention, two-thirds of all turtle species are being carefully monitored by the IUCN.

Saddleback giant The Galápagos tortoise (above) has a saddleback carapace. This condition is more often seen in adult male tortoises, due to enhanced mating success, from populations on the drier and more barren islands of the Galápagos.

Turtle skeleton A turtle's shell has an outer layer of epidermal scutes (usually 38 on the carapace and 16 on the plastron). Under these, a shell of fused ribs (the plastron) supports the body. The vertebrae are joined to the inside of the carapace.

retracting neck

claws   scute   carapace   plastron

Swimming sea turtle The forelimbs of sea turtles have been modified into flipper-shaped paddles that move synchronously, resembling aquatic flying rather than swimming. Sea turtles are so adept in the water that they rarely leave it except to nest. Freshwater turtles swim using all four limbs in turn.

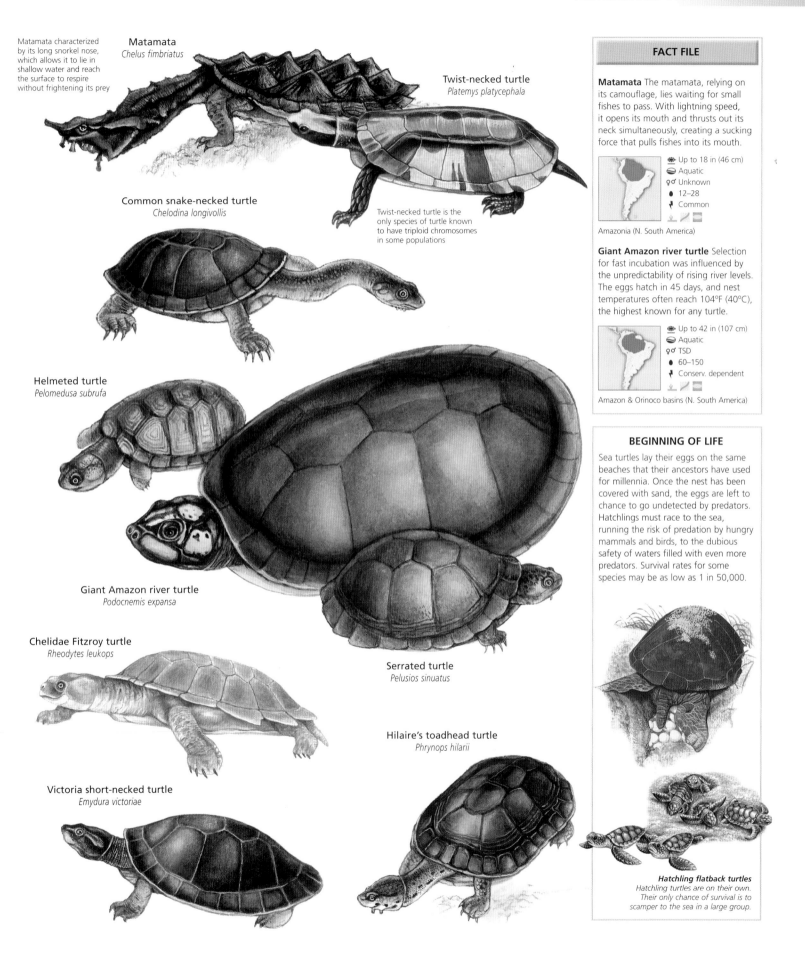

Matamata characterized by its long snorkel nose, which allows it to lie in shallow water and reach the surface to respire without frightening its prey

Matamata
Chelus fimbriatus

Twist-necked turtle
Platemys platycephala

Twist-necked turtle is the only species of turtle known to have triploid chromosomes in some populations

Common snake-necked turtle
Chelodina longivollis

Helmeted turtle
Pelomedusa subrufa

Giant Amazon river turtle
Podocnemis expansa

Chelidae Fitzroy turtle
Rheodytes leukops

Serrated turtle
Pelusios sinuatus

Hilaire's toadhead turtle
Phrynops hilarii

Victoria short-necked turtle
Emydura victoriae

FACT FILE

Matamata The matamata, relying on its camouflage, lies waiting for small fishes to pass. With lightning speed, it opens its mouth and thrusts out its neck simultaneously, creating a sucking force that pulls fishes into its mouth.

- Up to 18 in (46 cm)
- Aquatic
- Unknown
- 12–28
- Common

Amazonia (N. South America)

Giant Amazon river turtle Selection for fast incubation was influenced by the unpredictability of rising river levels. The eggs hatch in 45 days, and nest temperatures often reach 104°F (40°C), the highest known for any turtle.

- Up to 42 in (107 cm)
- Aquatic
- TSD
- 60–150
- Conserv. dependent

Amazon & Orinoco basins (N. South America)

BEGINNING OF LIFE

Sea turtles lay their eggs on the same beaches that their ancestors have used for millennia. Once the nest has been covered with sand, the eggs are left to chance to go undetected by predators. Hatchlings must race to the sea, running the risk of predation by hungry mammals and birds, to the dubious safety of waters filled with even more predators. Survival rates for some species may be as low as 1 in 50,000.

Hatchling flatback turtles
Hatchling turtles are on their own. Their only chance of survival is to scamper to the sea in a large group.

FACT FILE

Green turtle Green turtles migrate huge distances across the open seas between their feeding grounds and nesting beaches. They graze in shallow waters on submerged vegetation. Adults are primarily herbivorous, while juveniles are more carnivorous.

- Up to 5 ft (1.5 m)
- Aquatic
- ♀♂ TSD
- 50–240
- Endangered

Tropical oceans worldwide & Mediterranean Sea

Olive Ridley turtle This species is characteristic of turtles that nest in arribadas. Most of the population comes to nest within a 2–3 day period on the same beach. Arribadas in Orissa, India, have numbered more than 100,000 turtles nesting each year.

- Up to 31 in (79 cm)
- Aquatic
- ♀♂ TSD
- 30–168
- Endangered

Primarily tropical regions of Pacific, Indian & Atlantic oceans

SHELL SHAPES

Tortoises are high-domed to protect them from predators and store water. Pond turtles are more streamlined so that they can swim with less resistance. Semi-terrestrial turtles have higher domes for predator protection. Sea turtles are designed for least resistance to glide through the water.

Land tortoise

Semi-terrestrial

Sea turtle

Pond turtle

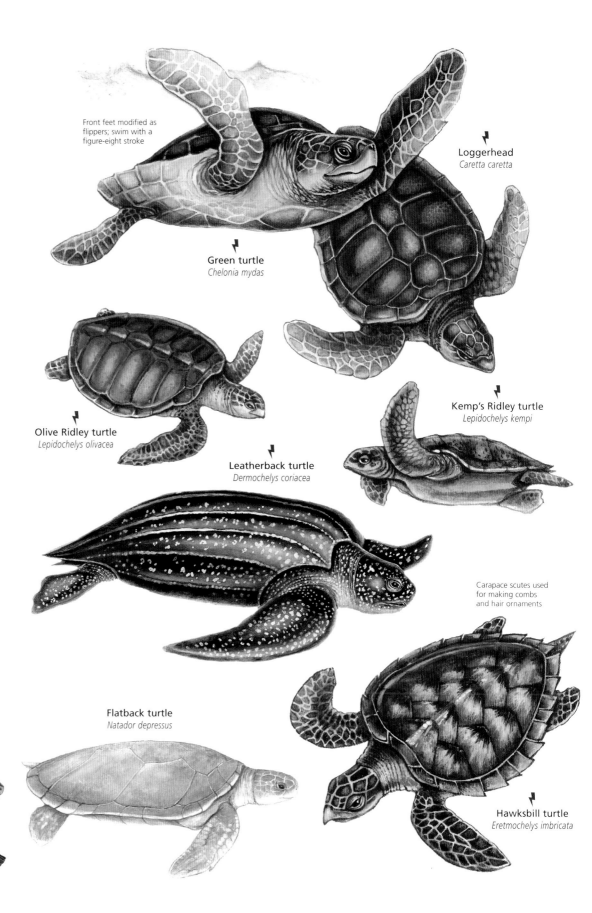

Front feet modified as flippers; swim with a figure-eight stroke

Loggerhead
Caretta caretta

Green turtle
Chelonia mydas

Olive Ridley turtle
Lepidochelys olivacea

Kemp's Ridley turtle
Lepidochelys kempi

Leatherback turtle
Dermochelys coriacea

Carapace scutes used for making combs and hair ornaments

Flatback turtle
Natador depressus

Hawksbill turtle
Eretmochelys imbricata

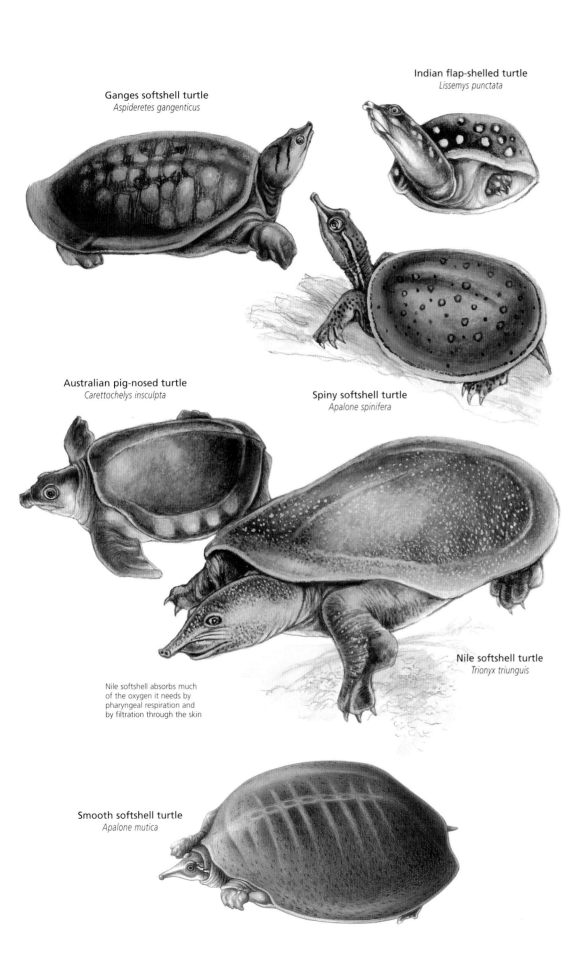

Ganges softshell turtle
Aspideretes gangenticus

Indian flap-shelled turtle
Lissemys punctata

Spiny softshell turtle
Apalone spinifera

Australian pig-nosed turtle
Carettochelys insculpta

Nile softshell turtle
Trionyx triunguis

Nile softshell absorbs much of the oxygen it needs by pharyngeal respiration and by filtration through the skin

Smooth softshell turtle
Apalone mutica

HEAT AND SEX

Sex in some species of turtles, as in most vertebrates, is genetic (referred to as GSD, or genetic sex determination). In most turtles studied, some lizards, all crocodiles, and the tuatara, sex is controlled by the incubation temperature (referred to as TSD, or temperature sex determination). The temperature during the middle third of the incubation period determines what the sex of the hatchling turtle will be. Females are produced at extreme low and high temperatures and males at intermediate temperatures. Thus a female can control the sex of her offspring by where she lays her eggs: nests out in the full sunlight produce females, while nests in the shade produce males; the first nests in summer produce females, while the last nests in the fall produce males.

Wood turtle hatching
Wood turtles are one of the few North American turtles in the family Emydidae to have GSD; most others have TSD.

FACT FILE

Diamond-back terrapin This is the only turtle to specialize in living in brackish water marshes. It was once driven to near extinction because of its popularity for the gourmet table.

- Up to 9½ in (24 cm)
- Aquatic
- ♀♂ TSD
- 4–18
- Near threatened

E. seaboard & Gulf Coast (USA)

Ringed sawback This species thrives in fast-moving water, where it forages for aquatic insect larvae. It is endangered due to pollution of the Pearl River. The pet trade and target practice have also reduced its numbers.

- Up to 8½ in (21 cm)
- Aquatic
- ♀♂ TSD
- 4–8
- Endangered

Pearl River, Mississippi (USA)

European pond turtle Only males hatch at incubation temperatures of 75–82°F (24–28°C), while at 86°F (30°C), 96 percent of the hatchlings are females. At higher temperatures, only females are produced.

- Up to 8 in (20 cm)
- Aquatic
- ♀♂ TSD
- 3–16
- Common

S. Europe & W. Asia

Painted turtle In spring, this cold-adapted species can be seen swimming under the ice and mating in iceflows. Hatchlings overwinter in the nest, super-cooling yet not freezing at 20°F (4°C).

- Up to 10 in (25 cm)
- Aquatic
- ♀♂ TSD
- 4–20
- Common

E. & C. USA

River cooter A complete herbivore, this species is often seen basking by the dozens on floating logs in order to raise its body temperature to speed digestion. Basking is also important for ridding the shell and limbs of fungal and algal colonies.

- Up to 17 in (43 cm)
- Aquatic
- ♀♂ TSD
- 6–28
- Common

S.E. USA

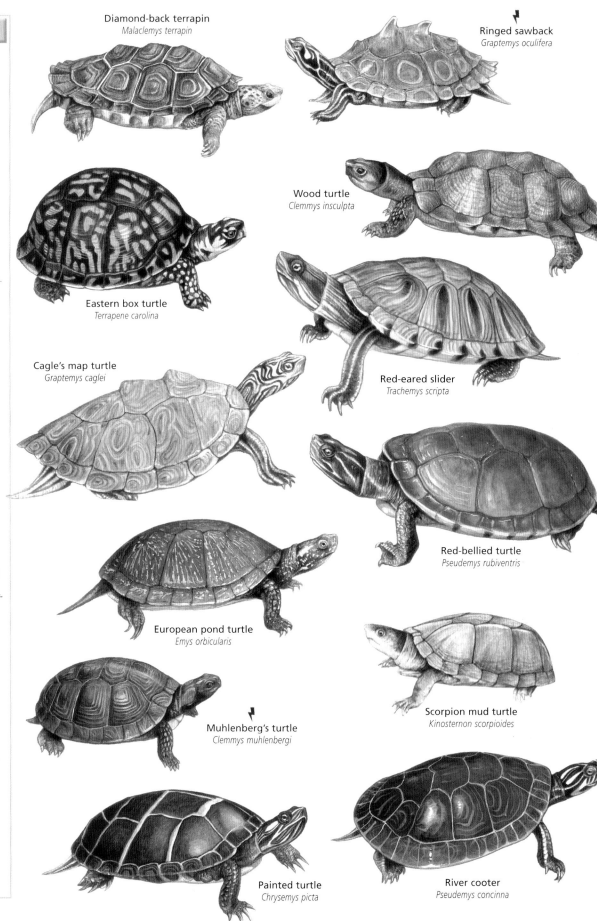

Diamond-back terrapin
Malaclemys terrapin

Ringed sawback
Graptemys oculifera

Wood turtle
Clemmys insculpta

Eastern box turtle
Terrapene carolina

Red-eared slider
Trachemys scripta

Cagle's map turtle
Graptemys caglei

Red-bellied turtle
Pseudemys rubiventris

European pond turtle
Emys orbicularis

Scorpion mud turtle
Kinosternon scorpioides

Muhlenberg's turtle
Clemmys muhlenbergi

Painted turtle
Chrysemys picta

River cooter
Pseudemys concinna

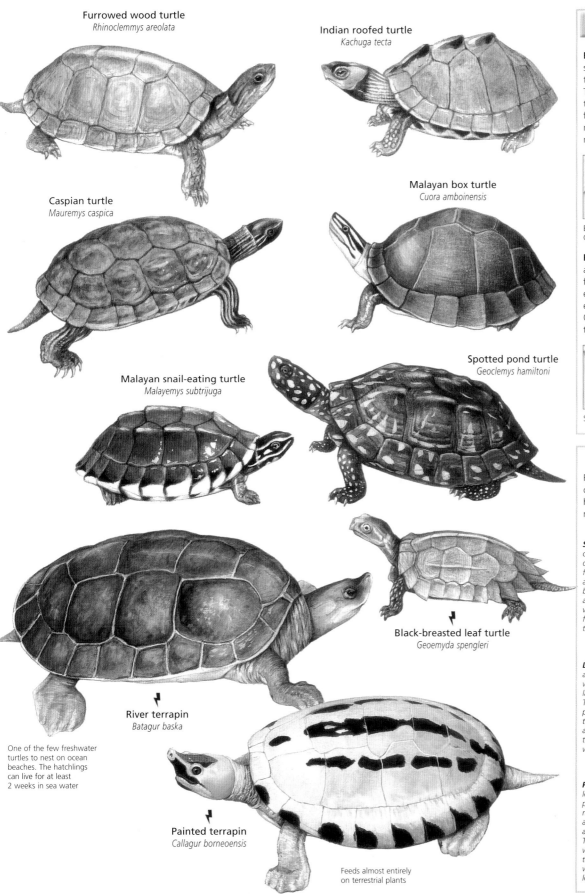

Furrowed wood turtle
Rhinoclemmys areolata

Indian roofed turtle
Kachuga tecta

Caspian turtle
Mauremys caspica

Malayan box turtle
Cuora amboinensis

Malayan snail-eating turtle
Malayemys subtrijuga

Spotted pond turtle
Geoclemys hamiltoni

Black-breasted leaf turtle
Geoemyda spengleri

River terrapin
Batagur baska

One of the few freshwater turtles to nest on ocean beaches. The hatchlings can live for at least 2 weeks in sea water

Painted terrapin
Callagur borneoensis

Feeds almost entirely on terrestrial plants

FACT FILE

River terrapin During the breeding season, from September to November, the male's head coloration changes. The nostrils become blue, the iris white, the head deep black, and the neck and front limbs deep red and black. Sand mining is destroying the preferred nesting beaches of this species.

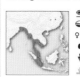

🐢 Up to 24 in (60 cm)
Aquatic
♀♂ Unknown
● 12–34
Critically endangered

E. India & Bangladesh to Burma, Thailand, Cambodia & Indonesia

Painted terrapin Painted terrapins are exploited for their eggs, which fetch five times the price of chicken eggs. Habitat destruction is also exacerbating the decline of the species. Only one or two rivers harbor more than a hundred nesting females.

🐢 Up to 30 in (76 cm)
Aquatic
♀♂ Unknown
● 10–15
Critically endangered

S. Thailand, Malaysia, Sumatra & Borneo

LEG ADAPTATIONS

From the shape of the leg, foot, and claws, it is possible to deduce what habitat the turtle was adapted for, but not necessarily where it is living today.

Sea turtle The forelimbs of sea turtles are aero-dynamically designed to fly through water. They are tapered from tip to base like the wings of an albatross. There is no webbing, as the toes are fused together within the flippers.

Land tortoise This animal is designed for walking with a load on land, not for swimming. The legs have armored plates, the unwebbed toes are elephantine, and the feet are flat to support the tortoise's weight on land.

Pond turtle The legs are only slightly paddle-shaped to navigate through aquatic vegetation and to walk on land. The toes are webbed, with long, claw-like toenails for traction when crawling up logs to bask.

FACT FILE

Leopard tortoise During courtship, the male trails the female, butting her into submission. After mounting, he extends his neck and releases a grunt-like bellow. Females lay 5–7 clutches of 5–30 eggs from May to October.

- ⊕ Up to 27 in (68 cm)
- ◯ Terrestrial
- ♀♂ Unknown
- ● 5–30
- ⚡ Common

S. Sudan & Ethiopia to Natal & South Africa

African tent tortoise Nesting takes place from September to December, when up to three ellipsoidal eggs are laid in a single yearly clutch. The eggs hatch between April and May. The hatchlings are 1 inch (2.5 cm) long.

- ⊕ Up to 5½ in (16 cm)
- ◯ Terrestrial
- ♀♂ Unknown
- ● 1–3
- ⚡ Common

S.W. Africa to Cape (South Africa)

Texas tortoise This species feeds on the pads, flowers, and fruit of cactus. In the Chihuahuan Desert, they are active early in the morning, and rest in the shade or in burrows during the heat of the day.

- ⊕ Up to 8½ in (22 cm)
- ◯ Terrestrial
- ♀♂ TSD
- ● 1–4
- ⚡ Vulnerable

S. Texas (USA) to N. Mexico

COURTSHIP

Courtship occurs in turtles that have sympatric congeners to ensure intra-specific mating. Males come face to face with the female, and present head bobs or titillations with the foreclaws to the face of the female. The number of bobs or vibrations and the length of the bout are species-specific.

Titillating a female Red-eared slider males are smaller than females. A courting male vibrates his foreclaws against the sides of the female's head. If the number of beats per minute is correct, it identifies him as a suitable male to breed with.

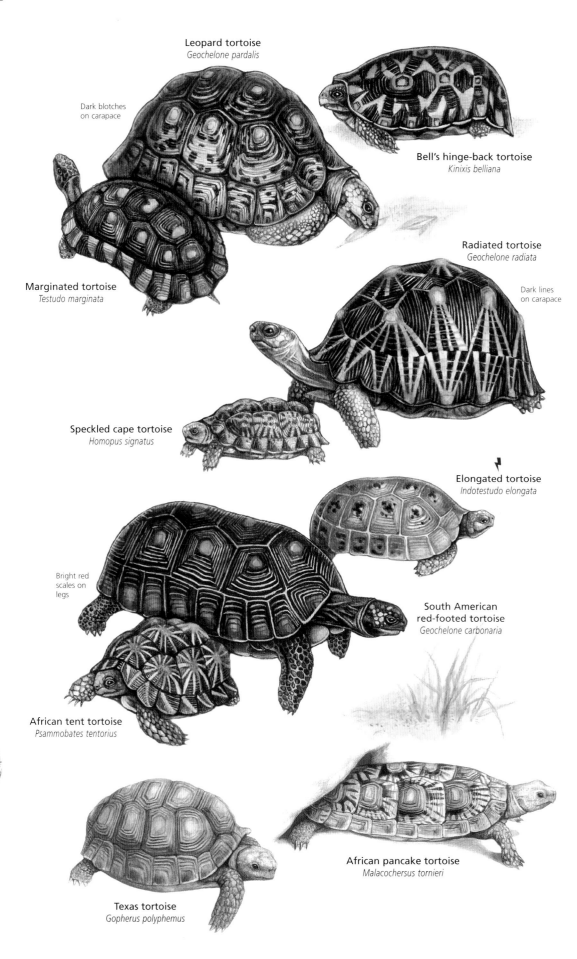

Leopard tortoise
Geochelone pardalis

Dark blotches on carapace

Bell's hinge-back tortoise
Kinixis belliana

Marginated tortoise
Testudo marginata

Radiated tortoise
Geochelone radiata

Dark lines on carapace

Speckled cape tortoise
Homopus signatus

Elongated tortoise
Indotestudo elongata

Bright red scales on legs

South American red-footed tortoise
Geochelone carbonaria

African tent tortoise
Psammobates tentorius

Texas tortoise
Gopherus polyphemus

African pancake tortoise
Malacochersus tornieri

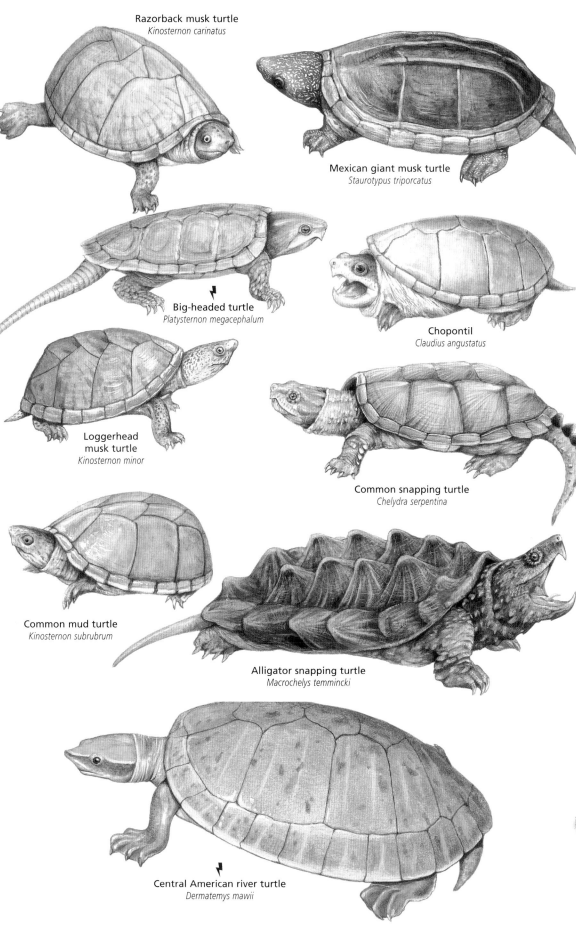

Razorback musk turtle
Kinosternon carinatus

Mexican giant musk turtle
Staurotypus triporcatus

Big-headed turtle
Platysternon megacephalum

Chopontil
Claudius angustatus

Loggerhead
musk turtle
Kinosternon minor

Common snapping turtle
Chelydra serpentina

Common mud turtle
Kinosternon subrubrum

Alligator snapping turtle
Macrochelys temmincki

Central American river turtle
Dermatemys mawii

FACT FILE

Common snapping turtle This species is known for its ability to lurch forward rapidly with snapping jaws, an adaptation for crayfish predation and for protection. These turtles are omnivores, feeding on crustaceans, carrion, duckweed, and aquatic plants.

⊕ Up to 19 in (48 cm)
⊜ Aquatic
♀♂ TSD
● 25–96
⌇ Common

S. Canada, E. & C. USA

Alligator snapping turtle The largest species of turtle in North America was being driven to extinction by the soup industry. Until recently, this rare beast could be found on American grocery store shelves in red-and-white cans.

⊕ Up to 31½ in (80 cm)
⊜ Aquatic
♀♂ TSD
● 8–52
⌇ Vulnerable

S.E. USA

Central American river turtle This highly aquatic turtle seldom leaves the water even to nest. They often nest by digging into the river bank under the water level. The eggs do not begin to develop until the river is lower.

⊕ Up to 26 in (66 cm)
⊜ Aquatic
♀♂ TSD
● 8–26
⌇ Endangered

S. Mexico, Guatemala, Belize

CAMOUFLAGE

The alligator snapping turtle is a master of disguise. With flaps of loose skin hanging on its neck and filamentous algae growing on its shell, it blends in well with the logs and plants among which it sits waiting to ambush its prey. Only its pink lure looks out of place.

Alligator snapping turtle
This turtle sits with its mouth open at the bottom of a river or lake, fishing with its own bright pink lure.

Bogged down The bog turtle (*Clemmys muhlenbergii*) is endemic to acidic wetlands of the Piedmont and Appalachian mountains, USA. Habitat fragmentation and destruction; and the pet trade have decimated this species and others such as the yellow-blotched map turtle (*Graptemys flavimaculata*) from Pascagoula River, Mississipi, USA.

DEATH ROW

During the last five years, the decimation of turtle populations has accelerated rapidly. The Turtle Survival Alliance (TSA) has been formed to monitor and attempt to reverse this trend. TSA shortlisted 25 of the most critically endangered species to raise awareness of the problem. Most of these species occur in hotspots for high biodiversity—areas that are important for the critical habitat of a number of other taxa as well. The turtles are in trouble because of over–exploitation for food or traditional remedies, the pet trade, restricted range, and habitat degradation. Only five of these are suffering due to habitat degradation—15 of the 25 are on the brink of extinction because of uncontrolled exploitation by humans.

THE WORLD'S MOST ENDANGERED TURTLES

1. MESOAMERICA HOTSPOT
Central American river turtle
Dermatemys mawii

2. CHOCÓ-DARIÉN–WESTERN ECUADOR HOTSPOT
Dahl's toad-headed tortoise
Batrachemys dahli

3. MEDITERRANEAN BASIN HOTSPOT
Egyptian tortoise
Testudo kleinmanni

4. MADAGASCAR AND INDIAN OCEAN ISLANDS HOTSPOT
Madagascar big-headed turtle
Erymnochelys madagascariensis

Ploughshare tortoise
Geochelone yniphora

Flat-tailed tortoise
Pyxis planicauda

5. SUCCULENT KAROO HOTSPOT
Southern speckled padloper tortoise
Homopus signatus cafer

6. CAPE FLORISTIC REGION HOTSPOT
Geometric tortoise
Psammobates geometricus

7. INDO-BURMA HOTSPOT
Striped narrow-headed softshell turtle
Chitra chitra

Chinese three-striped box turtle
Cuora trifasciata

Arakan forest turtle
Heosemys depressa

Burmese star tortoise
Geochelone platynota

Burmese roofed turtle
Kachuga trivittata

Leaf turtle
Mauremys annamensis

Yangtze giant softshell turtle
Rafetus swinhoei

8. SUNDALAND HOTSPOT
River terrapin
Batagur baska

Painted terrapin
Callagur borneoensis

9. PHILIPPINES HOTSPOT
Philippine forest turtle
Heosemys leytensis

10. WALLACEA HOTSPOT
Roti snake-necked turtle
Chelodina mccordi

Sulawesi forest turtle
Leucocephalon yuwonoi

11. SOUTHWESTERN AUSTRALIA HOTSPOT
Western swamp turtle
Pseudemydura umbrina

Reaping death There are now fewer than 400 ploughshare tortoises (below) in the wild; they are now restricted to the bamboo scrub near Baly Bay in northeastern Madagascar. Local consumption, the pet trade, and habitat degradation have led to their downfall. The tortoise's name comes from the long gular scute that extends under its head and is used in combat by the males.

Lonely giants Once there were 15 distinct island forms of Galápagos tortoises; some are extinct and now only one Abingdon Island tortoise (*Geochelone nigra*) remains. Human predation and feral mammals have had a devastating impact.

Rapid decline The painted terrapin (above) is extinct over much of Indochina due to harvesting of eggs and adults. A small population has been protected in Cambodia since 2001 and 30 hatchlings were released in 2002. However, the Mary River turtle (*Elusor macrurus*) of Australia, which was also on the verge of extinction, has been saved by conservation efforts.

CROCODILIANS

CLASS	Reptilia
ORDER	Crocodilia
FAMILIES	3
GENERA	8
SPECIES	23

Alligators, caimans, crocodiles, and gharials are all crocodilians, belonging to the lineage of archosaurs, which includes the dinosaurs and birds. Crocodilians are much more closely related to birds than they are to other reptiles, and have existed for 220 million years, since the Triassic period. Part of their success is a result of being the top aquatic predator in their domain. As the body form of crocodilians has stayed the same, they are often called living fossils, but these beasts have been evolving for millions of years and are very different from their ancestors in the age of the dinosaurs. Unlike most reptiles, crocodilians are very vocal, especially during courtship.

Distribution Crocodilians are found in tropical, subtropical, and temperate zones worldwide: Gavialidae in South Asia, and Alligatoridae in eastern North America, Central and South America, and eastern China. Crocodylidae inhabit estuaries and freshwater streams of Africa, India, Indonesia, Australia, northern South America, Central America, and the West Indies.

Nile crocodile Despite their ferocious look, these animals feed primarily on fishes. Those over 3 feet (1 m) mainly eat fishes that are predatory on human food fishes. Maintaining populations of this species in the wild may help the local fishing industry.

Nile crocodile baby When about to hatch, the young call from the egg. Their mother responds by scraping away the material covering the eggs. When they hatch, she gently gulps them into a pouch that has developed in the floor of her mouth, then transports them to their wetland nursery.

CANNIBALISM AND CARE

Crocodilians have an elongated, cylindrical body with short, muscular limbs and a laterally compressed tail. The massive skull is set on a short neck and features strongly toothed jaws. Crocodilians are aquatic, yet bask and nest on shorelines.

Crocodilians are oviparous, with internal fertilization. Clutches usually contain 12–48 eggs; all species studied have temperature–controlled sex determination, in which females are produced at high and low incubation temperatures and males only at a narrow range of intermediate temperatures.

The eggs are laid in nests made of mounds of vegetation or in nests dug in the sand. Nest site selection can control the sex of the young. Both males and females of some species guard the nest. Females of some species are known to respond to the grunts of the nearly hatched embryos by opening the nests for them. The female will also carry the hatchlings in her mouth to the water, where she has bulldozed a nursery pond for them.

Females will protect their young for the first 2 months. However, males are also known to protect and maintain their territories and food supplies by killing and eating any young male crocodilian in their territory, so the female is often protecting her young from their own father. Female American alligators often stay with their young near the nesting site for 1–2 years.

Walk Crocodilians walking on land hold the limbs vertically beneath the body.

Gallop Australian freshwater crocodiles often gallop over rough terrain.

Crawl Crocodiles crawl low to the ground when they are trying to conceal themselves from potential prey or predators.

Crocodile gaits Although crocodiles are primarily aquatic, they use their legs for walking on land and the tail for swimming. On land, the use of ball-and-socket vertebrae allows crocodilians to have varied gaits.

FACT FILE

American alligator Populations of
this species were low in the 1950s
and protected as endangered in 1967.
Populations rebounded in 20 years
to over 800,000 animals. Hunting of
some populations is now allowed, in
order to control their numbers.

- Up to 19 ft (5.8 m)
- Aquatic
- Oviparous
- 10–40
- Common

S.E. USA

Black caiman This species has recently
been reclassified from endangered in
Brazil. Conservation efforts over more
than 10 years were highly successful,
with populations recuperating rapidly.
A program to sustainably harvest this
species is being enacted.

- Up to 20 ft (6 m)
- Aquatic
- Oviparous
- 35–50
- Conserv. dependent

Amazon Basin (N. South America)

Chinese alligator This species spends
the majority of its life in a complex of
underground burrows. The alligators
build these systems with pools of water
above and below ground as well as air
holes for breathing.

- Up to 6½ ft (2 m)
- Aquatic
- Oviparous
- 10–40
- Critically endangered

Yangtze Valley (China)

ALLIGATOR ACTIVITY

Alligators frequently forage for fishes
beneath waterbird rookeries. On
occasion, for a change in diet, they
will launch themselves at birds as
well, using just the propulsion of
their tails. They can
reach amazing
speeds and
heights,
and it often
appears
as if they are
walking on
their tails.

American alligator
Alligator mississippiensis

Black caiman
Caiman niger

Cuvier's dwarf caiman
Paleosuchus palpebrosus

African dwarf crocodile
Osteolaemus tetraspis

Chinese alligator
Alligator sinensis

False gharial
Tomistoma schlegeli

Mugger
Crocodylus palustri

Saltwater crocodile
Crocodylus porosus

Orinoco crocodile
Crocodylus intermedius

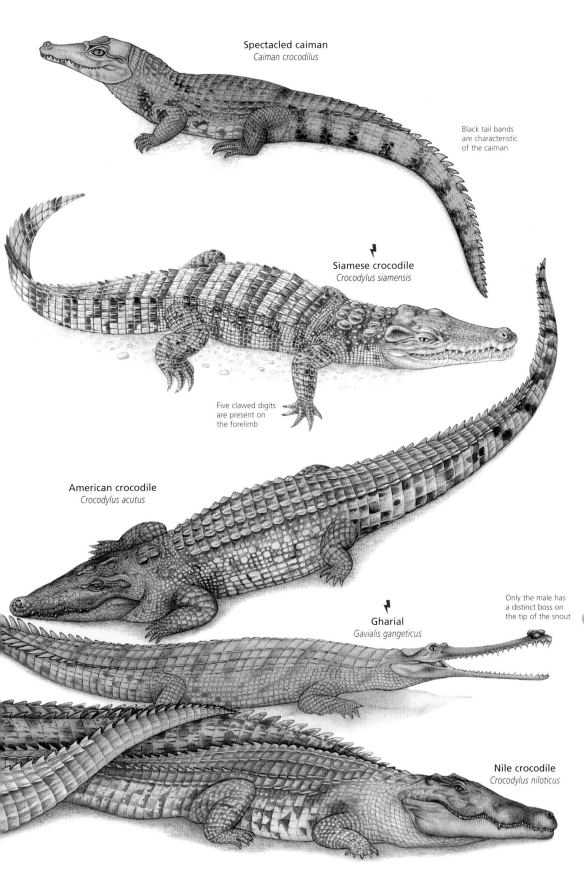

Spectacled caiman
Caiman crocodilus

Black tail bands
are characteristic
of the caiman

Siamese crocodile
Crocodylus siamensis

Five clawed digits
are present on
the forelimb

American crocodile
Crocodylus acutus

Only the male has
a distinct boss on
the tip of the snout

Gharial
Gavialis gangeticus

Nile crocodile
Crocodylus niloticus

FACT FILE

American crocodile This species was once abundant and widespread but was extirpated in many regions due to the skin trade and habitat destruction. Populations have not recuperated in many areas because of habitat loss and continued hunting.

⊬	Up to 23 ft (7 m)
🖙	Aquatic
○	Oviparous
●	30–40
🏌	Vulnerable

S. Florida (USA), Mexico to Colombia, Ecuador

Nile crocodile Maturity is reached in 12–15 years at 6–9 feet (1.8–2.8 m). The female guards the nest, opens it at hatching, and carries the hatchlings to the water. Both parents guard the young for up to 2 months.

⊬	Up to 19 ft (6 m)
🖙	Aquatic
○	Oviparous
●	16–80
🏌	Common

Sub-Saharan Africa

ANATOMY

Crocodilians have various adaptations to an aquatic life. The position of the eyes, ear openings, and nostrils at the highest part of the body allows them to lie concealed just below the surface of the water when stalking prey. A secondary palate lets them breathe with the mouth closed. A flap of skin in the throat prevents water from entering the throat when the jaws are being opened to capture prey.

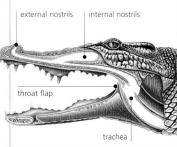

external nostrils   internal nostrils

throat flap

trachea

🏌 CONSERVATION WATCH

Fashion victims Skins from 15 species of crocodilians have been sold as luxury leather products. This has had a negative effect on wild populations of crocodilians. Crocodile farms, meanwhile, are vanishing due to high costs, lower demand, and lower prices. Sustainable use of wild populations seems to be more feasible in the long term.

TUATARA

CLASS	Reptilia
ORDER	Rhynchocephalia
FAMILY	Sphenodontidae
GENUS	Sphenodon
SPECIES	2

The tuatara is often called a "living fossil" and is now only to be found on the islands of New Zealand. It is the only survivor of a large group of reptiles that roamed with the dinosaurs over 225 million years ago, the rest of which became extinct 60 million years ago. Its tooth arrangement is unique: a single row in the lower jaw fits between two rows of teeth in the upper jaw. Lizards have visible ear openings but tuatara do not.

Distribution About 400 *Sphenodon guntheri* live on North Brother Island, New Zealand. More than 60,000 *S. punctatus* live on some 30 islands off the northeast coast of New Zealand's North Island.

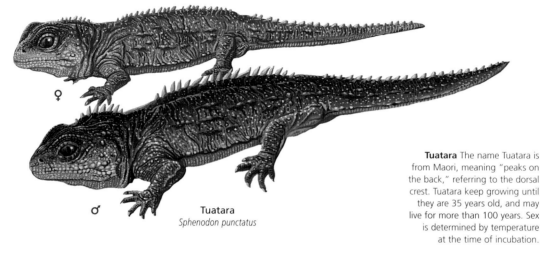

Tuatara
Sphenodon punctatus

♀

♂

Tuatara The name Tuatara is from Maori, meaning "peaks on the back," referring to the dorsal crest. Tuatara keep growing until they are 35 years old, and may live for more than 100 years. Sex is determined by temperature at the time of incubation.

AMPHISBAENIANS

CLASS	Reptilia
ORDER	Squamata
SUBORDER	Amphisbaenia
FAMILIES	4
GENERA	21
SPECIES	140

These legless squamates have reduced pectoral and pelvic girdles. They have an annulated pattern of scutes, and short tails. Amphisbaenians are built for burrowing, with heavily ossified skulls. Their brain is surrounded by the frontal bones. The right lung of amphisbaenians is reduced in size, while in other limbless lizards and snakes the left lung is smaller. Three of the four families of worm lizards have no limbs whatsoever, while the remaining family has enlarged forelimbs, which help it with locomotion and digging.

Distribution Amphisbaenians are found in tropical and subtropical regions of southern North America, South America to Patagonia, West Indies, Africa, the Iberian Penisula, Arabia, and western Asia.

Shovel-snouted worm lizard The illustration below shows how the worm lizard pushes its head against the ceiling of the tunnel to widen it. Worm lizards have large, interlocking upper and lower teeth, which allow them to grasp prey and drag it into their tunnel.

Two-headed legless lizard Amphisbaenians are often erroneously called two-headed snakes, as the tail is designed to mimic the head to confuse potential predators. A wound to the tail would be easier to survive than one to the head.

HOW THEY BURROW
The rings of scales behind the head are close together at the start of the stroke. During penetration the rings separate, pushing the head forward. To widen the tunnel, the head is lifted against the ceiling of the tunnel.

Round heads   *Shovel heads*

Keel heads   *Chisel heads*

LIZARDS

CLASS	Reptilia
ORDER	Squamata
SUBORDER	Sauria
FAMILIES	27
GENERA	442
SPECIES	4,560

Today, lizards occupy almost all landmasses except for Antarctica and some Arctic regions. At the end of the Cretaceous period, some 65 million years ago, lizards survived when the dinosaurs and other large reptiles died out. With more than 4,000 species, they are the largest group of living reptiles. Although the largest lizard, the Komodo dragon, reaches an impressive length of 10 feet (3 m), few lizards exceed 12 inches (30 cm) and this is one reason for their continued success. Lizards tend to be restricted to specific habitat niches, as mountains and water are significant barriers to their movement.

Distribution Lizards are found from New Zealand to Norway, and from southern Canada to Tierra del Fuego. They are also endemic to many islands in the world's oceans. The only continent they have not colonized is Antarctica.

The lizard assumes a threatening stance on all fours

The back is arched and the eyes stare firmly forward

The back feet leave the ground in an aggressive jump

Territorial defense A defined territory provides an area in which an adult male lizard can hunt for food and find a female for mating. If a rival invades its territory, a collard lizard does a series of "push-ups" to make itself look bigger and more threatening to the unwelcome interloper.

Lizard features The cone-like spines on the crest of the forest dragon make it appear to be larger and more formidable than it actually is, and its multicolored scales provide perfect camouflage in the mottled forest light.

Prehensile-tailed skink The Solomon Island skink (*Corucia zebrata*) is arboreal and herbivorous. It uses its prehensile tail to hold onto branches as it feeds on fruits and leaves in the treetops.

DEFENSE AND ESCAPE

Lizards are preyed upon by spiders, scorpions, other lizards, snakes, birds, and mammals. The Gila monster and the Mexican beaded lizard are the only two venomous species, but even these will resort to scare tactics at the start of a confrontation. Many others have developed an impressive array of tactics to defend themselves or to escape an attacker.

Most lizards are extremely well camouflaged and may keep absolutely still until a predator passes by. Chameleons, in particular, are well known for their ability to change color to blend in with their environment. Other lizards surprise or distract a predator to give themselves a chance to escape. The Australian frilled lizard, for example, opens its mouth, hisses loudly, and flourishes its neck frill before scampering away.

Some species have sharp spines that can injure a predator's mouth, or slippery scales that make them hard to grip. The armadillo girdle-tailed lizard curls itself into a ball and protects itself with a prickly fence of spikes, while the basilisk escapes by skimming on water before diving in to safety.

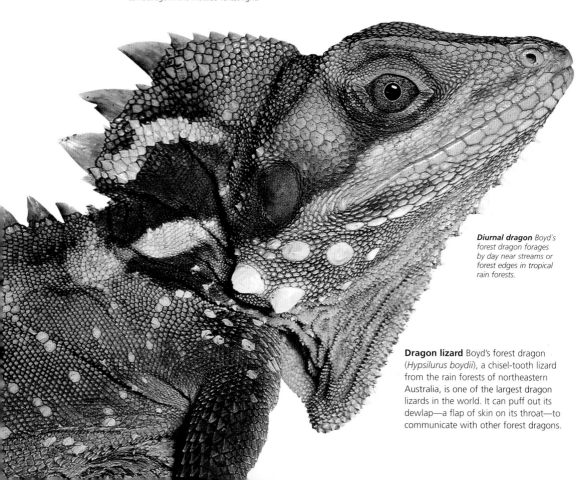

Diurnal dragon Boyd's forest dragon forages by day near streams or forest edges in tropical rain forests.

Dragon lizard Boyd's forest dragon (*Hypsilurus boydii*), a chisel-tooth lizard from the rain forests of northeastern Australia, is one of the largest dragon lizards in the world. It can puff out its dewlap—a flap of skin on its throat—to communicate with other forest dragons.

Australian shingleback

tree-living chameleon

Lizard tails Some lizards have tails that mimic leaves; others mimic heads. Some are used to hold onto branches, and many are expendable. If a predator grabs a skink's tail, the tail stays in the predator's mouth and the lizard escapes.

skink

leaf-tailed gecko

Underwater grazers Marine iguanas on the Galápagos Islands are herbivores from the time they hatch. They dive into the ocean to forage on algae. Before and after diving, they bask to increase their body temperatures to help them more efficiently digest their food, and also to increase swimming stamina in the usually cold seas.

Lizards use their tails for defense. Monitors and iguanas beat their attackers with their tails. Skinks and other small lizards may give up a little piece of tail in return for their lives. These lizards often have brightly colored tails that they will wave from side to side, inducing the predator to attack the tail and not the head. The tail continues to wriggle after the lizard has escaped. Shed tails grow back after time; the lizard loses some stored energy but remains alive to reproduce. In territorial bouts, some geckos attack and eat the tails of their opponents.

Horned lizards, when attacked by foxes and coyotes, will squirt a stream of bad-tasting blood out of their eyes to distract and discourage potential predators. Some lizards also attempt to scare off predators by sticking out their tongues. Australian skinks hiss and thrust their brightly colored tongues out to startle predators. Even though the Gila monster is venomous and brightly colored to warn predators of the risk of attacking, if molested it will display its bright purple tongue and hiss at its aggressor.

Rain-forest ranch The common green iguana (above) is completely herbivorous after hatching. The low-cholesterol meat is eaten as a delicacy in Meso-America.

Predatory dragon The Indonesian Komodo dragon (left) tests the air for the scent of warm-blooded prey. These lizards grow to be more than 10 feet (3 m) in total length and feed on large mammals such as deer, pigs, goats, and even water buffalo.

Fiji banded iguana
Brachylophus fasciatus, family Iguanidae

West Indian iguana
Iguana delicatissima, family Iguanidae

Marine iguana
Amblyrhynchus cristatus,
family Iguanidae

Galápagos
land iguana
Conolophus subcristatus,
family Iguanidae

Rhinoceros iguana
Cyclura cornuta,
family Iguanidae

The warmer male black
iguana (top) is lighter
in color; the other male
is colder and darker

Black iguana
Ctenosaura similis,
family Iguanidae

Green iguana
Iguana iguana, family Iguanidae

FACT FILE

Family Iguanidae This family contains terrestrial, rock-dwelling, marine, and arboreal species. They range from the 5½ inch (14 cm) snout–vent length *Dipsosaurus* to the more than 27½ inch (70 cm) *Cyclura*. Young iguanas of some species eat insects, but later become predominantly herbivorous, feeding on leaves, fruit, and even algae. All species are oviparous.

Genera 8
Species 36

USA to Paraguay,
Galápagos Is., Fiji,
West Indies

Old salts
Marine iguanas spend
so much time at sea that
they have a special gland to
exude salt from their bodies.

Long time coming
The Fiji crested
iguana (*Brachylophus
vitiensis*) has a 30-week
incubation—three times
that of other iguanas.

LIZARD TONGUES

The long forked tongues of monitors are used to capture scent information from the air and to transfer it to the Jacobson's organ for analysis. The long, sticky tongues of chameleons are used to capture prey, while the blue-tongued skink (below) flashes its tongue to deter attacking birds.

CONSERVATION WATCH

The 15 species of iguanas on the IUCN Red List are categorized as follows:

5 Critically endangered
2 Endangered
7 Vulnerable
1 Near threatened

CONSERVATION WATCH

Lizard losses One species of Crotaphytidae, the blunt-nosed leopard lizard (*Gambelia sila*), is listed as endangered on the IUCN Red List due to habitat encroachment. One species of Phrynosomatidae, the Coachella Valley fringe-toed lizard (*Uma inornata*) of North America, is on the IUCN Red List as endangered. It lives in moving dune areas which have now been stabilized by vegetation and construction. Populations of collard and leopard lizards, however, are abundant in the southwest deserts of the United States.

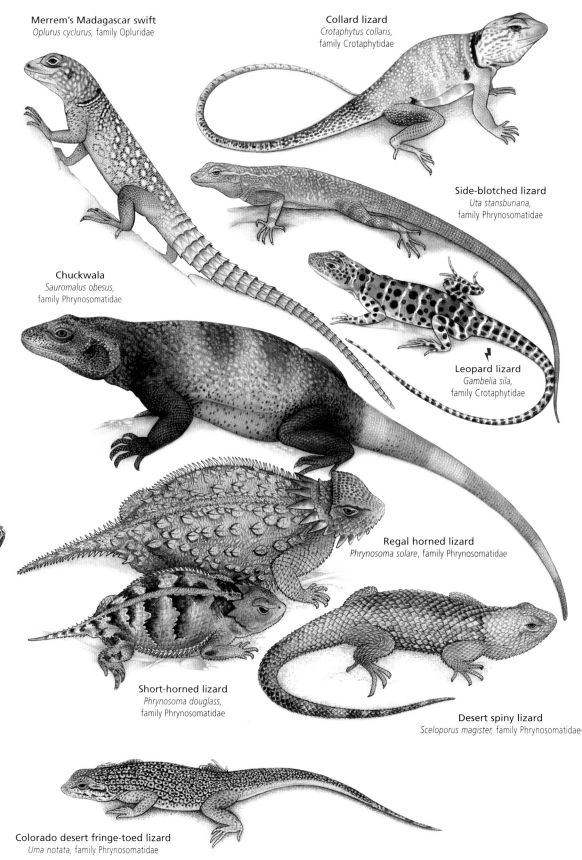

Merrem's Madagascar swift
Oplurus cyclurus, family Opluridae

Collard lizard
Crotaphytus collaris,
family Crotaphytidae

Side-blotched lizard
Uta stansburiana,
family Phrynosomatidae

Chuckwala
Sauromalus obesus,
family Phrynosomatidae

Leopard lizard
Gambelia sila,
family Crotaphytidae

Regal horned lizard
Phrynosoma solare, family Phrynosomatidae

Short-horned lizard
Phrynosoma douglass,
family Phrynosomatidae

Desert spiny lizard
Sceloporus magister, family Phrynosomatidae

Colorado desert fringe-toed lizard
Uma notata, family Phrynosomatidae

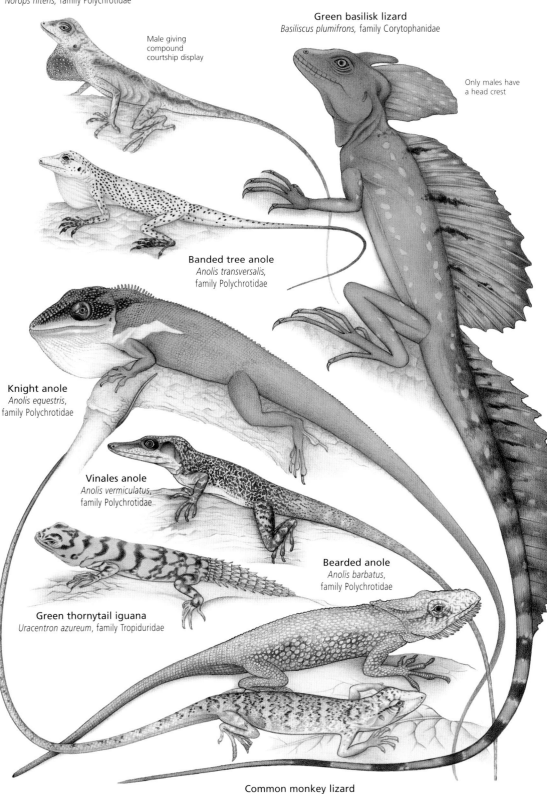

Blue-throated anole
Norops nitens, family Polychrotidae

Male giving
compound
courtship display

Green basilisk lizard
Basiliscus plumifrons, family Corytophanidae

Only males have
a head crest

Banded tree anole
Anolis transversalis,
family Polychrotidae

Knight anole
Anolis equestris,
family Polychrotidae

Vinales anole
Anolis vermiculatus,
family Polychrotidae

Bearded anole
Anolis barbatus,
family Polychrotidae

Green thornytail iguana
Uracentron azureum, family Tropiduridae

Common monkey lizard
Polychrus marmoratus, family Polychrotidae

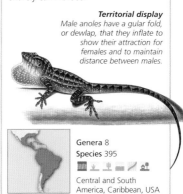

FACT FILE

Family Agamidae Chisel-tooth lizards are from Africa, Asia, and Australia. There are 52 genera, ranging from 2 to 14 inches (5 to 35 cm) in length from snout to vent. Forest species are green; desert species are brown, gray, or black. Sexual dimorphism in coloration is common; some can change coloration rapidly. The head is usually large, and distinct from the neck; the body form may be compressed, depressed, or cylindrical. The thick tongue is notched.

Genera 50
Species 420

Australia, Indonesia, Asia, Africa

Frilled lizard This arboreal lizard is active diurnally in dry woodlands. When escaping, it runs bipedally. If threatened, it erects its huge frilled collar to appear much larger than it is.

- Up to 11¼ in (28 cm)
- Arboreal
- Oviparous
- 8–23
- Common

N. Australia &
S. New Guinea

Carnivores
Frilled lizards feed on cicadas in the trees and will descend to the ground to feed on ants and crickets.

Thorny devil A hygroscopic system of grooves on this lizard's skin leads to the corners of its mouth, allowing it to drink the dew that falls on its back. It feeds only on ants, similar to the North American horned lizards.

- Up to 4½ in (11 cm)
- Terrestrial
- Oviparous
- 3–10
- Common

W. Australia

⚡ CONSERVATION WATCH

The five species of Agamidae on the 2003 IUCN Red List are categorized as follows:

    2 Endangered
    1 Vulnerable
    2 Data deficient

1   **Frilled lizard**
    Chlamydosaurus kingii, family Agamidae

2   **Banded agama**
    Laudakia stellio, family Agamidae

3   **Thorny devil**
    Moloch horridus, family Agamidae

4   **Eastern bearded dragon**
    Pogona barbata, family Agamidae

5   **Ocellated mastigure**
    Uromastyx ocellata, family Agamidae

6   **Sinai agama**
    Pseudotrapelus sinaitus,
    family Agamidae

7   **Iranian toad-headed agama**
    Phrynocephalus persicus,
    family Agamidae

8   **Persian agama**
    Trapelus persicus, family Agamidae

9   **Moroccan dabb lizard**
    Uromastyx acanthinura,
    family Agamidae

10 **Common agama**
    Agama agama, family Agamidae

1	Armored pricklenape *Acanthosaura armata*, family Agamidae	4	Giant forest dragon *Gonocephalus grandis*, family Agamidae	7	Indo-Chinese forest lizard *Calotes mystaceus*, family Agamidae
2	Five-lined flying dragon *Draco quinquefasciatus*, family Agamidae	5	Chinese water dragon *Physignathus cocincinus*, family Agamidae	8	Common green forest lizard *Calotes calotes*, family Agamidae
3	Sailfin lizard *Hydrosaurus amboinensis*, family Agamidae	6	Sumatra nose-horned lizard *Harpesaurus beccarii*, family Agamidae	9	Tropical forest dragon *Gonocephalus liogaster*, family Agamidae

TREE DRAGON

The semiarboreal tree dragon (*Diporiphora superba*) is one of the most slender agamids. It measures 3 inches (8 cm) in snout–vent length and its tail is up to four times its body length.

Treetop maneuvers
The tree dragon uses its long tail for balance while climbing and scampering through the branches.

LIZARD REPRODUCTION

Clutch size Geckos (top), regardless of size or nutrient condition, produce two eggs per clutch. Some species can vary clutch size and egg size (center). Large species (bottom) have large clutches of large eggs and the number and size of the eggs is proportionate to the size and physical condition of the female.

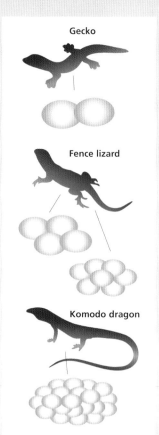

Gecko

Fence lizard

Komodo dragon

Reproductive patterns in lizards vary widely. Some lizard species mature rapidly, are short lived, and are continuously producing an egg. Other species take several years to mature and then lay large clutches of large eggs for many years. Between these two extremes there are all possible variations of numbers of clutches per year and viviparity. Some species are egg layers at low altitudes but populations at high altitudes or latitudes are viviparous. The female acts as an incubator, moving with the developing embryos into optimum incubation temperatures. Equally amazing are some species that are stuck in evolutionary inertia and produce no more than two eggs per clutch regardless of their size or the amount of stored energy.

Continuous ovulation Anoles of all sizes only produce one egg per clutch; they have continuous ovulation, first from one ovary then the other.

Skink with eggs Many species of skinks and glass lizards brood their eggs. The female stays with them, helping to fend off attacks from insect predators, and protecting them from fungus and dehydration until they hatch. Some skinks even lick their young as they are hatching.

Sceloporus with eggs Fence lizards (Sceloporus) are able to vary the number and size of their eggs according to the time of year and their physical condition. They put their energy into large eggs for the first clutches and many smaller eggs for later clutches that will have less time to develop before the onset of winter.

Iguana with eggs Iguanas normally dig tunnels in sandy beaches and deposit between 25 and 40 eggs, depending on the size of the female. The eggs hatch in 3 months and the hatchlings seek out other iguanas in order to eat their feces, thereby inoculating their guts with cellulose-digesting microbes.

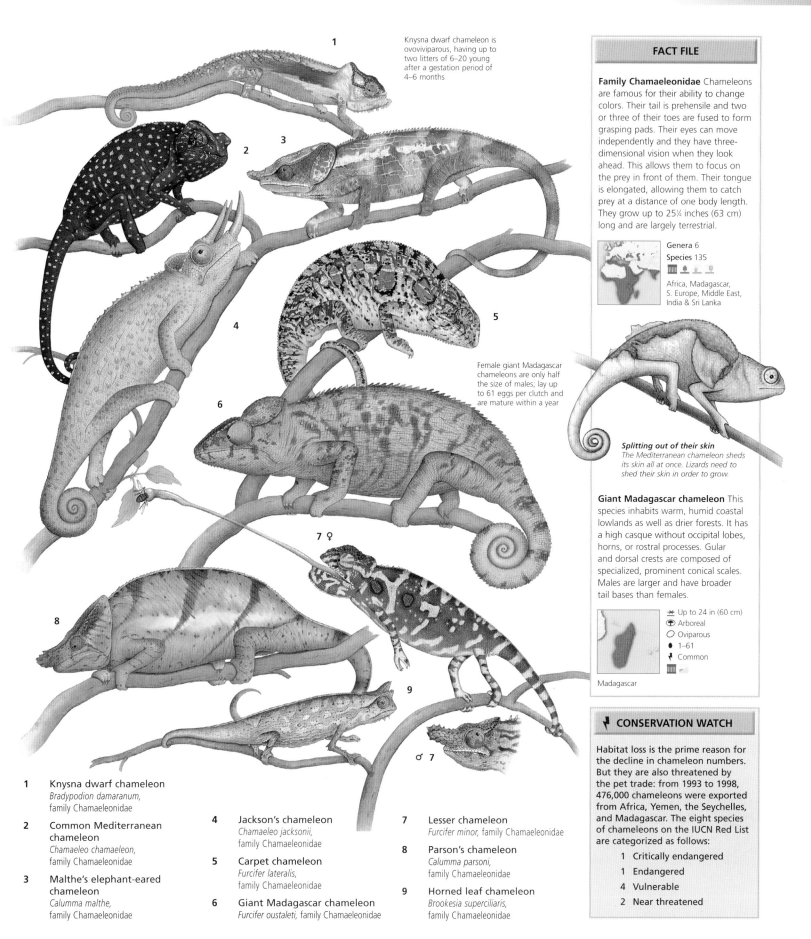

Knysna dwarf chameleon is ovoviviparous, having up to two litters of 6–20 young after a gestation period of 4–6 months

Female giant Madagascar chameleons are only half the size of males; lay up to 61 eggs per clutch and are mature within a year

FACT FILE

Family Chamaeleonidae Chameleons are famous for their ability to change colors. Their tail is prehensile and two or three of their toes are fused to form grasping pads. Their eyes can move independently and they have three-dimensional vision when they look ahead. This allows them to focus on the prey in front of them. Their tongue is elongated, allowing them to catch prey at a distance of one body length. They grow up to 25¼ inches (63 cm) long and are largely terrestrial.

Genera 6
Species 135

Africa, Madagascar, S. Europe, Middle East, India & Sri Lanka

Splitting out of their skin
The Mediterranean chameleon sheds its skin all at once. Lizards need to shed their skin in order to grow.

Giant Madagascar chameleon This species inhabits warm, humid coastal lowlands as well as drier forests. It has a high casque without occipital lobes, horns, or rostral processes. Gular and dorsal crests are composed of specialized, prominent conical scales. Males are larger and have broader tail bases than females.

Up to 24 in (60 cm)
Arboreal
Oviparous
1–61
Common

Madagascar

CONSERVATION WATCH

Habitat loss is the prime reason for the decline in chameleon numbers. But they are also threatened by the pet trade: from 1993 to 1998, 476,000 chameleons were exported from Africa, Yemen, the Seychelles, and Madagascar. The eight species of chameleons on the IUCN Red List are categorized as follows:

1 Critically endangered
1 Endangered
4 Vulnerable
2 Near threatened

1 Knysna dwarf chameleon
Bradypodion damaranum, family Chamaeleonidae

2 Common Mediterranean chameleon
Chamaeleo chamaeleon, family Chamaeleonidae

3 Malthe's elephant-eared chameleon
Calumma malthe, family Chamaeleonidae

4 Jackson's chameleon
Chamaeleo jacksonii, family Chamaeleonidae

5 Carpet chameleon
Furcifer lateralis, family Chamaeleonidae

6 Giant Madagascar chameleon
Furcifer oustaleti, family Chamaeleonidae

7 Lesser chameleon
Furcifer minor, family Chamaeleonidae

8 Parson's chameleon
Calumma parsoni, family Chamaeleonidae

9 Horned leaf chameleon
Brookesia superciliaris, family Chamaeleonidae

FACT FILE

Family Gekkonidae The geckos are the most speciose family of lizards, split into four subfamilies. Covered with small granular scales, they vary in size from ¾ inch to 13 inches (1.5 to 33 cm). The tails are usually fragile and break easily.

Tongue washing *Most species of geckos do not have eyelids and use the tongue to clean the eye spectacles, as in Cogger's velvet gecko.*

Genera 109
Species 970

Pan-tropical, S. North America, South America, Africa, S. Europe, S. Asia, Indo-Australia

Common leopard gecko Leopard geckos have moveable eyelids and lack toe pads. The sex is determined by incubation temperature.

Up to 10 in (25 cm)
Terrestrial
Oviparous
2
Common

Afghanistan, Pakistan, W. India, Iraq, Iran

Banded gecko This nocturnal gecko has large, moveable eyelids, no toe pads and pre-anal pores in a continuous row. Tails are easily lost.

Up to 4 in (10 cm)
Terrestrial
Oviparous
2
Common

S.W. USA to Mexico & Panama

ADAPTED FOR SAND

Fine free-flowing sand requires specialized feet to efficiently traverse the terrain. The African web-footed gecko (*Pallmatogecko rangeri*) uses its feet like snow shoes on the sand to keep it on the surface.

Sand shoes *Some lizards have fringes along the digits to allow them better traction on sand; others have paddle-like webbed feet.*

One of the few lizards native to New Zealand

Tail mimics head to distract predators

1 Tokashiki gecko
Goniurosaurus kuroiwae, family Gekkonidae

2 Common leopard gecko
Eublepharis macularius, family Gekkonidae

3 Prehensile tailed gecko
Aeluroscalabotes felinus, family Gekkonidae

4 Banded gecko
Coleonyx variegatus, family Gekkonidae

5 Green tree gecko
Naultinus elegans, family Gekkonidae

6 Thomas's sticky-toed gecko
Hoplodactylus rakiurae, family Gekkonidae

7 New Caledonia bumpy gecko
Rhacodactylus auriculatus, family Gekkonidae

8 Stellate knob-tail
Nephrurus stellatus, family Gekkonidae

9 Northern leaf-tailed gecko
Saltuarius cornutus, family Gekkonidae

Tail is flattened

Two-thirds of
length is tail

Enormous eyes,
bulbous head,
short tail

1   **Lined gecko**
    Gekko vittatus, family Gekkonidae

2   **Henkel's flat-tailed gecko**
    Uroplatus henkeli, family Gekkonidae

3   **Tokay gecko**
    Gekko gecko, family Gekkonidae

4   **Northern spiny-tailed gecko**
    Diplodactylus ciliaris, family Gekkonidae

5   **Marbled velvet gecko**
    Oedura marmorata, family Gekkonidae

6   **Marble-faced worm lizard**
    Delma australus, family Pygopodidae

7   **Burton's snake-lizard**
    Lialis burtonis, family Pygopodidae

8   **Gray's bow-fingered gecko**
    Cyrtodactylus pulchellus,
    family Gekkonidae

9   **Common wonder gecko**
    Teratoscincus scincus,
    family Gekkonidae

FACT FILE

Mourning gecko This arboreal gecko is covered with small scales. The tail is long and depressed with a lateral fringe of small, spinose scales.

🦎 Up to 2 in (5 cm)
🌳 Arboreal
○ Oviparous
● 2
🌾 Common

N.E. Australia, Malaysia to Oceania

Common wall gecko This gecko is strong and heavily built, with rows of keeled, tubercular scales. Males are territorial. The eggs take 10 weeks to hatch and the young 2 years to mature.

🦎 Up to 6 in (15 cm)
🌳 Arboreal
○ Oviparous
● 2
🌾 Common

Mediterranean & S. European coast

Kuhl's flying gecko This terrestrial species lays clutches of two eggs about 30 days apart. The eggs attach to bark or rocks and hatch in about 60 days.

🦎 Up to 6 in (15 cm)
🌳 Arboreal
○ Oviparous
● 2
🌾 Common

S.E. Asia

FLYING GECKO

At high speeds, the cutaneous flaps allow flying geckos to slow down and achieve shallower glide angles. The webbed feet function in gliding and their aerial locomotion is more similar to "flying" tree frogs than to other reptilian gliders.

Parachuting
The skin flaps along the body and tail flare out in flight and allow the Kuhl's flying gecko to break its fall.

⚡ CONSERVATION WATCH

The 27 species of Geckonidae on the IUCN Red List are categorized as follows:

2	Extinct
1	Critically endangered
3	Endangered
8	Vulnerable
7	Near threatened
3	Data deficient
3	Least concern

Broad-tailed day gecko is native to Madagascar but is well established on Hawaii

1   **Madagascar day gecko**
    Phelsuma madagascariensis,
    family Gekkonidae

2   **Broad-tailed day gecko**
    Phelsuma laticauda, family Gekkonidae

3   **Mourning gecko**
    Lepidodactylus lugubris,
    family Gekkonidae

4   **Common wall gecko**
    Tarentola mauritanica,
    family Gekkonidae

5   **Israeli fan-fingered gecko**
    Ptyodactylus puiseuxi, family Gekkonidae

6   **Kuhl's flying gecko**
    Ptychozoon kuhli, family Gekkonidae

7   **Anderson's short-fingered gecko**
    Stenodactylus petrii, family Gekkonidae

8   **Ruppell's leaf-toed gecko**
    Hemidactylus flaviviridis,
    family Gekkonidae

9   **Cradock thick-toed gecko**
    Pachydactylus geitje, family Gekkonidae

10 **Wiegmann's striped gecko**
    Gonatodes vittatus, family Gekkonidae

Long-tail whip lizard is more than two-thirds tail; the tail will break off, if grasped by a predator, so that the lizard can escape

Family Gerrhosauridae Plated lizards have large, symmetrical shields with bony plates, and the scales on the body are rectangular and overlapping. They are terrestrial and omnivorous, consuming insects and plants. Limbs are reduced in grassland species. Most species are viviparous. Clutches of between two and six eggs are laid.

Swimming through grass
The long-tail whip lizard is able to compress its legs against its body as it rapidly wriggles through grass stems to escape predators.

Genera 6
Species 32

S. Africa & Madagascar

Family Cordylidae Girdled lizards have large symmetrical scales with bony plates on the head. The rectangular, overlapping body scales are usually strongly keeled but are granular in flat lizards. Girdled lizards are terrestrial and produce live young.

Genera 4
Species 52

S. Africa

Rolled up in a ball
The armadillo girdled lizard (Cordylus cataphractus) bites its own tail to present an unswallowable form to predators.

⚑ CONSERVATION WATCH

The 11 species of Cordylidae on the IUCN Red List are categorized as follows:

1 Extinct
5 Vulnerable
5 Near threatened

1 Rough-scaled plated lizard
Gerrhosaurus major,
family Gerrhosauridae

2 Madagascar girdled lizard
Zonosaurus madagascariensis,
family Gerrhosauridae

3 Long-tail whip lizard
Tetradactylus tetradactylus,
family Gerrhosauridae

4 Lesser flat lizard
Platysaurus guttatus, family Cordylidae

5 Karoo girdled lizard
Cordylus polyzonus, family Cordylidae

6 Black crag lizard
Pseudocordylus melanotus,
family Cordylidae

7 Mole skink
Eumeces egregius, family Scincidae

8 Schneider's skink
Novoeumeces schneideri, family Scincidae

9 Sand fish
Scincus scincus, family Scincidae

FACT FILE

Family Scincidae Skinks are usually covered with overlapping smooth scales. The adults vary from 1 to 14 inches (2.5 to 35 cm) in length. The body shape varies from robust species to species with no external limbs. Limbless species are usually burrowers and the rest are terrestrial or arboreal. Tails are long to moderately long. Tail autonomy is present in most species. Skinks are active foragers, using both visual and olfactory cues to find prey. Most species lay eggs, but viviparity evolved in the family at least 25 times.

Genera 116
Species 993

Cosmopolitan in most terrestrial habitats

Telltale tails *Territorial male five-lined skinks (Eumeces fasciatus) recognize females and juveniles by their bright blue tails and allow them access to their territories.*

Hosmer's spiny-tailed skink The base of this skink's tail lacks enlarged and expanded scales, and long, rugose ear lobules almost conceal the ear. This is a diurnal rock-dwelling lizard found in rock outcrops and stony hillsides, where it lives in crevices, under boulders, and on tumbled rock slides.

⟷ Up to 7 in (18 cm)
◔ Terrestrial
○ Oviparous
• 2
🍴 Common

N.E. Australia

Centralian blue-tongued lizard This lizard has a bright blue tongue, relatively short five-toed limbs, and a short tail. It thrives in stony areas in desert and semidesert areas where it feeds on insects and other invertebrates. The tail is about half the body length.

⟷ Up to 12 in (30 cm)
◔ Terrestrial
🦎 Viviparous
• 10 live young
🍴 Common

N. & N.W. Australia

Solomon Island skink can grasp a branch and hang by its prehensile tail

1 Solomon Island skink *Corucia zebrata*, family Scincidae	**3** Hosmer's spiny-tailed skink *Egernia hosmeri*, family Scincidae	**5** Shingleback lizard *Tiliqua rugosa*, family Scincidae
2 Emerald skink *Dasia smaragdina*, family Scincidae	**4** Centralian blue-tongued lizard *Tiliqua multifasciata*, family Scincidae	**6** Three-lined burrowing skink *Androngo trivittatus*, family Scincidae
		7 Otago skink *Oligosoma otagense*, family Scincidae

AUSTRALIAN BLUE TONGUE PYGMY SKINK

Tiliqua adelaidensis was thought to be extinct, but in 1992 one was found in a snake's stomach. Since that time, a recovery plan has been in operation and numbers have now reached 5,500.

↯ CONSERVATION WATCH

The 43 species of Scincidae on the IUCN Red List are categorized as follows:

- 3 Extinct
- 2 Critically endangered
- 3 Endangered
- 21 Vulnerable
- 5 Near threatened
- 7 Data deficient
- 2 Least concern

1 Bridled mabuya
Mabuya vittata, family Scincidae

2 Christmas Island grass skink
Lygosoma bowringii, family Scincidae

3 Boulenger's legless skink
Typhlosaurus vermis, family Scincidae

4 Red-sided ctenotus
Ctenotus pulchellus, family Scincidae

5 Northwestern sandslider
Lerista bipes, family Scincidae

6 Cape York mulch skink
Glaphyromorphus crassicaudum, family Scincidae

7 Lined fire-tailed skink
Morethia ruficauda, family Scincidae

8 Juniper skink
Ablepharus kitaibelii, family Scincidae

9 Desert rainbow skink
Carlia triacantha, family Scincidae

10 Six-lined burrowing skink
Scelotes sexlineatus, family Scincidae

LIZARD COURTSHIP

Anole courtship displays Small, colorful arboreal lizards are most adapted to using visual communication for courtship. The males have species-specific, bright dewlap colors and head bobs, push-ups, or other motions that attract females to them for copulation. Variation exists between individuals, so that females can select a male by the way he courts her. The male's vigor in courtship is the component most often used by females in their selection of a mate.

Bobbing rapidly The carpenter anole (Norops carpenteri) (above) has a simple display: the dewlap, which is uniformly orange-colored, is extended and held open, while the head is bobbed at regular frequency. The male has a series of over a dozen rapid head bobs in his courtship display, while holding his dewlap extended the entire time.

Variable bobbing The silky anole (N. sericeus) (above) has a compound display: the dewlap has a central color that contrasts with the basal color. When the dewlap is extended only partway, the spot does not show. The head bob pattern is independent of the dewlap extension rhythm. The male begins bobbing rapidly for the first five bobs, then bobs in slow motion for the remainder of the sequence; the dewlap is extended and retracted twice.

Slow bobbing The display of the lichen anole (N. pentaprion) (above) is complex. The dewlap has a red basal color with blue lines: the number of blue lines exposed varies according to the extension of the dewlap. The slow bobbing sequence is synchronized with the extension of the dewlap—bob and extend, retract, bob and extend.

Courtship displays have evolved in lizards to ensure that gametes are not wasted on mating with the wrong species or inferior individuals. Males often maintain territories in resource-rich areas and will fight other males to maintain them. Females are allowed to enter males' territories and are encouraged to mate by energetic courtship displays. When there are many similar species or species in the same genus in the same habitat the courtship behavioral patterns are more complex. Courtship displays are most complex and have been most intensively studied in the family Polychrotidae. Courtship in monitor lizards (Varanidae) involves tongue flicks by males along different parts of the female's body during the initiation of courtship. Communication in skinks is primarily chemical.

Larger than life
When the frill is extended fully, it can reach 14 inches (35 cm) across, longer than its body length.

Rain-maker
Australian Aborigines will not hunt the frilled lizard because they believe that it calls the rain to come; without rain, the country falls into drought.

Pseudo-copulation In the whiptails (Cnemidophorus) of the southwestern deserts of the United States, females reproduce without males or their sperm (parthenogenetic reproduction). The genetic component of the female is identical to that of her offspring. Pseudo-copulation occurs in some species of these clones of all female lizards. One female behaves like a male and attempts to mount with another female. The courtship and pseudo-copulation stimulate ovulation.

Larger than life
By expanding its folded neck skin, the frilled dragon can appear much larger when threatening other males or attempting to attract females.

Expanding frill
Dominant male frilled lizards show off different display sequences during courtship of females or territoriality displays toward other males. Over 75 different sequences have been recorded, including head bobbing, push-ups, beard erection, color changes, body inflations, head licking, and jaw gaping. Apart from the changes in shape and size of the lizard, changes in color and flashes of color as they open the mouth are a major part of their repertoire.

Family Lacertidae Adult lacertids are 1½–10 inches (4–25 cm) in body length. The scales are variable, from large, overlapping smooth or keeled to small and granular. All species have limbs. Tails are long, sometimes over twice the body length. Most lacertids are terrestrial but some are arboreal. Most are oviparous, but some are viviparous and some populations are parthenogenetic. Almost all species are insectivorous and some eat seeds.

Genera 27
Species 220

Africa, Europe, Asia & N. East Indies

Giant Canary Island lizard Hatchlings take 3 years to reach maturity and live for about 12 years. Adults are primarily herbivorous and are important in seed dispersal. The disproportionately long hindlimbs of males allow them faster acceleration when escaping predators.

⚔ Up to 10½ in (27 cm)
◖ Terrestrial
○ Oviparous
● 10
♟ Common

Grand Canary Island (Canary Is.)

Tiger lizard These lizards actively hunt scorpions, which are dormant during the day and sparsely distributed, which makes them easy targets for predatory birds. Tiger lizards avoid predators by being active during the heat of the day at a body temperature of 102°F (39°C).

⚔ Up to 8 in (20 cm)
◖ Terrestrial
○ Oviparous
● 3–8
♟ Common

S. Namibia, S.W. Botswana, South Africa

The 13 species of Lacertidae on the IUCN Red List are categorized as follows:

1	Critically endangered
1	Endangered
5	Vulnerable
2	Near threatened
1	Data deficient
3	Least concern

1 European green lizard
Ablepharus kitaibelii, family Lacertidae

2 Giant Canary Island lizard
Gallotia stehlini, family Lacertidae

3 Zagrosian lizard
Timon princeps, family Lacertidae

4 Tiger lizard
Nucras tessellata, family Lacertidae

5 Jeweled lizard
Timon lepidus, family Lacertidae

6 Sand lizard
Lacerta agilis, family Lacertidae

7 Gallot's lizard
Gallotia galloti, family Lacertidae

8 Balkan emerald lizard
Lacerta trilineata, family Lacertidae

Family Xantusiidae Even though Xantusidae are called night lizards, many species are diurnal. They are small lizards, up to 4 inches (10 cm) long, with small granular dorsal scales and large ventral scales. All species are viviparous. Most species feed on invertebrates, although one cave-dwelling species feeds on figs. Night lizards are terrestrial and arboreal. In Mexico, Lepidophyma, a species of night lizard, are called scorpions and are mistakenly thought to be venomous. Like many lizards, their tails will break off if grasped; a new tail will regenerate but will be of a uniform color.

Liberated from males The yellow-spotted night lizard (Lepidophyma flavimaculata), is nocturnal and viviparous. Some populations are parthenogenetic.

Genera 3
Species 20

W. USA & E. Mexico, Central America & N. South America

Common wall lizard This is a colonial species. It is a good climber and basks on rocks. Wall lizards feed on invertebrates: beetles, flies, butterflies, and spiders. They are prey items for raptors and snakes, particularly young horned vipers or large whip snakes.

- Up to 4 in (10 cm)
- Terrestrial, arboreal
- Oviparous
- 2–8
- Common

Southern Europe & Balkans

1 Italian wall lizard
Podarcis sicula, family Lacertidae

2 Common wall lizard
Podarcis muralis, family Lacertidae

3 Menorca wall lizard
Podarcis perspicillata, family Lacertidae

4 Desert night lizard
Xantusia vigilis, family Xantusiidae

5 Granite night lizard
Xantusia henshawi, family Xantusiidae

6 Viviporus lizard
Lacerta vivipara, family Xantusiidae

7 Radd's rock lizard
Lacerta raddei, family Xantusiidae

8 Uzzell's rock lizard
Lacerta uzzeli, family Xantusiidae

9 Milo's wall lizard
Podarcis milensis, family Xantusiidae

Egyptian fringe-fingered lizard
The toes on these lizards have a fringe enabling better traction over windblown sand dunes. They also have shovel noses and countersunk lower jaws to allow them ease in plowing through sand. Ants make up most of their diet.

- Up to 8 in (20 cm)
- Terrestrial
- Oviparous
- 3–5
- Common

Algeria, Egypt, Israel, Jordan & Libya

Blue-throated keeled-lizard These diurnal lizards are the smallest lacertids in Europe, and forage for insects in vineyards and buildings. They emerge from hibernation and breed in April; breeding males have a bright blue throat and orange-red ventral surface.

- Up to 8 in (20 cm)
- Terrestrial, arboreal
- Oviparous
- 2–3
- Common

N.E. Italy to Gulf of Corinth & Ionian islands

Sawtail lizard Its flattened shape and striking coloration make this species unmistakable. This lizard uses its flat body and broad tail to glide through the air from tree to tree. They have long, stout trunks and tails and relatively strong hindlimbs.

Long jumper
The sawtail lizard jumps up to 33 feet (10 m) from tree to tree, its flattened body and tail assisting the feat.

- Up to 5 in (12.5 cm)
- Arboreal
- Oviparous
- 2
- Common

C., E. & W. Africa & Mozambique

Snake-eyed lizard This lizard gets its name from the large transparent disks that cover its eyes, so large that the eyelids no longer cover the eye. When escaping from a predator, they scamper from bush to bush and then pop up to look for the aggressor. They can also run short distances bipedally.

- Up to 2 in (5 cm)
- Terrestrial
- Oviparous
- 4–5
- Common

N. Africa, S.E. Europe to Middle East & India

1 **Egyptian fringe-fingered lizard**
Acanthodactylus pardalis, family Lacertidae

2 **Rapid racerunner**
Eremias velox, family Lacertidae

3 **Algerian psammodromus**
Psammodromus algirus, family Lacertidae

4 **Blue-throated keeled-lizard**
Algyroides nigropunctatus, family Lacertidae

5 **Small-spotted lizard**
Mesalina guttulata, family Lacertidae

6 **Asian grass lizard**
Takydromus sexlineatus, family Lacertidae

7 **Sawtail lizard**
Holaspis guentheri, family Lacertidae

8 **Mourning racerunner**
Heliobolus lugubris, family Lacertidae

9 **Slender sand lizard**
Meroles anchietae, family Lacertidae

10 **Snake-eyed lizard**
Ophisops elegans, family Lacertidae

FACT FILE

Family Gymnophthalmidae The microtiids are small, oviparous lizards, up to 2½ inches (6 cm) long, with a wide variation of scale patterns. Some species have reduced limbs. Tails are autonomous. Most of the lizards in this diverse family live within the forest-floor litter. A few species are semiaquatic. All species consume invertebrates.

Genera 36
Species 160

S. Central America &
N.W. South America

Family Teiidae Whiptail lizards and tegus, which are oviparous, vary in adult size from 2 to 16 inches (5 to 40 cm) in snout–vent length. Dorsal and lateral scales are small and granular, while the ventral scales are larger, rectangular, and in rows. The tails are long and autonomic. Smaller whiptails prefer deserts, grasslands, and open areas in the forest where they prey on invertebrates. The larger tegus prefer open forests and are omnivorous.

Sexless clones
*The checkered whiptail
(Cnemidophorus
tesselatus) reproduces
asexually; only females
are present in the
population.*

Genera 9
Species 118

N. USA to South America

Golden tegu This heavy-bodied lizard is one of the main predators of turtle eggs in the Amazon Basin. To protect their own eggs from predation, they lay them in arboreal termite nests.

Up to 12 in (30 cm)
Terrestrial
Oviparous
4–32
Common

N. South America

🗡 CONSERVATION WATCH

The six species of Teiidae on the IUCN Red List are categorized as follows:

2 Extinct
1 Critically endangered
1 Vulnerable
2 Data deficient

Heliothermic species that feeds on ants and spiders in the leaf litter

1 Ocellated tegu
Cercosaura ocellata,
family Gymnophthalmidae

2 Thomas's bachia
Bachia panoplia,
family Gymnophthalmidae

3 Two-ridged neusticurus
Neusticurus bicarinatus,
family Gymnophthalmidae

4 Rainbow lizard
Cnemidophorus lemniscatus,
family Teiidae

5 Green calango
Kentropyx calcarata, family Teiidae

6 Four-toed tegu
Teius teyou, family Teiidae

7 Slow worm
Anguis fragilis, family Anguidae

8 Common worm lizard
Ophiodes intermedius, family Anguidae

9 Southern alligator lizard
Elgaria multicarinata, family Anguidae

Family Xenosauridae The xenosaurian or knob-scaled lizards are covered with granular scales and large tubercules. These insectivorous lizards inhabit mountainous tropical rain forests in southern Mexico and Guatemala, where they live in rock crevices or tree holes. The Chinese crocodile lizard, their widely disjunct relative, forages for fishes and tadpoles in mountain streams.

Genera 2
Species 5

S. China & S. Mexico & Guatemala

Family Anguidae Anguids have heavily armored scales with underlying osteoderms. Most have limbs, but a large number of them are limbless with long tails that are two-thirds of their total length. They are commonly called glass snakes, because when attacked by a predator the tail breaks into several pieces.

Prehensile tails
Cope's arboreal alligator lizard (Abronia aurita) is adapted for living high in the canopy of tropical rain forests; they hold on with their prehensile tails.

Genera 13
Species 101

S. Asia, S.W. Asia, Europe & Americas

The 10 species of Anguidae listed on the IUCN Red List are categorized as follows:

1	Extinct
3	Critically endangered
1	Endangered
1	Vulnerable
1	Near threatened
3	Data deficient

Lives in the low branches of trees above the water; the tail is high and flattened dorso-laterally for swimming

1 Giant ameiva
Ameiva ameiva, family Teiidae

2 Banded galliwasp
Diploglossus fasciatus, family Anguidae

3 Chinese crocodile lizard
Shinisaurus crocodilurus,
family Xenosauridae

4 Golden tegu
Tupinambis teguixin, family Teiidae

5 European glass lizard
Pseudopus apodus, family Anguidae

6 Slender glass lizard
Ophisaurus attenuatus
family Anguidae

7 Crocodile tegu
Crocodilurus lacertinus, family Teiidae

8 Paraguay Caiman lizard
Dracaena paraguayensis, family Teiidae

FACT FILE

Family Helodermatidae The Gila monster and the Mexican beaded lizard are the only known venomous lizards. They have broad, flattened heads, and stocky bodies, strong limbs, and thick tails that are used for fat storage. Both species are slow-moving, oviparous, and diurnal. They feed on nestlings and lizard or birds' eggs.

Genera 2
Species 2

S.W. USA to Guatemala

Family Lanthanotidae These earless monitors have ptergoid teeth and lack a parietal eye. They are related to the Varanidae and Helodermatidae. The species is nocturnal and semi-aquatic, living along and in forest streams. Monitors forage in the water and on land for small vertebrates and invertebrates. They are oviparous with clutches of up to six eggs.

Genera 1
Species 1

Borneo

SHEDDING SKIN

The outer layer of a lizard's skin (the epidermis) is composed of keratin; scales are thickenings of this layer. As the lizard grows, the outer layer of keratin is shed in large flakes.

Splitting out
All lizards need to shed their skin periodically in order to grow.

CONSERVATION WATCH

Added protection Both species of Helodermatidae are listed on the IUCN Red List as vulnerable. The Gila monster is given complete protection in Arizona, United States, to keep it from wanton slaughter and being engulfed by the pet trade. Mexico lists both species, so the lizards cannot be legally sold on the international pet market and cannot be killed, stuffed, and then sold as curios for the tourist trade.

Tail is round in cross section, with no evidence of a dorsal keel

1 **Mexican beaded lizard**
Heloderma horridum,
family Helodermatidae

2 **Spiny-tailed monitor**
Varanus acanthurus, family Varanidae

3 **Roughneck monitor**
Varanus rudicollis, family Varanidae

4 **Emerald monitor**
Varanus prasinus,
family Varanidae

5 **Gila monster**
Heloderma suspectum,
family Helodermatidae

6 **Borneo earless monitor**
Lanthanotus borneensis,
family Lanthanotidae

7 **Pygmy Mulga monitor**
Varanus gilleni, family Varanidae

Komodo dragons have an extremely
virulent symbiotic bacteria living in
their mouths; within a few hours of
being bitten, wounded prey will lose
energy due to a fever caused by the
bacteria, then drop to the ground.
The dragon trails the animal and
eats it when it is down

1   Crocodile monitor
Varanus salvadorii, family Varanidae

2   Perentie
Varanus giganteus, family Varanidae

3   Gray's monitor
Varanus olivaceus, family Varanidae

4   Desert monitor
Varanus griseus, family Varanidae

5   Sand monitor
Varanus gouldii, family Varanidae

6   Nile monitor
Varanus niloticus, family Varanidae

7   Komodo dragon
Varanus komodoensis, family Varanidae

FACT FILE

Family Varanidae Monitors are
large, long-necked lizards with
thick skin and many rows of
small, rounded scales circling the
body. Their tails are long and
lack caudal autonomy. Their
tongues are long and forked.
The largest of the monitors
is the komodo dragon.

Standing tall *The sand
monitor has an extremely
thick tail, allowing it a
firm tripod stance when
searching for mates or prey.*

Genera 1
Species 50

Africa, Asia, Australia & Pacific Is.

JACOBSON'S ORGAN

A large number of lizards sense the
air around them with their tongues,
picking up chemical cues regarding
food, conspecifics, likely mates, and
predators. The Jacobson's organ has a
pair of cavities lined with sensory cells
on the roof of the mouth. The particles
collected on the lizard's tongue are
transported to ducts leading to these
cavities by the tongue, explaining why
the tongue is forked. The vomeronasal
nerve then transmits the information
collected to the brain for action.

Tongue testing
*Monitors and many
other lizards pick up
airborne scents on
their forked tongues.*

⚡ CONSERVATION WATCH

Monitoring monitors Many species
of monitors are killed for their
skins and meat. In Asia and Africa,
they are exploited for traditional
medicines; they also make up part
of the diet of Australian indigenous
people. More than a million Nile
and other Asiatic monitors are killed
annually for their skins, which are
used in the manufacture of luxury
shoes, belts, purses, and accessories.

SNAKES

CLASS	Reptilia
ORDERS	Squamata
FAMILIES	17
GENERA	438
SPECIES	2,955

At nearly 3,000 species, the variety in snakes is enormous. They range from the tiny burrowing blind snakes of a few inches (10 cm) long to huge constrictors over 33 feet (10 m) in length. Snakes have evolved special methods of locomotion, different ways of gathering environmental cues, and diverse venom delivery systems. Lizards appeared in the fossil record before snakes, and the presence of vestigial pelvic girdles and spurs in some primitive snakes indicates that snakes have evolved from them; the left lung is reduced or absent in snakes and legless lizards, but the right lung is reduced in amphisbaenians. Most of the organs of snakes are reduced in girth and elongated.

Tropic lovers Snakes are found on all continents except Antarctica, and ranges of some even pass above the Arctic circle. Some islands are also devoid of snakes, such as New Zealand, Ireland, and Iceland, and sea snakes are absent from the Atlantic. Snake biodiversity is highest in the tropics.

rattle (series of interlocking shells) — stomach — single lung — hollow, hinged fang — heat-sensitive pit — eye — small intestine — liver — ribs (up to 450 pairs) — venom gland — forked tongue

Snake anatomy As in the example of the Eastern diamondback rattlesnake (above), most snake organs have been reduced in diameter and have increased in length. Lungs in most species have been reduced to one, but males have two functional reproductive organs.

Defensive display Most species of cobras, such as the Cape cobra (*Naja nivea*) (right), have a hood that they can spread to look larger than life in order to frighten enemies or to transfix prey. The dorsal surface of the hood of some species is marked with large eye-like spots to suggest the eyes of a much larger animal.

Hidden fangs When pit vipers, including timber rattlesnakes (below), threaten with an open mouth they keep their fangs relaxed, so they do not obstruct the functioning of their pit organs. These scan for infrared signals from predators or prey.

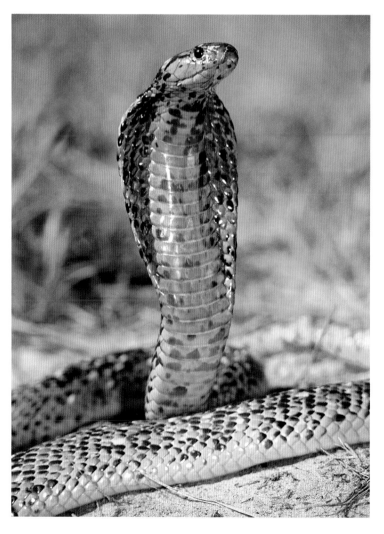

AN EAR TO THE GROUND

Snakes are very close to their environment. In fact, their bellies are in contact with the substrate most of the time—only when they are gliding between trees, swimming, or climbing trees are they free from this close contact with the ground. It is through this earthy contact that they pick up sound vibrations and follow the scent trails of prey and receptive females.

The shape of the snake determines where it will live and what it will do. Shovel-nosed snakes and worm snakes remain within the ground with modified snouts for burrowing and feeding on their subterranean prey. The slender, thin-necked, arboreal snakes are adapted for gliding through the branches and stretching out to reach the next branch only a nose away. They have small clutches of elongate eggs and eat thin, elongate prey, such as lizards or frogs. Short, thick-bodied snakes, like some vipers, are sit-and-wait predators and often gorge on a meal that weighs more than they do. Their awkward shape does not affect them, as they do not move much anyway, and many are venomous. Long-bodied, agile, fast-moving snakes are the athletes in the group, chasing down lizards and other snakes, and using their speed for escape. It is amazing how fast mambas and whip snakes can move

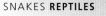

SNAKE SKIN TYPES

Snake skin is made up of scales, which are not separate items, but a thickened part of the skin connected to other scales by thinner areas of elastic skin. Fine, granular scales are common in boas, the smooth, glossy overlapping scales are common in racers, and strongly keeled scales are characteristic of rattlesnakes.

Granular scales

Smooth scales

Keeled scales

Poised to strike
This young green tree python is coiled, half in the air, ready to strike.

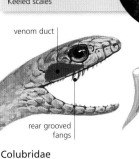

Fang varieties Rear grooved fangs are associated with Duvernoy's gland secretions in Colubridae. Elapidae (cobras, coral snakes, sea snakes, and taipans) have fixed short front fangs. The vipers all have hinged front fangs.

venom duct

rear grooved fangs

Colubridae

venom duct

fixed front hollow fangs

Elapidae

venom duct

swinging front hollow fangs

Viperidae

Infrared sensors
Green tree pythons have heat-sensing receptors embedded in the labial scales, which enable them to receive a visual image of light and heat.

Green constrictors The green tree python is an arboreal predator, feeding on birds, mammals, and lizards. Grasping a bird or bat on the wing with its long teeth, it simultaneously throws a coil around the prey and constricts it. The hatchlings of the green tree python are 11–14 inches (28–35 cm) long and are colored differently from the adults. The bright juvenile color pattern transforms to a vivid green in 6–8 months.

Keen vision The king cobra has large, round pupils adapted for acute diurnal vision. They are designed for detecting the slightest motion of their preferred prey—other snakes—within the vegetation.

through the forest canopy: they do not slither, but flow like a stream of water. Sea snakes have modified their shape to have a paddle-like tail, useful for a pelagic life. Many species never touch land, but feed, breed, and give birth at sea.

All male snakes have two hemipenes in the base of the tail; they are usually used alternately, each receiving sperm from only one of the testicles. This system perhaps evolved from the selective advantage of having a fast recovery time when participating in mass spring orgies following emergence from hibernation. Sperm can be stored for months or more than a year before it is utilized to fertilize eggs.

Females have evolved a range of modified behavior patterns to enhance their genes. Most snakes lay eggs, but many of the more recent snakes have evolved viviparity and some parental care. Through muscle

contractions, pythons can raise their body temperatures when brooding their eggs. Female cobras guard their nest of eggs in a loose construction of leaves built over the nest.

Some of the most fantastic adaptations of modern snakes are the mechanisms they have developed for finding, capturing, killing, and swallowing prey. Highly developed chemical receptors on the roof of the mouth help snakes to identify mates, enemies, and prey. Infrared receptors possessed by pit vipers, boas, and pythons allow them to visualize warm-blooded prey in terms of heat. The venom produced by Viperidae, Elapidae, and Colubridae allow them to stop prey in its tracks and help in swallowing and digesting the meal. Obviously some snakes have evolved more than others, and many are now losing ground—humans are changing the environment faster than snakes can evolve.

Hatchlings emerge Most pythons guard and incubate their eggs. However, once their first week outside the shell is over, the young shed their skins, leave the protective coil of the mother, and disperse, like the young green tree python below.

BOA AND PYTHON SKULLS

The kinetic jaws of snakes are designed to swallow objects up to five times their diameter. Teeth are curved so that by first moving one side and then the other, the food is pushed down the throat.

resting jaw

Full gape The snake's lower jaw is free at the chin to move sideways. Flexible tendons allow the snake to drop its jaw both posteriorly and anteriorly.

distended jaw

Male Mexican rosy boas have well-developed spurs; those of the female are smaller

Tatar sand boas are sold for high prices in central Asia for medicinal purposes

1 **Mexican rosy boa**
Charina trivirgata, family Boidae

2 **Wood snake**
Tropidophis melanurus, family Tropidophiidae

3 **New Guinea ground boa**
Candoia aspera, family Boidae

4 **Calabar ground python**
Calabaria reinhardtii, family Boidae

5 **Rubber boa**
Charina bottae, family Boidae

6 **East African sand boa**
Gongylophis colubrinu, family Boidae

7 **Schaefer's dwarf boa**
Xenophidion schaeferi, family Tropidophiidae

8 **Isthmian dwarf boa**
Ungaliophis continentalis, family Tropidophiidae

9 **Tatar sand boa**
Eryx tataricus, family Boidae

10 **Feick's dwarf boa**
Tropidophis feicki, family Tropidophiidae

Because of its gentle disposition and beautiful pattern, the Indian python has been prized in the pet trade for decades; now most individuals sold are captive-born

Tongue is used to collect airborne scents

Heat-sensing pits are located in the labial scales

Family Boidae This family includes the boas, pythons, and sand boas—the largest living snakes—but some species are less than 20 inches (50 cm) long. The largest may reach 33 feet (10 m) and feed on large mammals, capybaras, deer, and caimans. Boas and sand boas are viviparous; pythons are oviparous.

Egg brooding
The children's python (Antaresia childreni) coils around its eggs to conceal and protect them. It increases body temperature by muscle contractions.

Genera 20
Species 74

Worldwide except Europe and Antarctica

Common boa constrictor Boas are heavy-bodied arboreal snakes that kill their prey by constriction. They have vestigial legs as spurs on either side of the cloaca, which suggests that they are of ancient origin.

- Up to 14 ft (4.2 m)
- Terrestrial, arboreal
- Viviparous
- 30–50 live young
- Common

S. Mexico to Argentina

Reticulated python One of the two largest snakes in the world, this python is more massive than the anaconda. Its prey includes large reptiles, such as lizards and crocodilians, and medium to large mammals, even humans.

- Up to 33 ft (10 m)
- Terrestrial
- Oviparous
- 80–100
- Common

S.E. Asia

1 **Common boa constrictor**
Boa constrictor, family Boidae

2 **Indian python**
Python molarus, family Boidae

3 **Madagascar ground boa**
Acrantophis madagascariensis, family Boidae

4 **African rock python**
Python sebae, family Boidae

5 **Reticulate python**
Python reticulatus, family Boidae

6 **Anaconda**
Eunectes murinus, family Boidae

7 **Emerald tree boa**
Corallus caninus, family Boidae

FACT FILE

Green tree python This nocturnal constrictor feeds on mammals and birds. It is an example of parallel evolution: the emerald tree boa (*Corallus caninus*) of South America evolved in the same habitat and is similar in color and form.

- Up to 6½ ft (2 m)
- Arboreal
- Oviparous
- 12–18
- Uncommon

N.E. Australia, New Guinea

Polymorphic colors
The young differ in color from the bright-green adults; young are bright yellow to brick red when they hatch.

Cook's tree boa This boa feeds on small lizards when young, progressing to rodents and birds as it grows. Prey is ambushed: in one motion, the boa bites and wraps several coils of its body around its victim while suspended from a branch by its prehensile tail.

- Up to 6¼ ft (1.9 m)
- Arboreal
- Viviparous
- 30–80 live young
- Common

Panama, N. South America, West Indies

Black-headed python This python is nocturnal in warmer months and diurnal in cooler months. Its diet consists of monitor lizards, frogs, birds, mammals, and snakes—even death adders. Dingos are its main predator.

- Up to 8½ ft (2.6 m)
- Terrestrial
- Oviparous
- 5–10
- Common

N. Australia

Blood python Blood pythons are stocky, robust, and semiaquatic, spending much time underwater in swamps or streams. They feed primarily on mammals and small birds. Blood python populations are diminishing due to the skin trade: the colorful skin is prized for the luxury leather market.

- Up to 10 ft (3 m)
- Terrestrial, aquatic
- Oviparous
- 18–30
- Common

S.E. Asia

Green tree python
Morelia viridis, family Boidae

Cook's tree boa
Corallus cookii, family Boidae

Carpet python
Morelia spilota, family Boidae

The ventral scales are a yellowish cream color with gray streaking

White-lipped python
Leiopython albertisii, family Boidae

Cuban boa
Epicrates angulifer, family Boidae

Black-headed python
Aspidites melanocephalus, family Boida

Ball python
Python regalis, family Boidae

Blood python
Python curtus, family Boidae

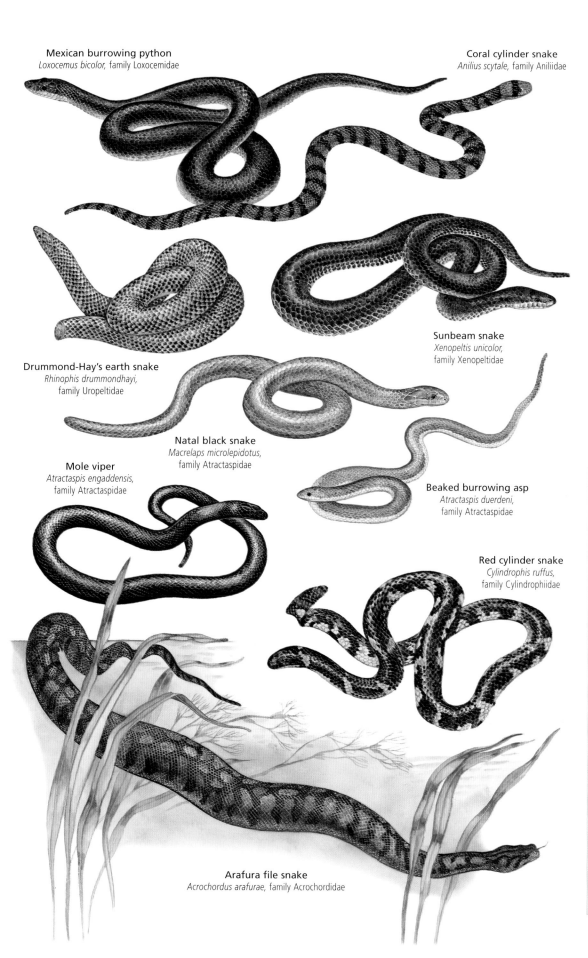

Mexican burrowing python
Loxocemus bicolor, family Loxocemidae

Coral cylinder snake
Anilius scytale, family Aniliidae

Drummond-Hay's earth snake
Rhinophis drummondhayi,
family Uropeltidae

Sunbeam snake
Xenopeltis unicolor,
family Xenopeltidae

Natal black snake
Macrelaps microlepidotus,
family Atractaspidae

Mole viper
Atractaspis engaddensis,
family Atractaspidae

Beaked burrowing asp
Atractaspis duerdeni,
family Atractaspidae

Red cylinder snake
Cylindrophis ruffus,
family Cylindrophiidae

Arafura file snake
Acrochordus arafurae, family Acrochordidae

FACT FILE

Mexican burrowing python This nocturnal python forages for small mammals and reptiles, and sea turtle and lizard eggs. Its pointed snout is useful for burrowing into reptile nests. The large plates on the head suggest those of more recent colubrid snakes, rather than the closely related boas.

Up to 4¼ ft (1.4 m)
Terrestrial, burrowing
Oviparous
2–4
Rare

S. Mexico to Costa Rica

Family Atractaspidae These oviparous snakes are called stiletto vipers because they have a large semi-erect fang on each maxillary bone (upper jaw). They prey on burrowing rodents: the tight spaces mean it is impossible for them to gape their mouths to strike, so they wiggle alongside their prey, shift their jaw to the opposite side from the prey, and expose their long fangs. They then proceed to envenomate their prey, stabbing it with a backslash motion.

Genera 1
Species 18

Africa & Middle East

Family Aniliidae These brightly colored coral-snake mimics live in leaf litter and feed on earthworms, caecilians, eels, amphisbaenians, and snakes. They are on occasion found in the water, but are probably burrowers. When handled, they roll up into a ball.

Genera 1
Species 1

Amazonia (South America)

Family Acrochordidae These snakes have small, strongly keeled scales. File snakes are one of the most aquatic snakes, and are almost incapable of moving on land. They are nocturnal, and feed on fishes and crustaceans.

Genera 1
Species 3

India, S.E. Asia, Australia

Paddle tail
The laterally compressed tail of the little file snake (Acrochordus granulatus) is an adaptation for swimming.

SNAKE DEFENSE STRATEGIES

Looping in alarm The bandy-bandy (*Vermiculla annulata*) is a nocturnal, venomous elapid snake. It throws its body into loops off the ground when it is alarmed. It is possible that the snake is attempting to appear larger than it is by doing this, or that it is striking in a new direction to catch the predator off guard.

Snakes have many different strategies to avoid becoming a meal. Camouflage—utilizing color, pattern, and shape—is the most common tactic. Many arboreal snakes have long, slender heads and necks like twigs so that they blend in with their favored habitat. Escape works if you are very fast, like the red racer (*Masticophis flagellum*), which is built for speed. Many defensive maneuvers were designed to be effective against birds or mammals. The Indian cobra (*Naja naja*) raises half its body off the ground, spreads its hood, and displays large eye spots so that it appears to be a much larger animal. The Arizona coral snake (*Micruroides euryxanthus*) raises its tail and pops its cloaca to distract predators from attacking its head. The prairie ringneck snake (*Diadophis punctatus*) is black dorsally; when threatened, it hides its head in its coils and raises a coiled tail which is bright orange ventrally to startle its attacker. Many snakes will hiss, thrash, bite, and defecate to dissuade unwanted attention.

Rattling good tail When disturbed, a rattlesnake will vibrate its tail and make a loud rattling sound. The noise and the movement distract the potential prey or predators, who end up watching the tail and not the striking head. Many species of non-venomous snakes vibrate their tails as well.

Master of disguise The eyelash viper (*Bothriechis schlegelii*), an arboreal pit viper, is perfectly camouflaged. It chooses an appropriate perch on which to wait for passing mice or frogs. Its color and shape blend in with the vegetation so that predatory birds are not alerted to its presence. The "eyelashes" may help to protect its eyes from abrasion as it slips through the rain-forest canopy.

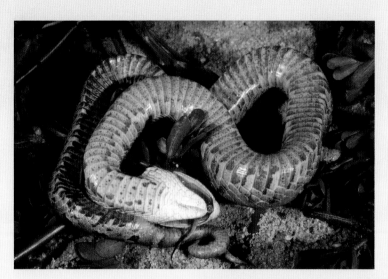

Surprise under the sand Waiting for a meal to pass, the Peringuey's sidewinding adder (*Bitis peringueyi*) (below) becomes invisible as the shifting sand of the Namibian desert blows over it. The adder's pattern and coloration blend in with the golden sand; only its eyes and the black tip of its tail remain visible. Hiding is a good defense against canids and raptors.

Mimicking danger Many nonvenomous snakes have evolved color patterns similar to those of venomous species in their region, to reap the benefit this warning coloration has on predators. This adaptation is called Batesian mimicry. The long-tailed false coral snake (*Pliocercus elapoides*) of the Yucatán peninsula, Mexico, is one of these imitators (far right). It closely resembles the Mayan coral snake (*Micrurus hippocrepis*) (right).

Feigning death When molested, the Eastern hognose snake (above) hisses and strikes with a closed mouth. If this fails to deter a predator, the snake writhes and contorts its body; its mouth is open, and it discharges fetid cloacal fluids. After a few minutes it will roll onto its back and lie limply with its mouth open as though dead. The impact is lost if you turn the snake over, as it will immediately roll onto its back again.

Aging rattles The rattle grows one button each time the snake sheds its skin. This can be four to six times a year.

Snake in the grass When threatened, a bull snake (*Pituophis melanoleucus*) raises its head off the ground and expels air from its trachea; vibrating a cartilage at the tracheal opening creates a loud hissing sound. The tail is vibrated simultaneously, which produces a rattling sound in dry leaves or grasses. These effects combine to scare off most predators.

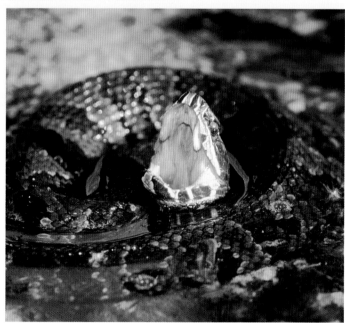

Threat display The venomous Florida cottonmouth (*Agkistrodon piscivorous*) opens its jaws to reveal a startlingly white mouth. This alerts predators to its presence and to the imminent danger. Sympatric nonvenomous water snakes have a similar color pattern and mimic this behavior for their defense.

FACT FILE

Family Colubridae About 63 percent of all species of snakes are included in this family, which utilizes all available reproductive styles and habitats. There are six loosely defined groups within the colubrids: Natricinae are small aquatic or terrestrial snakes; the largest group, Colubrinae, exploit all snake habitats except marine; the primarily oviparous Xenodontinae contains small, New World tropical and terrestrial species; Dipsadinae have diversified in Central and South America and occur in all available habitats; Homalopsinae contains 11 genera of diverse aquatic snakes occurring from northern Australia to Asia; and Aparallactinae are small snakes that range from sub-Saharan Africa to the Middle East.

Genera 320
Species 1,800

Worldwide, except Antarctica & polar regions

Snake trade
The brightly colored corn snake (Elaphe guttata) has been sought after in the pet trade for over 50 years because of its attractive colors and mild disposition. Captive breeding colonies are now providing most pet snakes sold today.

COLUBRID VENOM

People often ignore the fact that most species of colubrids produce venom in the Duvernoy's gland. The venom is released and flows along grooved erect fangs in the back of the mouth. Since the venom is not forced through hollow fangs under pressure, as in front-fanged venom delivery (common to vipers and elapids), only about half enters the wound.

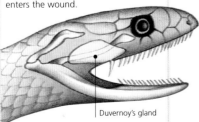

Duvernoy's gland

Non-lethal venom *When dispensed via a wound from the rear teeth, the venom from colubrids can be deadly. Herpetologists have died after underestimating the venom's potency.*

Chinese rat snake
Ptyas karros, family Colubridae

Large whip snake
Coluber jugularis, family Colubridae

Aesculapian snake
Elaphe longissima, family Colubridae

Desert whip snake
Masticophis flagellum, family Colubridae

Green whip snake
Coluber viridiflavus, family Colubridae

Black-banded trinket snake
Elaphe porphyracea, family Colubridae

Red-tailed green ratsnake
Gonyosoma oxycephalum, family Colubridae

Dahl's whip snake
Coluber najadum, family Colubridae

Beauty snake
Elaphe taeniura, family Colubridae

Tropical ratsnake
Spilotes pullatus, family Colubridae

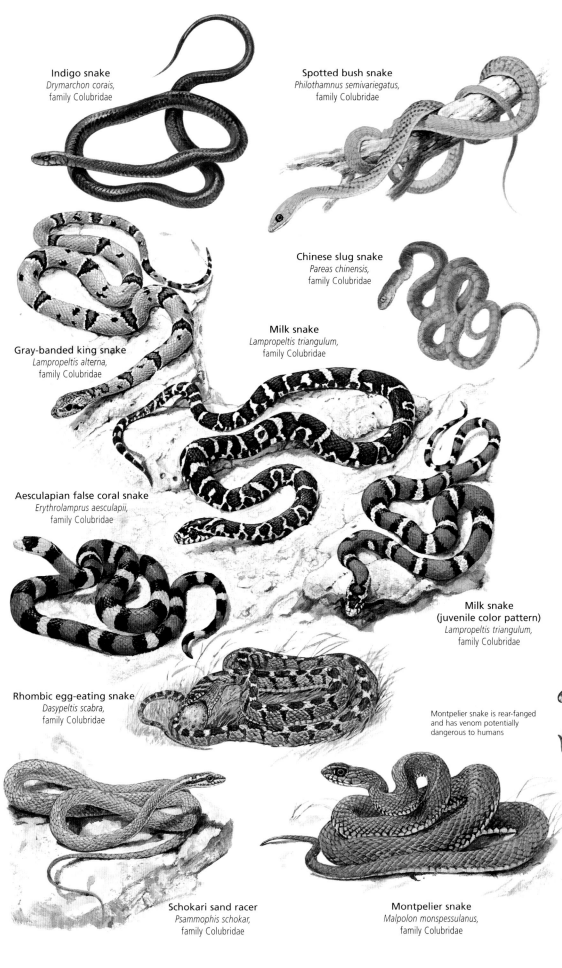

Indigo snake
Drymarchon corais,
family Colubridae

Spotted bush snake
Philothamnus semivariegatus,
family Colubridae

Chinese slug snake
Pareas chinensis,
family Colubridae

Milk snake
Lampropeltis triangulum,
family Colubridae

Gray-banded king snake
Lampropeltis alterna,
family Colubridae

Aesculapian false coral snake
Erythrolamprus aesculapii,
family Colubridae

Milk snake
(juvenile color pattern)
Lampropeltis triangulum,
family Colubridae

Rhombic egg-eating snake
Dasypeltis scabra,
family Colubridae

Montpelier snake is rear-fanged
and has venom potentially
dangerous to humans

Schokari sand racer
Psammophis schokar,
family Colubridae

Montpelier snake
Malpolon monspessulanus,
family Colubridae

FACT FILE

Indigo snake This large diurnal snake is highly prized by the pet trade for its dark, blue-black coloration and docile temperament. Indigos feed on turtle eggs, reptiles, amphibians, birds, small mammals, and snakes.

🐍 Up to 8¾ ft (2.7 m)
◯ Terrestrial
◯ Oviparous
● 15–26
🏃 Uncommon

S.E. USA, Mexico to Paraguay

Milk snake This wide-ranging species is divided into 24 diverse subspecies. Milk snakes often mimic the color pattern of coral snakes for defense.

🐍 Up to 4 ft (1.2 m)
◯ Terrestrial
◯ Oviparous
● 8–12
🏃 Common

E. USA, Mexico to Venezuela & Ecuador

Schokari sand racer This slender, fast-moving, diurnal predator searches its desert habitat for prey. They have rear fangs and are mildly venomous.

🐍 Up to 5¼ ft (1.6 m)
◯ Terrestrial
◯ Oviparous
● 8–16
🏃 Common

N.W. India, Afghanistan, Pakistan to N. Africa

SPECIALIZED EGG-EATERS

African egg-eating snakes have evolved vertebrae with blunt spines that pierce the egg as it is forced down by muscle contraction. The contents are squeezed out and the eggshell regurgitated.

Egg room By not swallowing the eggshell, the snake has more space in its stomach for high-protein egg yolk.

⚡ CONSERVATION WATCH

Hobby farming In the 1970s in Texas, United States, the rare gray-banded king snake was protected, as it was popular with the pet trade. Hobbyists have since bred so many that wild populations have recovered and the species no longer needs protection.

FACT FILE

Western ground snake This snake is secretive, inhabiting areas with loose alluvial sand in dry washes, creosote bushes, desert flats, and rocky hillsides. It prefers to hunt for prey at night and consumes centipedes, spiders, crickets, grasshoppers, and insect larvae.

- Up to 20 in (50 cm)
- Terrestrial
- Oviparous
- Unknown
- Uncommon

S.W. USA & N.W. Mexico

Common bronze-back snake Bronze-backs are primarily arboreal in rain forest, coconut plantations, and urban areas. Frogs and lizards, including flying lizards (Draco), are consumed.

- Up to 3¼ ft (1 m)
- Terrestrial, arboreal
- Oviparous
- Unknown
- Common

India, Burma, W. Malaysia, Indonesia, S. China

Ring-neck snake When attacked, these small woodland snakes hide their head and raise a coiled tail exposing the bright orange ventral surface. They feed on slugs, beetles, frogs, salamanders, and small snakes.

- Up to 28 in (71 cm)
- Terrestrial
- Oviparous
- 1–7
- Common

S.E. Canada, USA, N. Mexico

GARTER SNAKE

In Canada, garter snakes (*Thamnophis sirtalis*) hibernate en masse in deep crevices below the frost line. In spring, thousands emerge simultaneously to bask and breed. Males trail receptive females by the scent trails they lay down; up to a hundred males can be in a ball courting the same female. After copulating, the male leaves a gelatinous sperm plug in the female, giving his sperm time to fertilize the embryos before other males' sperm can enter.

Different fathers
DNA studies have shown that litters often have multiple paternities.

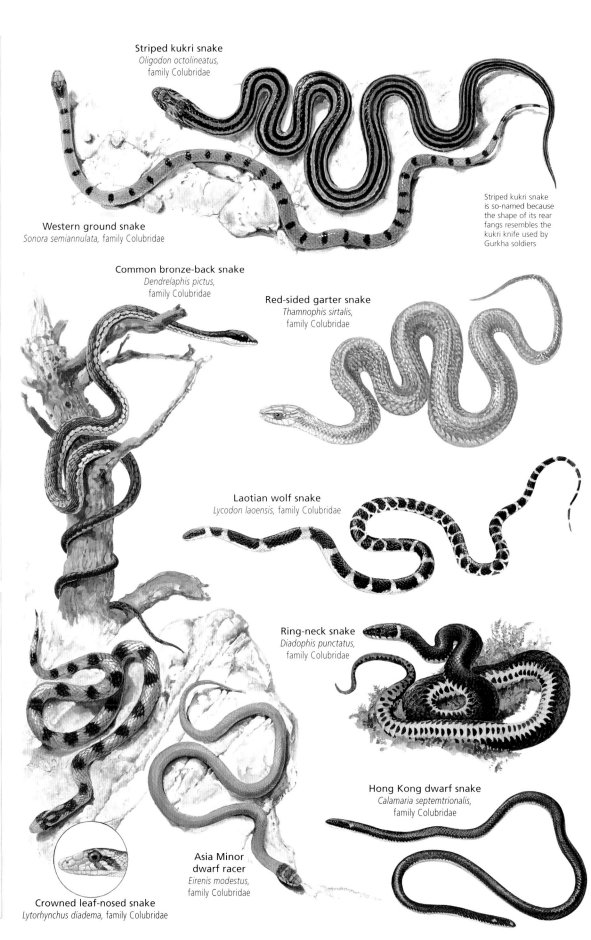

Striped kukri snake
Oligodon octolineatus,
family Colubridae

Striped kukri snake is so-named because the shape of its rear fangs resembles the kukri knife used by Gurkha soldiers

Western ground snake
Sonora semiannulata, family Colubridae

Common bronze-back snake
Dendrelaphis pictus,
family Colubridae

Red-sided garter snake
Thamnophis sirtalis,
family Colubridae

Laotian wolf snake
Lycodon laoensis, family Colubridae

Ring-neck snake
Diadophis punctatus,
family Colubridae

Hong Kong dwarf snake
Calamaria septemtrionalis,
family Colubridae

Asia Minor dwarf racer
Eirenis modestus,
family Colubridae

Crowned leaf-nosed snake
Lytorhynchus diadema, family Colubridae

New Guinea bockadam
is tolerant of salt water

Rainbow
water snake
is important to
the snake-skin
leather industry

FACT FILE

European grass snake This is one of the few reptiles to live inside the arctic circle and above 7,000 feet (2,121 m). Frogs are one of their main dietary items. Declining frog populations mean grass snake numbers are falling.

Dead or alive?
When grass snakes are attacked, they inflate with air, hiss, bite, release a foul-smelling liquid from the cloaca, and writhe around with their mouth open before lying limp as if dead.

⟊ Up to 6½ ft (2 m)
Terrestrial, aquatic
○ Oviparous
● 15–35
Common

Europe, W. Asia, N.W. Africa

Queen snake The queen snake is endangered in parts of its range due to habitat destruction and pollution. This water snake inhabits cool, clear streams, where it forages for newly molted crayfish under flat rocks.

⟊ Up to 36½ in (93 cm)
Aquatic
Ovoviviparous
5–23 live young
Status

S.E. Canada, E. USA

Masked water snake This nocturnal aquatic snake feeds on fishes and frogs. It has well-developed Duvernoy's glands and grooved, posterior maxillary teeth. Duvernoy's secretions are used to incapacitate prey animals, which makes them easier to eat.

⟊ Up to 4 ft (1.2 m)
Aquatic
Viviparous
Unknown
Common

S.E. Asia

Rainbow water snake This tropical water snake feeds primarily on fresh-water fish and is not tolerant of salt water. It is the main aquatic snake in most wetland habitats in Southeast Asia, but is at risk from the intrusion of salt water, associated with El Niño, into its habitats.

⟊ Up to 32 in (81 cm)
Aquatic
Viviparous
Unknown
Common

S.E. Asia

1 Blue-necked keelback
Macropisthodon rhodomelas, family Colubridae

2 Red-necked keelback
Rhabdophis subminiatus, family Colubridae

3 European grass snake
Natrix natrix, family Colubridae

4 Northern water snake
Nerodia sipedon, family Colubridae

5 Queen snake
Regina septemvittata, family Colubridae

6 Masked water snake
Homalopsis buccata, family Colubridae

7 New Guinea bockadam
Cerberus rynchops, family Colubridae

8 Tentacle snake
Erpeton tentaculatum, family Colubridae

9 Rainbow water snake
Enhydris enhydris, family Colubridae

BROWN VINE SNAKE

These diurnal snakes forage in the lower branches of neotropical forests, where they easily strike and capture passing ground-dwelling lizards. They also feed on arboreal lizards, frogs, small birds, and small mammals.

Look, no hands
The brown vine snake is a rear-fanged snake and kills its prey so that it is easier to manipulate and has less chance of dropping to the ground.

Rear-fanged nocturnal predator of lizards and birds; mildly venomous

1 Mangrove snake *Boiga dendrophila*, family Colubridae	**4** Boomslang *Dispholidus typus*, family Colubridae	
2 Brown vine snake *Oxybelis aeneus*, family Colubridae	**5** Paradise flying snake *Chrysopelea paradisi*, family Colubridae	**7** Mediterranean cat snake *Telescopus fallax*, family Colubridae
3 Long-nosed tree snake *Ahaetulla nasuta*, family Colubridae	**6** Cape twig snake *Thelotornis capensis*, family Colubridae	**8** Forest flame snake *Oxyrhopus petola*, family Colubridae

SNAKES AS PREDATORS

All snakes are carnivorous. The variety of prey sizes and taxa ranges from termites to crocodiles. Small snakes that feed on invertebrates search for their prey by sight or smell, often attacking them in their nests. Snakes use their tongues to collect scent data on where their prey has been and often trail them or wait for them to return; many of the large vipers and constricting snakes wait along rodent or game trails for prey to come to them. The large-eyed diurnal racers and whipsnakes are visual predators and chase down lizards and other snakes. The venom that vipers, elapids, and some colubrids inject to kill their prey also helps in the digestion of the animal, since venom is an enzyme. Many large snakes eat a meal only a few times a year, but sometimes this meal has a greater mass than they do.

Strike force The eyelash viper (*Bothriechis schlegelii*) (above) is an arboreal sit-and-wait predator, ready to rapidly identify prey through visual, infrared, and olfactory cues. It strikes on a moment's notice, as a bird, bat, lizard, frog, or in this case, rodent, passes by.

Heat vision Carpet pythons (Morelia spilota), with their labial heat-sensing pits, are able to detect and identify the size of a warm-blooded object before seeing it optically.

Snake-eaters Many species of snakes, including the king cobra (above), feed on other snakes such as coral snakes, king snakes, indigo snakes, and mussuranas. Snakes are easy to swallow and the protein is easily digestible.

Egg-eaters The egg-eater snake (*Dasypeltis scabra*) has a gland behind each eye that may supply extra fluids to the mouth to lubricate egg shells for swallowing. It can swallow an object about three times its diameter.

Gone fishing The mild venom of the Duvernoy's gland is sufficient to paralyze a fish. The grass snake (*Natrix natrix*) (above) can then more easily manipulate it for swallowing. All snakes swallow their prey whole.

Suffocation Many snakes, not just pythons, boas, and anacondas, constrict their prey to kill it. The amethyst python (*Morelia amethistina*) (left) captures prey in its teeth and simultaneously wraps several coils around it. The coils get tighter as the animal exhales, and it dies from suffocation. Normally no bones are broken in this process.

Catesby's snail eater
Dipsas catesbyi, family Colubridae

Mountain sipo
Chironius monticola, family Colubridae

Blunthead tree snake
Imantodes cenchoa, family Colubridae

Amazon false ferdelance
Xenodon severus, family Colubridae

Mussurana
Clelia clelia, family Colubridae

Ringed hognose snake
Lystrophis semicinctus, family Colubridae

Eastern hognose snake
Heterodon platyrhinos, family Colubridae

Rainbow snake
Farancia erytrogramma, family Colubridae

False water cobra
Hydrodynastes gigas, family Colubridae

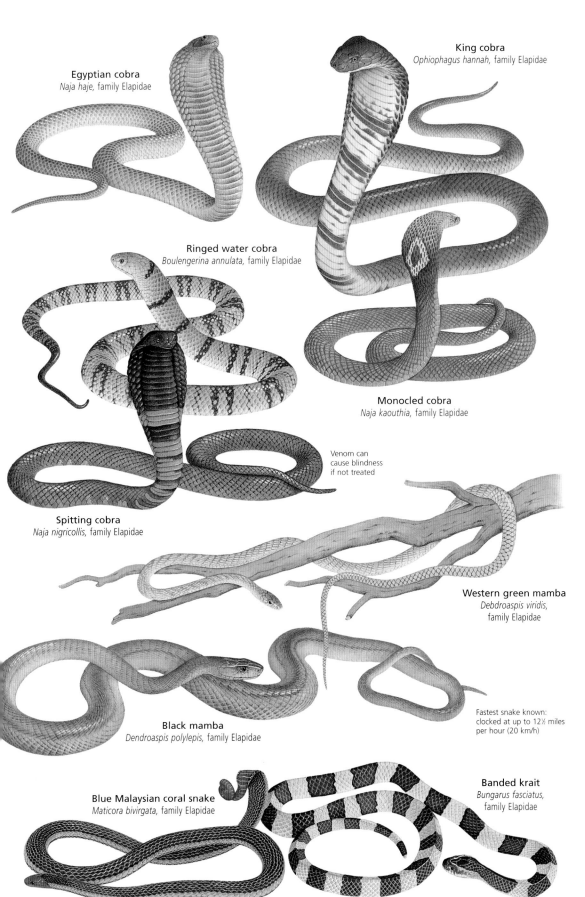

Egyptian cobra
Naja haje, family Elapidae

King cobra
Ophiophagus hannah, family Elapidae

Ringed water cobra
Boulengerina annulata, family Elapidae

Monocled cobra
Naja kaouthia, family Elapidae

Venom can cause blindness if not treated

Spitting cobra
Naja nigricollis, family Elapidae

Western green mamba
Debdroaspis viridis,
family Elapidae

Fastest snake known: clocked at up to 12½ miles per hour (20 km/h)

Black mamba
Dendroaspis polylepis, family Elapidae

Blue Malaysian coral snake
Maticora bivirgata, family Elapidae

Banded krait
Bungarus fasciatus,
family Elapidae

FACT FILE

Family Elapidae This family comprises the cobras, kraits, seasnakes, coral snakes, death adders, and allies. Elapids are venomous, with anterior erect fangs on each maxilla. Only the mambas and tree cobras are arboreal. Many are burrowing or leaf-litter snakes and have bright coloration. Most terrestrial species are oviparous or viviparous. All true sea snakes are viviparous, giving birth in the water. The sea kraits lay eggs on land.

Genera 62
Species 300

Worldwide except Antarctica & Atlantic

Spitting cobra Although this species usually does not bite, it can squirt its venom accurately up to 9 feet (2.6 m), aiming for its attacker's eyes.

Up to 7¼ ft (2.2 m)
Terrestrial
Oviparous
10–22
Common

Sub-Saharan Africa

Black mamba This large snake carries enough neuro-toxic venom to kill up to 10 adult humans. It is one of the fastest and most fearless snakes known. It can strike out to 40 percent of its length (most snakes only manage 25 percent).

Up to 14 ft (4.2 m)
Terrestrial, arboreal
Oviparous
12–14
Common

Africa

SPITTING COBRA

Spitting cobras have an opening on the anterior surface of the fang above the tip. For better accuracy, the inside of the fangs have spiral grooves that put a spin on the projected venom.

Safe spitting
Spitting cobras avoid contact with potential predators by spitting venom in their eyes; this avoids injuries to their fangs and mouths.

FACT FILE

Eastern coral snake Even though it has neuro-toxic venom, this snake is not very dangerous to humans because of its small size. Several non-venomous snakes mimic the color pattern.

- ↔ Up to 4 ft (1.2 m)
- ⬯ Terrestrial
- ◯ Oviparous
- ● 3–13
- ⚑ Common

S.E. USA & E. Mexico

Redtail coral snake Eggs are laid in January and hatch in March. Hatchlings are 6¾ inches (17 cm) long. Cope's false coral snake (*Pliocercus euryzona*) mimics the color pattern in Costa Rica.

- ↔ Up to 3½ ft (1.1 m)
- ⬯ Terrestrial
- ◯ Oviparous
- ● 15–18
- ⚑ Uncommon

S. Central America & N.W. South America

Common death adder These nocturnal snakes spend the day buried in sand or leaf litter, often at the base of trees or shrubs. Death adders have large fangs and toxic venom.

- ↔ Up to 3¼ ft (1 m)
- ⬯ Terrestrial
- ◉ Ovoviparous
- ● 10–20
- ⚑ Common

Australia & Papua New Guinea

SNAKE EYES

The habits of a snake can be seen in their eyes. Small degenerate eyes suggest burrowers. Vertical elliptical pupils are nocturnal species. Large round eyes are active diurnal predators that chase down their prey.

⚡ CONSERVATION WATCH

Sea snake status Crocker's sea snake (*Laticauda crockeri*) is listed on the IUCN Red List as vulnerable in Oceania. It is the only species of Hydrophiinae listed and the only species of sea snake to be found primarily in fresh water. It is vulnerable because of its limited distribution in the Solomon Islands.

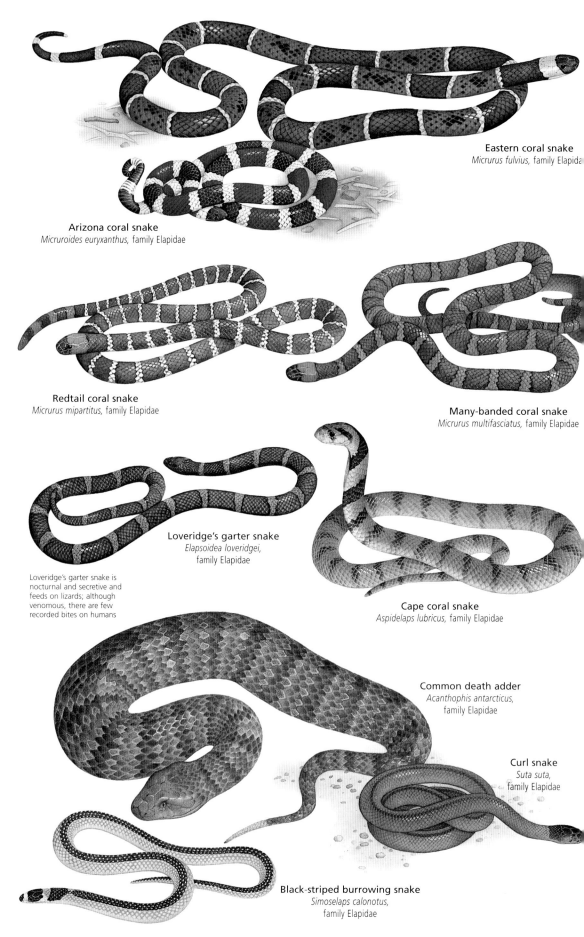

Eastern coral snake
Micrurus fulvius, family Elapidae

Arizona coral snake
Micruroides euryxanthus, family Elapidae

Redtail coral snake
Micrurus mipartitus, family Elapidae

Many-banded coral snake
Micrurus multifasciatus, family Elapidae

Loveridge's garter snake
Elapsoidea loveridgei,
family Elapidae

Loveridge's garter snake is nocturnal and secretive and feeds on lizards; although venomous, there are few recorded bites on humans

Cape coral snake
Aspidelaps lubricus, family Elapidae

Common death adder
Acanthophis antarcticus,
family Elapidae

Curl snake
Suta suta,
family Elapidae

Black-striped burrowing snake
Simoselaps calonotus,
family Elapidae

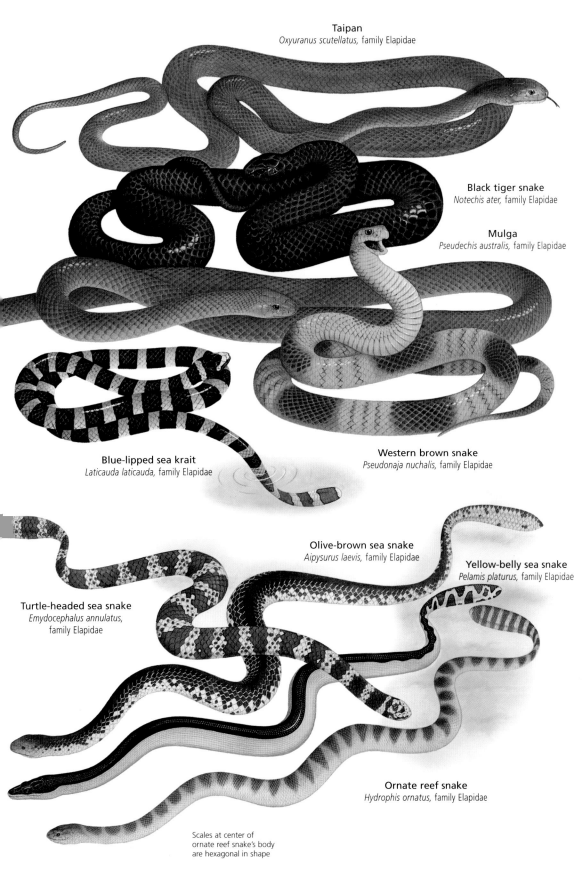

Taipan
Oxyuranus scutellatus, family Elapidae

Black tiger snake
Notechis ater, family Elapidae

Mulga
Pseudechis australis, family Elapidae

Blue-lipped sea krait
Laticauda laticauda, family Elapidae

Western brown snake
Pseudonaja nuchalis, family Elapidae

Olive-brown sea snake
Aipysurus laevis, family Elapidae

Yellow-belly sea snake
Pelamis platurus, family Elapidae

Turtle-headed sea snake
Emydocephalus annulatus,
family Elapidae

Ornate reef snake
Hydrophis ornatus, family Elapidae

Scales at center of
ornate reef snake's body
are hexagonal in shape

FACT FILE

Taipan The taipan is the world's
deadliest snake, due to the toxicity
of its venom. It inhabits wet tropical
forests as well as dry forests and open
savanna, and feeds on small mammals.

✦ Up to 6½ ft (2 m)
◯ Terrestrial
◯ Oviparous
● 3–20
✦ Common

S. New Guinea, Indonesia & Australia

Blue-lipped sea krait Unlike other
sea snakes, sea kraits are oviparous
and lay their eggs on land. They do not
have reduced ventral scales or a well-
developed paddle-like tail. They often
come to shore to digest large meals,
another point of difference with other
sea snakes, and possess muscles that
are well developed for moving on land.

✦ Up to 3¼ ft (1 m)
◯ Aquatic
◯ Oviparous
● 1–10
✦ Common

Indian & Pacific oceans

SEA SNAKES

Sea snakes were once grouped with
Hydrophiidae, but are now part of
the family Elapidae. They have many
similar characteristics: all are venomous, and all except the sea krait
(*Laticauda*) are viviparous and give
birth at sea. All of these snakes have
laterally compressed bodies, paddle-
like tails, reduced ventral scales, and
are incapable of moving well on land.
There are 15 genera and 70 species
distributed in Papua New Guinea,
Australia, and tropical Pacific and
Indian oceans.

No table *Sea snakes evolved
a very potent neuro-toxic
venom so that they
could stun fishes
rapidly, and
then easily
manipulate
them into
their mouths
without
dropping
them to the
ocean floor.*

✦ CONSERVATION WATCH

The nine species of Elapidae on
the IUCN Red List are categorized
as follows:

7 Vulnerable
2 Near threatened

FACT FILE

Family Viperidae All vipers are venomous, and possess movable front fangs. The pit vipers (rattlesnakes and allies) have an external loreal pit for infrared detection. Adults range from 1 to 12½ feet (0.3 to 3.75 m) in length. The vipers lack the loreal pit; adults range from 1 to 6½ feet (0.3 to 2 m) in length. Most vipers have thick bodies and triangular-shaped heads. Young often eat amphibians, lizards, or snakes and change to a diet of mammals and birds as adults.

Retractable fangs
Vipers are characterized by large retractable front fangs in the upper jaw, which are used to inject a potent venom to prey and predators alike.

Genera 32
Species 221

Central & South America, Africa, Europe, Asia

SIDEWINDER

The sidewinder (*Crotalus cerastes*) moves in loose sand by sidewinding. The head and neck are held off the sand and thrown sideways while the body remains in place. As soon as the head and neck hit the sand, the body and tail are hurled after it. As the tail touches the ground, the head and neck become airborne again, resulting in a continuous looping motion.

Sidewinding
Vipers in African deserts and side-winder rattlesnakes in North American deserts evolved this skill separately for moving across windblown sand.

Lichtenstein's night adder
Causus lichtensteini,
family Viperidae

Adder
Vipera berus,
family Viperidae

Persian horned viper
Pseudocerastes persicus,
family Viperidae

Wagner's viper
Vipera wagneri,
family Viperidae

Green bush viper
Atheris squamigera,
family Viperidae

Saw-scaled viper
Echis carinatus,
family Viperidae

Russel's viper
Daboia russelii,
family Viperidae

Horned viper
Cerastes cerastes, family Viperidae

Fea viper
Azemiops faae,
family Viperidae

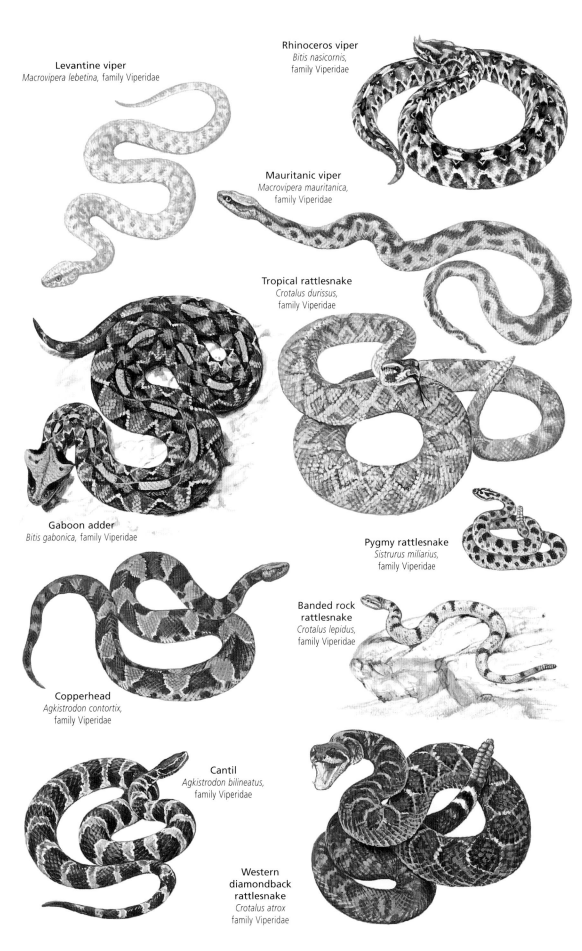

Levantine viper
Macrovipera lebetina, family Viperidae

Rhinoceros viper
Bitis nasicornis,
family Viperidae

Mauritanic viper
Macrovipera mauritanica,
family Viperidae

Tropical rattlesnake
Crotalus durissus,
family Viperidae

Gaboon adder
Bitis gabonica, family Viperidae

Pygmy rattlesnake
Sistrurus miliarius,
family Viperidae

Copperhead
Agkistrodon contortix,
family Viperidae

**Banded rock
rattlesnake**
Crotalus lepidus,
family Viperidae

Cantil
Agkistrodon bilineatus,
family Viperidae

**Western
diamondback
rattlesnake**
Crotalus atrox
family Viperidae

FACT FILE

Rhinoceros viper This heavy-bodied viper has two to three horns on the tip of its snout and is venomous but not aggressive. It is a sit-and-wait predator and mostly preys on mammals.

⌖ Up to 4 ft (1.2 m)
◯ Terrestrial
🜬 Viviparous
● 6–35 live young
▦ Common

C. & W. Africa

Pygmy rattlesnake The genus *Sistrurus* is distinguished by having nine large scales on the dorsal surface of the head. Young pygmy rattlesnakes have a bright yellow tail tip, which they wiggle as a lure to attract small prey.

⌖ Up to 31½ in (80 cm)
◯ Terrestrial
🜬 Viviparous
● 6–10 live young
⚘ Common

S.E. USA

Western diamondback rattlesnake One of the most abundant rattlesnakes in the United States, it is responsible for more snake bites there than any other snake. Diet is primarily rodents, but the young prey on lizards.

⌖ Up to 7½ ft (2.3 m)
◯ Terrestrial
🜬 Viviparous
● 4–25 live young
⚘ Common

S.W. USA & N.W. Mexico

RATTLE

Rattlesnakes have a unique rattle at the end of their tails. It is made up of interlocking segments of keratin; each time the snake sheds its skin, a new segment is added. When the tail is vibrating, the hollow segments bang against each other, making the anti-predator rattling sound.

🍂 CONSERVATION WATCH

The 20 species of Viperidae on the IUCN Red List are categorized as follows:

7	Critically endangered
4	Endangered
7	Vulnerable
1	Data deficient
1	Least concern

FACT FILE

Tiger rattlesnake This small nocturnal rattlesnake can often be found resting in pack rat (*Neotoma*) mounds in the daytime. At night it feeds on rodents and lizards. Although small, it has long fangs and potent venom.

- Up to 36 in (92 cm)
- Terrestrial
- Viviparous
- 2–5 live young
- Common

Sonoran Desert (S.W. USA & N.W. Mexico)

Massasauga Massasauga means great river mouth in the Chippeawa language. The preferred habitat for this species is river-bottom forest in the floodplains of large rivers. They hibernate in cray-fish burrows after foraging for rodents and frogs during the summer. When vibrated, their small rattle sounds like the buzz of a cricket.

- Up to 30 in (76 cm)
- Terrestrial
- Viviparous
- 8–20 live young
- Rare

S.E. Canada, N.E. USA to N.W. USA, N. Mexico

Black-tailed rattlesnake In the spring, males follow the chemical trails of females to court them. Courtship and mating often last several days. Females give birth in August and stay with their young until they have shed for the first time. They find prey by following animal scent trails to burrows or nests and waiting for their chosen prey to return.

- Up to 4¼ ft (1.3 m)
- Terrestrial
- Viviparous
- 3–13 live young
- Common

S.W. USA & N.W. Mexico

Timber rattlesnake These rattlesnakes have communal dens in rock out-croppings, usually on the south side of hills or mountains. Breeding usually takes place in the spring at the dens before the snakes disperse. The young follow the scent trails of the adults to reach the dens in the fall. Although this species is primarily terrestrial, young have been found in the lower branches of trees and recent studies have found adults in the treetops hunting squirrels.

- Up to 5 ft (1.5 m)
- Terrestrial
- Viviparous
- 6–15 live young
- Common

N.E. USA

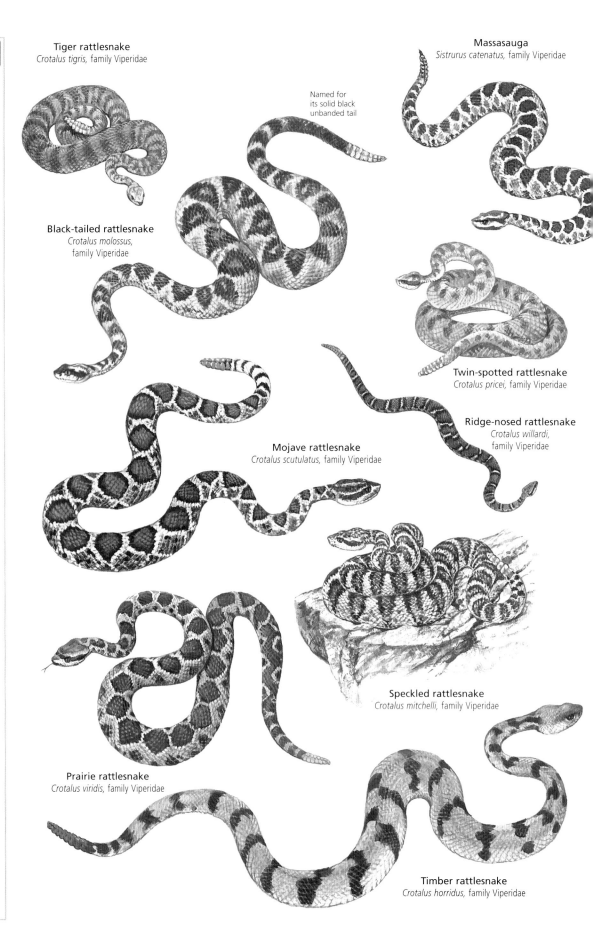

Tiger rattlesnake
Crotalus tigris, family Viperidae

Massasauga
Sistrurus catenatus, family Viperidae

Named for its solid black unbanded tail

Black-tailed rattlesnake
Crotalus molossus, family Viperidae

Twin-spotted rattlesnake
Crotalus pricei, family Viperidae

Ridge-nosed rattlesnake
Crotalus willardi, family Viperidae

Mojave rattlesnake
Crotalus scutulatus, family Viperidae

Speckled rattlesnake
Crotalus mitchelli, family Viperidae

Prairie rattlesnake
Crotalus viridis, family Viperidae

Timber rattlesnake
Crotalus horridus, family Viperidae

Wagler's palm viper
Tropidolaemus wagleri,
family Viperidae

White-lipped tree viper
Trimeresurus albolabris, family Viperidae

Yellow-blotched
palm pit viper
Bothriechis aurifer, family Viperidae

Speckled forest pit viper
Bothriopsis taeniata,
family Viperidae

Malayan pit viper
Calloselasma rhodostoma,
family Viperidae

Brazil's lancehead
Bothrops brazili,
family Viperidae

Hump-nosed moccasin
Hypnale hypnale, family Viperidae

Bushmaster
Lachesis muta, family Viperidae

Jararacussu
Bothrops jararacussu, family Viperidae

Hognosed pit viper
Porthidium nasutum, family Viperidae

FACT FILE

Wagler's palm viper This viper can
be identified by its keeled chin scales. It
has long fangs and the venom is hemo-
toxic, causing cell and tissue destruction.

- Up to 3¼ ft (1 m)
- Arboreal
- Viviparous
- 3–10 live young
- Common

S.E. Asia

Bushmaster This is the largest
venomous snake in the Americas and
the largest viper in the world. They are
sit-and-wait predators, traveling short
distances between sites then waiting
for days or weeks for a meal. The eggs
are often laid in mammal burrows.

- Up to 14¼ ft (4.3 m)
- Arboreal
- Oviparous
- 8–13
- Uncommon

Amazonia (N. South America)

Hognosed pit viper These stocky
snakes are called jumping vipers, as
their whole body appears to jump
forward when they strike. In reality
they can only strike about half their
length. This viper often swallows food
morsels weighing more than it does.

- Up to 20 in (50 cm)
- Terrestrial
- Viviparous
- 6–9 live young
- Common

Central America to Colombia & Ecuador

PIT VIPER

Pit vipers have an infrared sensing gland
that they use along with light data from
their eyes to create a visual image. They
can sense a mouse that is only 5°F (1°C)
warmer than its surrounds when it is
within 23 feet (7 m).

maxilla

heat-sensitive pit

jaw muscle

venom duct

compressor muscle

venom gland

AMPHIBIANS

AMPHIBIANS

PHYLUM	Chordata
CLASS	Amphibia
ORDERS	3
FAMILIES	44
GENERA	434
SPECIES	5,400

Amphibians arose from early lobe-finned fishes about 360 million years ago to become the first vertebrates established on land. There are three main modern groups. The earthworm-like caecilians have bullet-shaped heads, tails, and no limbs. Salamanders have cylindrical bodies, long tails, distinct heads and necks, and well-developed limbs. Anurans—frogs and toads—differ from all other vertebrates in having stout, tail-less bodies with a continuous head and body and well-developed limbs. All amphibians are ectothermic and none has scales or claws. Anurans and salamanders lay eggs, while some caecilians give birth to live young.

Burrowing forms The ringed caecilian (*Siphonops annulatus*) is typical of an animal built for subterranean life. It has no limbs, but a fortified, bullet-shaped head and muscular segmented body designed for adept tunneling. Eyes, being of little use in a dark environment, are greatly reduced. Some salamanders also spend most of their lives foraging underground.

stratified epithelium   mucus gland

chromatophore

poison gland   connective tissue

Remarkable organ Amphibian skin does much more than provide physical protection for internal organs and tissues. Kept moist by glandular mucous secretions, it maintains water balance and often allows respiration. Potent antiviral, antifungal, and antibacterial secretions are common. Some amphibians—usually those with bright warning coloration—also secrete poisons that are distasteful or even toxic to predators.

TERRESTRIAL LIFE

Features that have allowed amphibians to exploit terrestrial environments include a tongue, to help moisten and move food in the mouth; eyelids and associated glands to protect the cornea and keep it damp; an outer dead skin-cell layer that is regularly shed; external ear drums; a larynx in the throat for sound production; and the chemosensory Jacobson's organ in the roof of the mouth, for taste and smell.

Amphibian skin plays an active role in water-balance control. In frogs, for example, the skin's permeability changes according to their activity. When foraging on land, it increases for better water absorption. In water, permeability is greatly reduced. Some terrestrial frogs have a pelvic skin patch richly supplied with blood vessels that can absorb water from any moist area. When frogs hibernate in an aquatic environment, they must alter skin permeability and the ionic balance in their body fluids to reduce water absorption. Some desert toads retain urea in their urine to create an osmotic gradient across the skin that allows water to be absorbed from seemingly dry soil.

All adult amphibians are carnivorous, although a few frog species reportedly eat certain fruits. Most larval amphibians are also carnivorous, feeding on invertebrates, tadpoles, and small fish. The tadpoles of most frog species are herbivorous. In this way, they are not competing with the adults for food. The digestive system of the tadpole must change as it is transforming to the adult stage.

Regenerative powers Newts, such as the warty newt (larval form above), can regenerate body parts lost in tussles with predators or through other means. This capability is more pronounced in the hind part of the body and in younger individuals.

Frog view Like those of other land vertebrates, amphibian eyes have a cornea, iris, lens, and retina. Most amphibians have an immovable upper eyelid and a movable lower eyelid, of which the upper part—known as the nictitating membrane—is usually transparent. Anurans have true color vision. In addition to their role in visual perception, frogs blink their eyes to help push food from their mouths down their throats.

AMPHIBIANS THROUGH THE AGES

Evolutionary biologists cannot be sure which early fish or fishes gave rise to the amphibians. The most likely candidates were among the lobe-finned rhipidistians, a freshwater group common during the Devonian period (408–360 million years ago). The relationship is indicated by several key common features not evident in other fish groups. Labyrinthidonts are the earliest known amphibians, the oldest fossils of which come from Greenland, from around the end of the Devonian. These had a fish-like tail and the remnants of a bony gill-cover in the cheek region. Among the labyrinthidonts were the reptiliomorphs and the batrachomorphs. The former included the ancestor of reptiles, birds, and mammals; the latter gave rise to the modern amphibians.

ANCIENT FORMS

None of the modern amphibians bears much physical resemblance to their earliest ancestors. The links are often gleaned from small skeletal details, such as features of the skull relating to the structure of the middle ear.

It is believed all three living orders arose from the long-extinct batrachomorph order Temnospondyli. One ancient representative was *Dendrerpeton*, a predominantly terrestrial amphibian thought to have been able to hear seismic, but not airborne, vibrations. Another was *Eryops*, a fierce swamp-dwelling predator that could swim better than run

and which, at 5 feet (1.5 m) in length, was the biggest land animal known from the Permian (290–248 million years ago). During the next 40 million years, the seas inundated the northern continents and many amphibians grew to astonishing sizes. In *Metoposaurus* and *Cyclotosaurus*, the skull alone was 3¹/₄ feet (1 m) long. These kinds of large creatures were evolutionary dead-ends.

The earliest frogs are known from about 245 million years ago; salamanders appear in the fossil record from about 150 million years ago; and caecilians appear from about 65 million years ago.

Ancient frog *Messelobatrachus* (above) was an aquatic frog that survived during the early Eocene when Earth's climate was largely tropical. It is known from a fossil found in a rich deposit in the sediments of a lake in Grube Messel, in Germany, which dried up about 50 million years ago. The fossil does not reveal color or pattern details.

Transitional life *Eusthenopteron*, an ancient lobe-finned fish (below), was probably similar to ancestors of the first amphibians. Having lungs as well as gills, it could breathe air when necessary. Its fins were like those from which tetrapod limbs evolved—paired and supported by muscular lobes with bony elements.

CLASSIFICATION

Lissamphibia, the living amphibians, includes three orders: the frogs and toads (Anura); the salamanders, newts, and sirens (Caudata); and the caecilians (Gymnophiona). Amphibians are monophyletic—they are all derived from the same common ancestor. Smooth skin without scales is their main common feature. Biological classifications inevitably change as scientists gather more information and discover new species. The Malayan horned frog (right), for example, has been assigned six different scientific names since first described in 1858. At various times, the two species in the genus *Megophrys*, which look very similar, have been mistakenly considered the same species.

KINGDOM
Animalia
Malayan horned frog; tiger, coral, sponge, lizard, shark

PHYLUM
Chordata
Malayan horned frog, domestic cat, grizzly bear, human

CLASS
Amphibia
Malayan horned frog, all frogs, all toads, salamanders, newts, caecilians,

ORDER
Anura
Malayan horned frog, all frogs, all toads,

FAMILY
Megophryidae
Malayan horned frog, shaping frog, Karin hills frog, Asian toad

GENUS
Megophrys
Malayan horned frog; Asian spadefoot toad

SPECIES
Megophrys nasuta
Malayan horned frog

AMPHIBIANS

Class Amphibia

Order Caudata
Salamanders and newts

Order Gymnophiona
Caecilians

Order Anura
Frogs and toads

Order Anura, page 100

BIOLOGY AND BEHAVIOR

Most amphibians are nocturnal and active only in moist environmental conditions. Some, however, exhibit water-conserving behavior and even behavior to regulate body temperature. Day-active frogs living in cool climates often bask in the Sun to raise their body temperature before foraging. Some periodically enter water to acquire moisture and lower their temperature. The North American bullfrog regulates its temperature by changing position in relation to the Sun's rays, and by evaporative cooling through mucous secretions and periodic rewetting of the skin. Gray tree frogs (*Hyla versicolor*) change their body color from dark brown or gray when they want to be warmer, to light green when they are warm enough and want to reflect, rather than absorb, light.

STAYING SAFE

Feigning death is a widespread anti-predator response among amphibians, particularly frogs. Toads commonly inflate the body to appear bigger while raising themselves up, sometimes tilting their paratoid glands at predators and even squirting mild venom from these glands.

Some South American leptodactylid frogs have groin glands resembling "eyespots," suggestive of a bigger animal. Large frogs may leap and snap at predators. Many emit loud screams when grasped, to frighten predators and warn other frogs.

Salamanders with poison glands on the tail lash it at predators; others, with cephalic glands, butt with their heads. Many exhibit caudal autonomy—a tail portion breaks in a predator's grasp and the salamander can escape while the predator is distracted by the piece of wriggling tail.

PERNICIOUS PREDATORS

Most amphibians are opportunistic sit-and-wait predators that react to potential prey when it comes within reach. Some heavy-bodied frogs, such as the South American horned frogs, lure agile prey by waving the long toes on their hind feet. Other diurnal frogs, especially the small poison frogs of tropical America, actively forage for insects using visual cues.

Changing names Common names are often inconsistent. The frogs at left, for example, are called mission golden-eyed tree frogs, Amazon milk frogs, and blue milk frogs. There is no ambiguity about the scientific name—*Phrynohyas resinifistrix*.

Independent offspring Tadpoles are not always at the mercy of predators and the environment as they seem to be. Many exhibit some control over body temperature by moving into shallow water on sunny days. Some are also toxic to potential predators, a fact advertised by bright warning coloration. Others school in big groups, appearing to be a larger animal to avoid predation.

Frog pharmacy The bright coloration of green and black poison dart frogs, from Central and South America, warns of toxic skin secretions. Medical researchers are investigating a substance from this frog's skin as a potential painkiller for humans, up to 200 times more potent than morphine, without side-effects.

Fountain of youth Larvae of the barred tiger salamander usually become adults within five months of hatching. This species is neotenic—under certain conditions, individuals will retain gills and other larval features throughout life. Although they reproduce, they never complete metamorphosis to a terrestrial existence. This allows them to live permanently in water.

MATING SONGS

Males of most frog species have a unique mating call recognized by other individuals of the same species. Many frogs in seasonal environments have short breeding periods during which males move to temporary ponds and produce simple calls intended to attract females. Those active year-round, in tropical and subtropical regions, typically have more complex calls with courtship and territorial components.

Although some salamanders bark and squeak, they are not known to use vocalizations during sexual behavior. Some mark territories with scent trails, recognized by members of the same species, and courtship is often elaborate and well developed. Male redbacked salamanders have a mental gland on their chin which is used to release hormones directly into the brain of females to stimulate them to mate. The only frogs with elaborate courtship are among the aquatic tongueless frogs.

NURSERY CARE

Some terrestrial frogs and toads actively care for their young. Female South American marsupial frogs, for example, transport eggs on their backs or in a dorsal pouch. Male Darwin's frogs, from Chile, gather hatchling tadpoles from their egg clutches to carry them in a vocal sac until development is complete. Likewise, male hip-pocket frogs, from Australia, transport tadpoles in flank pockets. Female Australian gastric-brooding frogs swallow fertilized eggs. Tadpoles complete development in the stomach, which shuts down digestion during brooding. The tadpoles of South American pond frogs often move in schools. Their mothers protect them by leaping aggressively at potential predators. Some tropical rain-forest frogs nourish free-living tadpoles in tree holes or bromeliads with unfertilized eggs. The females of many terrestrial salamanders protect their eggs until they hatch.

Egg brooders Most amphibians that deposit their eggs in water immediately abandon them to develop at the whims of the surrounding environment. It is common in species that deposit their eggs on land, however, for a parent to stay with them to prevent their theft by predators.

Male display This male crested newt (below) is in breeding condition. Usually, the sexes look very similar, but during breeding season the male's dorsal and tail crests increase in size. After courtship in the water, the eggs are fertilized internally and deposited singly on vegetation.

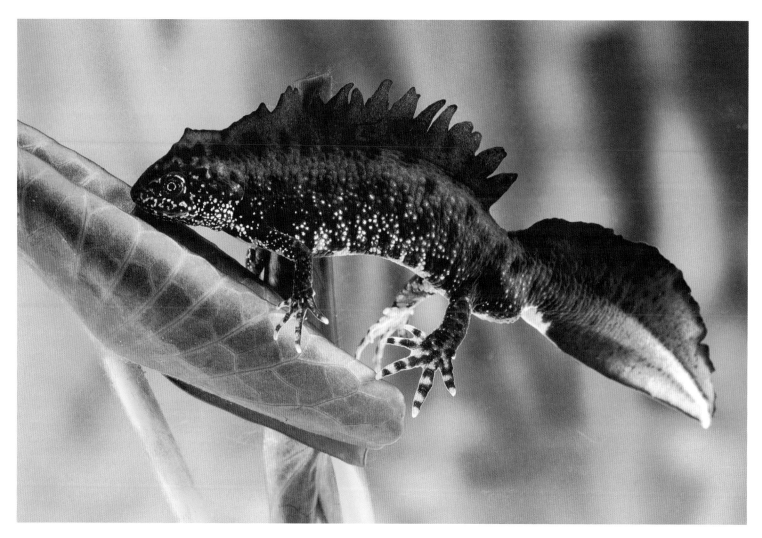

HABITATS AND ADAPTATIONS

Because amphibians are ectothermic and their body temperature is largely at the mercy of environmental conditions, few manage to be active in cold surroundings. They do not occur naturally in Antarctica or the extreme northern parts of Europe, Asia, and North America. Amphibians are also noticeably absent from most oceanic islands: their need for fresh water does not make them good candidates for rafting across expanses of salt water, which is the way island fauna often begins. Caecilians are found throughout the tropics although they are absent from Madagascar, New Guinea, and Australia. Salamanders are widely distributed in the temperate regions of the Northern Hemisphere. Even though they are small, their biomass can exceed that of mammals in some northern temperate forests. One family—the lungless salamanders—reaches its highest diversity in tropical Central and northern South America. In contrast, frogs have a worldwide distribution, with species diversity greatest in the tropics. Some Amazonian rain forests boast higher numbers of amphibian species than the entire United States.

HABITAT VARIETY

Most salamanders, caecilians, and about half of the frog species are terrestrial. Some, especially the caecilians, spend most of their time below ground and are highly adapted to a subterranean lifestyle. One eel-like South American subfamily (*Typhlonectinae*) is strictly aquatic, living in lakes and rivers. Many frogs and a few salamanders live in trees.

Practically all adult frogs can swim. But members of two frog families are particularly specialized. South America's paradox frogs have extremely powerful hindlimbs and huge, fully webbed feet. These are active near the surface of ponds and their eyes protrude dorsally. Africa's clawed frogs and the Surinam toad and its relatives in South America also have fully webbed feet, but they have slightly flattened bodies and relatively small eyes. They rest and feed on the bottom of ponds, coming to the surface periodically to gulp air. If ponds dry up, these frogs burrow into the mud where they stay until the ponds fill with water again. The *Eleutherodactylus* frogs are free from standing water. They lay small clutches of large, yolked eggs in humid soil in shallow nests. Males guard the eggs until they hatch directly into miniature froglets—they have no tadpole stage. Often, a male will guard more than one nest from different females in the area.

AQUATIC AMPHIBIANS

Four salamander families in North America—mudpuppies, giant salamanders and hellbenders, Congo eels, and sirens—are strictly aquatic. So are the giant salamanders of China and Japan, and the olm in south-eastern Europe. The olm and some North American aquatic salamanders are neotenic—never completely transforming into adults, but retaining the larval form. These include some of the largest salamanders. They breathe by means of gills and have larval tail fins.

The sirens and Congo eels are limbless, or nearly so, and swim like snakes. In contrast, mudpuppies, giant salamanders, and hellbenders have somewhat flattened bodies and normal limbs. They crawl about on the bottom of lakes or rivers and are more sedentary in their habits.

Most of the so-called pond frogs of the genus *Rana* have powerful hindlegs and fully webbed feet, well adapted for leaping from land into water and swimming. Toads from the genus *Bufo* have small hindlimbs modified for short hopping on land. They do not have fully webbed toes and are not well adapted for swimming. One subfamily of caecilians (Typhonectinae) in South America is strictly aquatic.

Treetop breeders Many frogs attach eggs to leaves or branches from which tadpoles later drop into water below. Others deposit eggs in water-filled tree holes or bromeliads. In this way, adults do not need to leave trees to reproduce.

Juvenile form The red-spotted newt (below) is aquatic for its first few months. It then develops lungs and loses its gills, to become a red-skinned terrestrial form called an eft. Two years later it metamorphoses again, returning to the water to breed.

ARBOREAL AMPHIBIANS

The ends of the fingers and toes of many tree frogs are expanded into specialized pads that help them cling to vertical surfaces. Their long, slender bodies and long limbs are adapted to perching on and leaping from leaves and branches. In the genus *Phyllomedusa*, found in the American tropics, the innermost fingers and toes are elongated and, like primate thumbs, are opposable to the outer digits. This allows these frogs to climb by grasping branches. Some tree frogs in Southeast Asia have huge, fully webbed hands and feet as well as fringes of extra skin along the limbs. These modifications provide an extensive surface area when the limbs are extended and the fingers and toes spread. By gliding on these wing-like structures, the tree frogs are able to travel considerable distances between tree branches, or even glide from tree to tree.

Some of the American tropic's casque-headed tree frogs have hard skin on the head that is firmly attached to underlying bones. They have a greatly reduced blood supply to this skin. To reduce water loss during dry seasons, these frogs back into holes or bromeliad plants containing small amounts of water, flexing their heads at right angles to secure themselves in place.

Frogs have responded to the challenge of reproduction in the trees with a range of effective adaptations. Perhaps the ultimate for arboreal reproduction occurs in some of the South American marsupial frogs in which fertilized eggs develop into miniature froglets in a pouch on the mother's back. In this way generations pass without any individuals leaving the trees.

There are small poison frogs in the family Dendrobatidae which forage on the forest floor in Central and South America. The males guard the eggs until they hatch in terrestrial nests. They then carry the tadpoles on their backs up trees and deposit them in water-filled tree holes to finish development. The reverse happens as well, many treefrogs (Hylidae) forage in the trees but descend to temporary terrestrial ponds in order to breed.

Safe flashing Species in the genus *Bombina* are gregarious aquatic toads. When alarmed, they arch the back and flash their bright underbelly to confuse predators. Eggs are laid on pond surfaces as the Sun's warmth accelerates development.

Push and pull Caecilians propel themselves through soil by concertina locomotion. Part of the body remains in static contact with the earth while adjacent sections are pushed or pulled forward at the same time.

BURROWING AMPHIBIANS

Of all the amphibians, caecilians are most adept at burrowing. Worm-like and limbless, they have muscular bodies and compact skulls. With eyes covered by skin or bone, caecilians are blind but detect prey, such as earthworms, using a protrusible, chemosensory head tentacle.

Many groups of frogs have a large, keratinized, spade-like tubercle on the inner edge of each hind foot. They use this to bury themselves quickly in soft dirt or mud. Other burrowing frogs use calloused or pointed snouts, and tunnel head-first. Some bury themselves for daytime retreat. Others do so for longer periods, existing in a kind of suspended animation during dry seasons. They fill their urinary bladder with water before burrowing to avoid desiccation. Some further reduce the risk by secreting mucus which hardens around them to form a cocoon. Australian desert species are known to have remained alive underground for over a year between rainy seasons.

AMPHIBIANS IN DANGER

Since 1980, it is believed that at least 122 amphibian species have gone extinct. One third—just over 1,850 in number—are now facing the same fate according to IUCN figures. The fate of a further 113 remains uncertain because they have not been studied in sufficient detail to know their status in the wild today. While the figures on amphibian decline are worrying enough for the group itself, they have set alarm bells ringing in wider scientific and environmental communities because of what they mean for all life-forms. The highly permeable skin of amphibians makes them extremely sensitive to environmental shifts, particularly pollution and temperature change. This means they are excellent biological indicators of habitat health. Current figures detailing amphibian losses confirm fears that Earth is experiencing a period of significant environmental decline. There are more herpetologists studying frogs now, however, than ever before so what we are documenting may be natural fluctuations in frog populations.

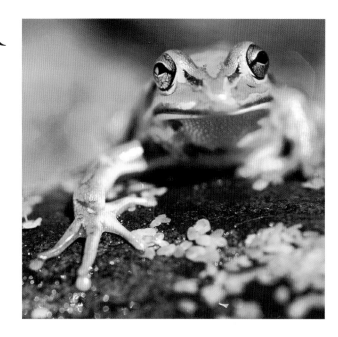

ALARMING DECLINES

There are several possible reasons for the amphibian losses observed around the world since the mid-1970s. Some of these are linked, and the impact of each varies from country to country. For example, the infectious fungal disease known as chytridiomycosis is thought to have been a major cause of decline among the amphibian fauna of Australia, the Caribbean, and the Americas; there have also been smaller outbreaks in Asia, Africa, and Europe. The disease is caused by the chytrid fungus. It interferes with the skin's permeability, and death by suffocation is the inevitable outcome. Recently, this fungus has been shown to have arisen in Africa in the 1930s. It was perhaps spread around the world by the use of the African clawed frog (*Xenopus laevus*) in pregnancy tests and the aquarium pet trade.

Habitat loss and modification, and collection for the international pet trade—particularly of some of the more colorful or physically spectacular frog and salamander species—are other serious problems.

Rising temperatures that are linked to global climate change; increased UV exposure due to declining levels of ozone in Earth's atmosphere; and herbicide and pesticide pollution have also played critical roles in the decline of amphibians. Developing nations in tropical areas, particularly those in Central and South America, are reporting the worst losses.

Small, isolated populations are more likely to be eradicated by disease or natural disaster than large ones. Because some disappearing species exist only in what appear to be pristine environments, it is not entirely clear whether or not all losses are caused by human activity.

Medical argument Skin secretions of toads and frogs, such as Australia's green and golden bell frog (above), are receiving increasing attention as potential sources of new medications for humans. This is a compelling reason to preserve amphibian biodiversity, but too many species are disappearing before researchers can investigate their potential.

Mysterious losses Golden toads, (below) are inhabitants of Central American high mountain cloud forest. They congregate in the breeding season to mate at small ponds and streams. During the 1980s, this was one of many highland species worldwide that suffered a catastrophic and largely unexplained decline, in many cases to apparent extinction.

SALAMANDERS AND NEWTS

CLASS	Amphibia
ORDER	Caudata
FAMILIES	10
GENERA	60
SPECIES	472

Salamanders, newts, mudpuppies, waterdogs, and sirens belong to the order Caudata. All have tails and most have four legs. Most species are very secretive, living terrestrially in leaf litter or rotting logs, underground, in arboreal bromeliads, or underwater. Some live terrestrially but return to the water to reproduce. Although seldom seen, they are not uncommon; astoundingly, in some deciduous forests in North America, the biomass of salamander populations is greater than that of the birds and mammals. All salamanders and their larvae are carnivorous, and they in turn become prey for many larger carnivores, such as snakes, birds, and mammals.

Distribution Salamanders are widely distributed in North and Central America, northern South America, Europe, northern Africa, and Asia.

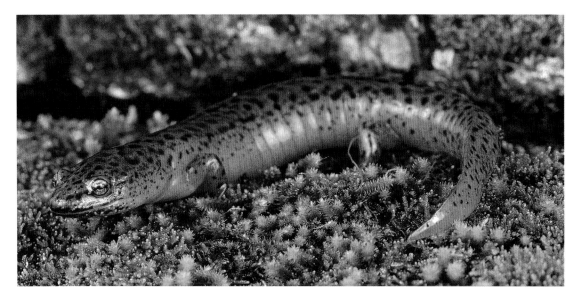

Warning colors The red salamander (*Pseudotriton ruber*) is semiaquatic, living in or under moss or flat rocks in or near springs or spring creeks. It prefers cool, clear water that flows through woods or meadows. Many species of salamanders are brightly colored to warn their principal predators—birds—that they are distasteful.

Four-toed salamander *Hemidactylium scutatm* lays up to 24 eggs under logs or in moss near clear-water creeks. The female guards them until they hatch; then the larvae enter the water to finish development.

five toes on hindlimb

pelvic girdle

four toes on forelimb

frontal bone

tail   hindlimb   vertebrae   forelimb   eye socket

Salamander skeleton A salamander's vertebral column is rigid to support the head, pelvic and pectoral girdles, and viscera, but is also flexible, permitting lateral and dorsoventral movements. Salamanders have 10–60 presacral vertebrae and a variable number of postsacral vertebrae: 2–4 precaudals and a number of caudal vertebrae.

SILENT CARNIVORES

Salamanders evolved to live on land, with four legs and a tail. Some species have secondarily returned to live permanently in the water and have reduced limbs; these are known as sirens.

Salamanders more closely resemble early fossil amphibians than do frogs and toads. Unlike frogs, they do not emphasize vocal communications during breeding. The skin of salamanders is generally smooth, moist, and flexible, with oxygen exchange taking place through the skin. Many species have lungs as well, but some families lack lungs and respire entirely cutaneously. As the salamander grows, the skin is regularly shed. Because it is made up of the salamander's own cells and is easy to digest, the animal usually devours its own skin as it is sloughed.

Salamanders and their larvae are completely carnivorous. Adults consume insects, spiders, snails, slugs, worms, and other invertebrates. The larvae devour mosquito larvae and other insects. As they grow, they eat larger prey, including tadpoles and the larvae of the dragonfly that was once their feared predator. Some species of salamanders are able to extend their tongues rapidly for half the length of their body to capture prey.

Salamanders have moist, slippery skin, while newts, both in their aquatic and terrestrial phases, have rough, dry skin. Some species of newts live on land as adults, coming to the water only to breed, while the adults of some species are aquatic. Red-spotted newts are equally at home in the water or on land. The aquatic larvae metamorphose into a terrestrial red eft, and after 1–2 years on land return to the water to breed.

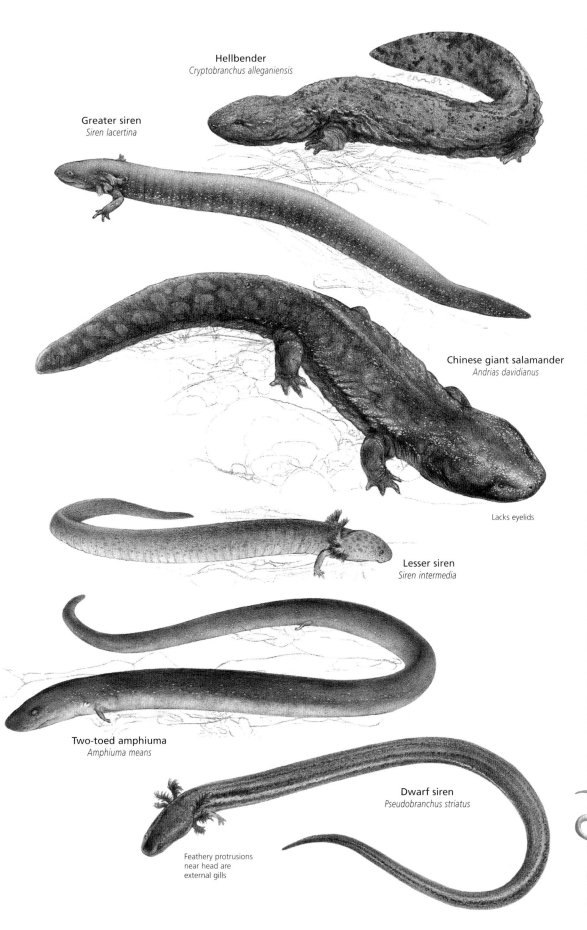

Hellbender
Cryptobranchus alleganiensis

Greater siren
Siren lacertina

Chinese giant salamander
Andrias davidianus

Lacks eyelids

Lesser siren
Siren intermedia

Two-toed amphiuma
Amphiuma means

Dwarf siren
Pseudobranchus striatus

Feathery protrusions
near head are
external gills

FACT FILE

Hellbender Hellbenders live under rocks and thrive in streams, where they forage for crayfish, mollusks, and small fishes. They are harmless but extremely slimy; in order to pick them up, they must be grasped firmly around the head.

- Up to 29½ in (74 cm)
- Aquatic
- Fall
- Common

E.C. USA

Greater siren Although most salamanders are silent, greater sirens when first caught will sometimes yelp. They also make clicking sounds, which perhaps may be used in intraspecific communication.

- Up to 38½ in (98 cm)
- Aquatic
- Unknown
- Common

S.E. USA

Chinese giant salamander Breeding takes place in an underwater cavity where the female lays up to 500 eggs in a cylindrical string. The male fertilizes the eggs externally and guards them until they hatch, in 50–60 days.

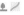

- Up to 6 ft (1.8 m)
- Aquatic
- Fall
- Data deficient

E.C. China

SALAMANDER REPRODUCTION

During courtship, males of species that fertilize their eggs internally deposit sperm packets, or spermatophores, which are picked up by the cloacal lips of the females. Species with direct development lay eggs in moist areas, and the females guard the eggs until a miniature version of the adult emerges. Eggs laid in ponds or streams and attached to vegetation hatch within 1–2 weeks into free-swimming carnivorous larvae. Some species do not develop past their final larval stage.

Courtship consequences
After courtship, the male deposits his spermatophore below the female. She picks it up with her cloacal lips and the eggs are fertilized internally.

Mudpuppy
Necturus maculosus

Extremely slimy skin

Olm
Proteus anguinus

Vestigial eyes

Siberian salamander
Ranodon sibiricus

Fischer's clawed salamander
Onychodactylus fischeri

Dybowski's salamander
Salamandrella keyserlingii

Sichuan salamander
Liua shihi

Chinese salamander
Hynobius chinensis

Paghman mountain salamander
Batrachuperus mustersi

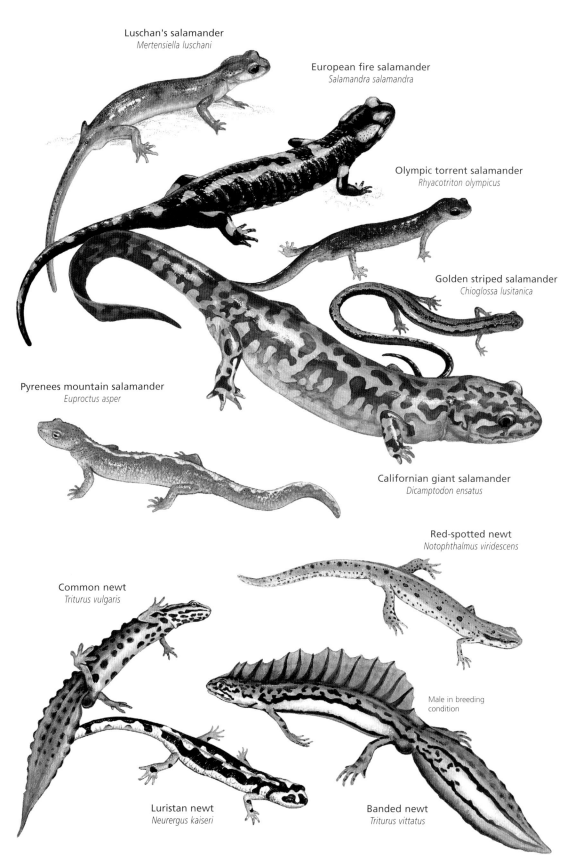

Luschan's salamander
Mertensiella luschani

European fire salamander
Salamandra salamandra

Olympic torrent salamander
Rhyacotriton olympicus

Golden striped salamander
Chioglossa lusitanica

Pyrenees mountain salamander
Euproctus asper

Californian giant salamander
Dicamptodon ensatus

Red-spotted newt
Notophthalmus viridescens

Common newt
Triturus vulgaris

Male in breeding
condition

Luristan newt
Neurergus kaiseri

Banded newt
Triturus vittatus

FACT FILE

Ringed salamander This species has narrow crossbands, a slate-colored belly, and a light gray stripe along the sides of its thin body, unlike the marbled and tiger salamanders.

 Up to 9 in (23 cm)
 Aquatic, burrowing
 Fall
 Common

S.C. USA

Tiger salamander These salamanders are fossorial for most of the year, only emerging to breed once the early spring rains begin. After breeding in ponds or marshes, the adults retreat underground.

 Up to 13 in (33 cm)
 Aquatic, burrowing
 Early spring
 Common

S. Canada to Mexico

Marbled salamander This species congregates to lay up to 230 eggs in dry depressions from September to December. Females remain wrapped around the eggs, protecting them from predation and desiccation, until fall rains fill the pools.

 Up to 5 in (13 cm)
 Terrestrial, aquatic
 Fall
 Common

S.E. USA

Japanese firebelly newt Males of this species differ from females by having swollen cloacas. The tails of breeding males develop a bluish iridescent sheen and a small filament at the tip.

 Up to 5¼ in (13.2 cm)
 Aquatic
 Spring
 Common

Japan

Vietnam warty newt This is the largest species of the genus. It is characterized by a distinct belly pattern of orange-yellow or reddish blotches, each with black or dark brown mottling.

 Up to 8 in (20 cm)
 Aquatic
 Spring
 Vulnerable

N. Vietnam

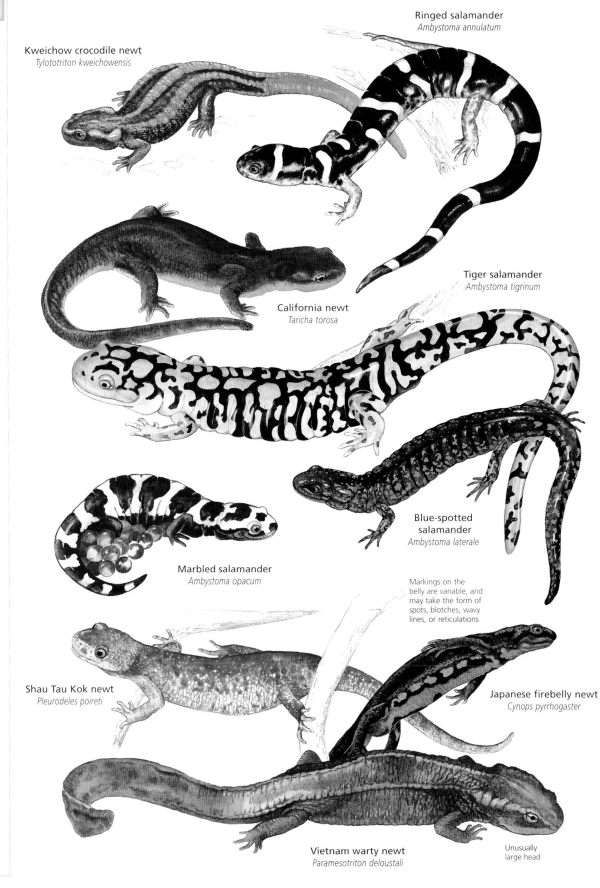

Ringed salamander
Ambystoma annulatum

Kweichow crocodile newt
Tylototriton kweichowensis

California newt
Taricha torosa

Tiger salamander
Ambystoma tigrinum

Blue-spotted salamander
Ambystoma laterale

Marbled salamander
Ambystoma opacum

Markings on the belly are variable, and may take the form of spots, blotches, wavy lines, or reticulations

Shau Tau Kok newt
Pleurodeles poireti

Japanese firebelly newt
Cynops pyrrhogaster

Vietnam warty newt
Paramesotriton deloustali

Unusually large head

Apennines salamander
Speleomantes italicus

Jackson's mushroomtongue salamander
Bolitoglossa jacksoni

Cave salamander
Eurycea lucifuga

Arboreal salamander
Aneides lugubris

Ensatina
Ensatina eschscholtzii

Spring salamander
Gyrinophilus porphyriticus

Northern dusky salamander
Desmognathus fuscus

Tennessee cave salamander
Gyrinophilus palleucus

Red back salamander
Plethodon cinereus

Four-toed salamander
Hemidactylium scutatum

Slimy salamander
Plethodon glutenosus

FACT FILE

Arboreal salamander This aggressive species has a heavily ossified skull, strong jaws, hypertrophied jaw muscles, and enlarged, flattened, blade-like, monocuspid teeth. Scarred individuals are often found, presumably having survived conspecific attacks.

- Up to 4 in (10 cm)
- Terrestrial, arboreal
- Spring
- Common, declining

Coast Ranges of California (USA)

Tennessee cave salamander This species is primarily neotenic, although some individuals transform into the adult form, losing their gills. This salamander has vestigial eyes and reduced skin pigment.

- Up to 9 in (23 cm)
- Aquatic
- Spring
- Common

Central Tennessee, N. Alabama (USA)

Slimy salamander Recently, each of the 13 genetic populations has been shown to be a distinct species. All are black with glue-like skin gland secretions.

- Up to 8 in (20 cm)
- Terrestrial
- Spring
- Common

S.E. USA

LUNGLESS SALAMANDERS

Plethodontidae is the most diverse family of salamanders, with 269 species. Jordan's salamander (*Plethodon jordani*) inhabits the leaf litter and rotting logs on the humid forest floor of the Appalachian Mountains, in the eastern United States. It is adapted to cool, moist habitats up to 6,643 feet (1,993 m). Highly vascularized blood vessels near the skin's surface mean it can respire through the skin and lining of the mouth.

Desirable colors
The Jordan's salamander has a variety of color morphs. There are other species that mimic the color pattern of this red-cheeked morph, presumably because it has a bad taste to predators.

AMPHIBIAN LIFE-CYCLES

Most amphibians have a dual life-cycle involving a court-ship ritual, the deposition of sperm and eggs, external fertilization, an aquatic larval stage, and transformation into the adult life form. Modifications made to this cycle involve internal fertilization, direct development, viviparity, neoteny, or parental care. There is a trade-off between multitudes of small eggs with no parental care and a few large eggs with parental care.

Swollen egg sacs The egg sac of the Jefferson salamander (*Ambystoma jeffersonianum*) is much larger than the adult after the eggs have absorbed water. This species does not brood or guard its eggs.

Salamander life-cycle Pheromones stimulate courtship behavior in sala-manders. Males then deposit sperm as spermatophores on the substrate below the female. She retrieves the spermatophores with her cloacal lips, fertilizing the eggs internally as she deposits them in water or in a moist substrate. Aquatic larvae hatch from the eggs in the water or direct develop-ment may occur in terrestrial eggs.

terrestrial adult

larva with fully developed limbs and gills

egg

larva with gill buds

larva with developing gills and forelimbs, and hindlimb buds

1. Mating *The male clasps the female around the middle. The female carries the male until she is ready to lay her eggs. The male then sheds his sperm over the eggs as they are laid.*

5. Change complete *After 6 weeks, the metamorphosis from tadpole to adult frog is complete, and the young frog begins to hunt insects.*

2. Egg development *The eggs float in large masses while the embryos develop inside. The eggs are covered in a jelly-like substance that swells when it comes into contact with water.*

Safe development Marsupial frogs (*Gastrotheca*) have one or two pouches, similiar to those of marsupials, which open dorsally to the cloaca. Eggs are placed in the pouch as the male fertilizes them. Thus the eggs develop in a moist and safe environment. The young emerge as tadpoles or froglets, depending on the species.

Frog life-cycle Frogs and toads have a complex life-cycle. Males call to attact females, and shed sperm over the eggs as the female deposits them in a selected site. The eggs absorb water and in a few days develop into free-swimming tadpoles, which are normally herbivorous. After a few weeks, months, or years (depending on the species) the tadpoles meta-morphose into identical small replicas of the adults. It then takes months or years of a carnivorous diet before sexual maturity is reached.

4. Tadpole development *Lungs begin to form after 3 weeks, and legs after 4 weeks, the hindlimbs developing first. The tadpole's tail shrinks and its gills are reabsorbed.*

3. Tadpoles emerge *After 2 weeks, the eggs hatch into tadpoles. When the mouth develops, the tadpoles feed on algae. They breathe through external gills.*

CAECILIANS

LASS Amphibia
RDER Gymnophiona
AMILIES 6
ENERA 33
PECIES 149

Caecilians have radiated to a variety of aquatic and terrestrial habitats, with specialized characteristics for a fossorial life not present in any other vertebrates—chemo-sensing tentacles, an extra set of jaw-closing muscles, and skin that is ossified to the skull. Adults range in size from just under 3 inches (7 cm) to 5¼ feet (1.6 m). Fertilization is internal. Some species are oviparous; others have direct development; and about half of the known species are viviparous. They feed on earthworms, beetle larvae, termites, and crickets.

Distribution Caecilians have a limited pantropical distribution in India, southern China, Malaysia, the Philippines, Africa, Central America, and South America. No species are known from Europe, Australia, or Antarctica.

Caecilian skull Caecilians are built for burrowing, with massive, bullet-shaped skulls. They are streamlined, but reinforced for burrowing through soil or protruding into the substrate in search of invertebrate prey. They move through the soil by undulating the body: the muscles move in a wave from the head to the tail. The body curves resist the soil or water, and forward motion is achieved.

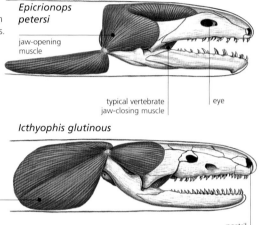

Epicrionops petersi

jaw-opening muscle

typical vertebrate jaw-closing muscle

eye

Icthyophis glutinous

strong jaw-closing muscles

nostril

Gymnophis multiplicate All species in the family Caeciliidae are chacterized by distinct annuli, which have caused some people to confuse them with earthworms. Caecilians have a retractable tentacle on each side of the head, which helps them to search for prey by transmitting chemical clues to the nasal cavity.

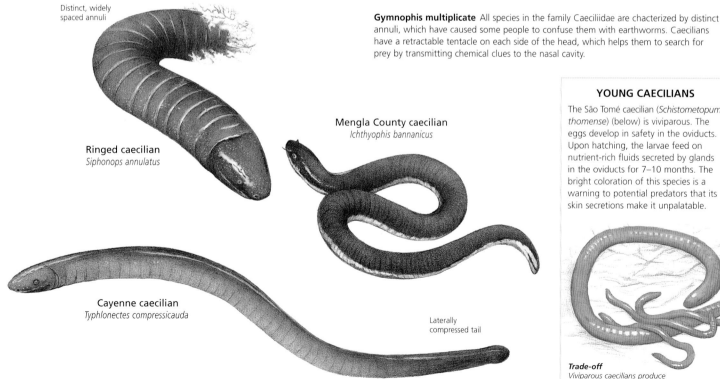

Distinct, widely spaced annuli

Ringed caecilian
Siphonops annulatus

Mengla County caecilian
Ichthyophis bannanicus

Cayenne caecilian
Typhlonectes compressicauda

Laterally compressed tail

YOUNG CAECILIANS

The São Tomé caecilian (*Schistometopum thomense*) (below) is viviparous. The eggs develop in safety in the oviducts. Upon hatching, the larvae feed on nutrient-rich fluids secreted by glands in the oviducts for 7–10 months. The bright coloration of this species is a warning to potential predators that its skin secretions make it unpalatable.

Trade-off
Viviparous caecilians produce fewer young than oviparous species but provide better care.

FROGS AND TOADS

CLASS Amphibia
ORDER Anura
FAMILIES 28
GENERA 338
SPECIES 4,937

Anuran is the collective term for this group of tailless amphibians. This is the largest order of amphibians, with nearly 5,000 known species. Anurans come in all shapes and sizes, from the tiny Brazilian Izecksohn's toad (*Psyllophryne didactyla*), which is less than half an inch (1 cm) long, to the African goliath frog (*Conraua goliath*), which is 12 inches (30 cm) long and weighs 7⅓ pounds (3.3 kg). Frogs and toads are easily identified by their long hindlegs, short trunk, moist skin, and lack of tail. Anurans are the only amphibians that are extremely vocal when breeding. The largest genus of frogs—*Eleutherodactylus* (rain frogs)—is also the largest genus of all vertebrates.

Distribution Frogs and toads occur on all continents except Antarctica. More than 80 percent of species are tropical; at one site alone, 67 species have been recorded. Two species extend north of the Arctic Circle.

Flying frogs The Java flying frog (*Rhacophorus reinwardtii*) has broad webs of skin between its toes, allowing it to parachute between trees or guiding it in a controlled fall to another branch. This adaptation is important for life in the rain-forest canopy.

SINGING FOR THEIR LIVES

A notable feature of frogs and toads is the voices of the males calling for mates. These calls herald spring in the temperate zone and the onset of the rainy season in the tropics. Each species of frog has a specific call that distinguishes it from all other species. Females can assess the size of the male, and thus his fitness, by the tone of his call. Only males call, and females come to the calling male to mate. These calls also have the disadvantage of attracting some predators, notably bats.

In some species, calling sites are at a premium and males defend them against other calling males. To avoid confrontations, satellite males wait silently near the calling male in hopes of intercepting a gravid female before she reaches him. This lessens their chance of being eaten by a bat, and reduces the energy lost by calling or by fighting with the dominant male.

The above are characteristics of frogs with long breeding seasons. Many other species are explosive breeders, coming to the breeding ponds with the first heavy rains, breeding by the thousands for 2–3 days, and then retreating until the following year. These species

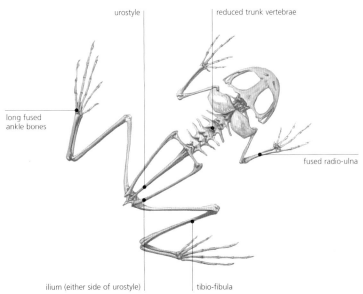

urostyle | reduced trunk vertebrae

long fused ankle bones

fused radio-ulna

ilium (either side of urostyle) | tibio-fibula

Tongue lashing Frogs and toads have long, sticky tongues, like the Japanese toad (*Bufo japonicus*) (above), which they use to capture prey. Once the insect is inside the mouth, the toad blinks its eyes and the eyes push the food out of the mouth and down the throat. Males also use their tongues in combat, lashing them into the eyes of other males in territorial battles or in bouts over access to a female.

Frog skeleton Anurans have a shortened vertebral column of nine or fewer vertebrae. The epipodial elements of both fore and hindlimbs are fused; also, the ankle is elongated and made up of two fused elements. The postsacral vertebrae are uniquely fused into a rod-shaped urostyle. The long hindlimbs give frogs the propulsive force to propel themselves forward. A short, compact body is easier to move forward. The reinforced pectoral girdle and forelimbs are built to absorb the shock of landing.

Calling for a mate During the breeding season, male frogs and toads call to attract the females to mate. Each species has a distinct attraction call. This natterjack toad (*Bufo calamita*) (above) has his gular sac inflated and is making a trilling sound.

Energy transfers The northern leopard frog (*Rana pipiens*) (right) leaps to escape a predator. Frogs and tadpoles transform the energy in their food (algae, detritus, and insects) into larger packets of energy that are then available to bigger predators.

usually have loud, carrying calls and lay thousands of small eggs. To avoid predation of their eggs by aquatic predators, many species of tree frogs (*Hylidae*) lay their eggs in vegetation overhanging their breeding ponds. When the eggs hatch, the tadpoles fall into the water, where they complete their development. Other species of casque-headed tree frogs (*Osteocephalus*) lay a few large fertilized eggs in tree holes. The female returns regularly to deposit unfertilized eggs in the nest to feed her tadpoles. Many species of poison frogs (*Dendrobatidae*) guard their eggs in terrestrial nests and, upon hatching, carry their tadpoles to the water, or in some cases up trees and into bromeliads. Many species of *Eleutherodactylus* lay 15–25 large yolked eggs in terrestrial nests, the eggs having direct development. Midwife toads, Surinam toads, and gastric-brooding frog females carry the eggs with them until they hatch into small frogs. Other *Leptodactylid* and *Rhacophorid* frogs build foam nests to deposit their eggs and rear their tadpoles.

Frogs are indicators of environmental pollution. Since the 1970s, there has been growing worldwide evidence that frog populations are declining on a massive scale and that many species are going extinct, even though their populations appear to be within pristine areas. The decline may be the result of a number of factors, including pollution, pesticides (such as DDT), herbicides (such as Atrizine), road salts, UV radiation, global warming, lower rainfall, or lower humidity. At present, the fungus chytridiomycosis seems to be the greatest threat. The fungus, which probably originated in Africa, invades the skin and lowers the frogs' immune system so they are more susceptible to diseases.

> **⚡ CONSERVATION WATCH**
>
> The 342 species of anurans on the IUCN Red List are categorized as follows:
>
> | | |
> |---:|---|
> | 7 | Extinct |
> | 27 | Critically endangered |
> | 27 | Endangered |
> | 64 | Vulnerable |
> | 1 | Conservation dependent |
> | 15 | Near threatened |
> | 67 | Data deficient |
> | 134 | Least concern |

FACT FILE

Brown New Zealand frog Males of this species do not have a prominent breeding call. Call notes are made by resonance frequencies in the head and body, not by the vibration frequency of the vocal cords.

- ► Up to 2 in (5 cm)
- ◯ Terrestrial
- ⇌ Spring
- ↯ Vulnerable

Stephens & Maud Islands (New Zealand)

Oriental firebelly toad This toad is one of the most common in its range, constituting up to a third of the total anurans at some localities. The density at breeding sites can reach three toads per square foot (nine toads per sq. m).

- ► Up to 2½ in (6 cm)
- ◯ Terrestrial
- ⇌ Summer
- ↯ Common

Russia, Korea, China

Tailed frog This frog has no breeding call. Its "tail"—used for internal fertilization in fast-moving streams— is unique among anurans. Eggs are deposited in strings under rocks in streams. Tadpoles take 1–4 years to metamorphose to juveniles, and then 7–8 years to first breeding.

- ► Up to 2 in (5 cm)
- ◉ Terrestrial, aquatic
- ⇌ Summer
- ↯ Common

N.W. USA

ANURAN FERTILIZATION

Fertilization of the eggs usually occurs while the frogs are in amplexus. As the female deposits her eggs, males release sperm above them in the water. The coqui and some other terrestrial species achieve internal fertilization by cloacal apposition; only the tailed frog has an intermittent organ.

Frogs in amplexus
The female carries the male to an appropriate spot to deposit the eggs.

Brown midwife toad
Alytes cisternasii

Yellowbelly toad
Bombina variegata

Brown New Zealand frog
Leiopelma hamiltoni

Olive midwife toad
Alytes obstetricans

Hochstetter's
New Zealand frog
Leiopelma hochstetteri

Oriental firebelly toad
Bombina orientalis

Painted frog
Discoglossus pictus

Belly and underside of limbs are flashed as a warning to predators

Corsica painted frog
Discoglossus montalentii

Tailed frog
Ascaphus truei

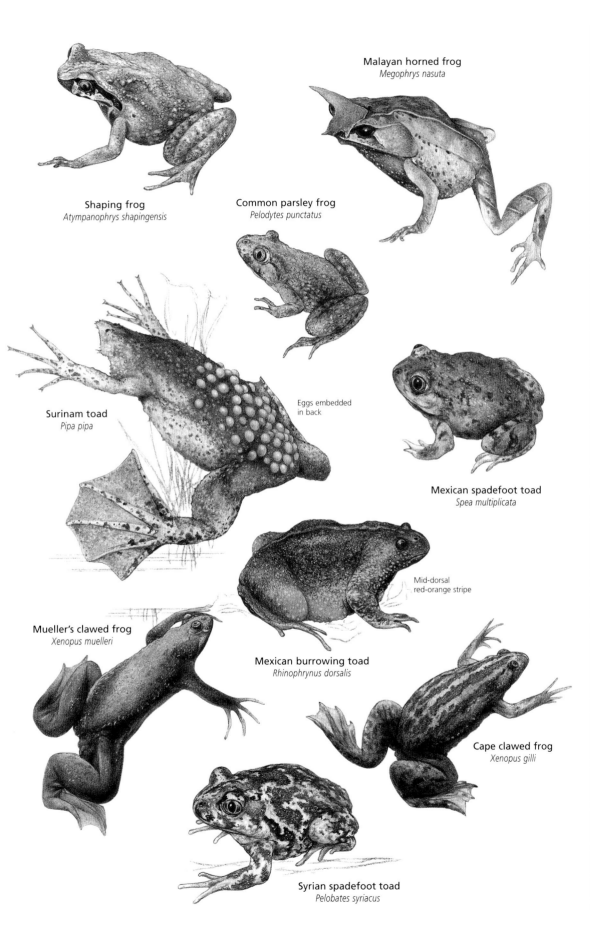

Malayan horned frog
Megophrys nasuta

Shaping frog
Atympanophrys shapingensis

Common parsley frog
Pelodytes punctatus

Surinam toad
Pipa pipa

Eggs embedded
in back

Mexican spadefoot toad
Spea multiplicata

Mueller's clawed frog
Xenopus muelleri

Mid-dorsal
red-orange stripe

Mexican burrowing toad
Rhinophrynus dorsalis

Cape clawed frog
Xenopus gilli

Syrian spadefoot toad
Pelobates syriacus

FACT FILE

Common parsley frog Male parsley
frogs can be heard calling from below
the surface of the water. The tadpoles
are larger than the adult frogs, at up
to 2½ in (6 cm) in length. The eggs are
laid in strings across aquatic plants.

Up to 2 in (5 cm)
Terrestrial, aquatic
Spring
Common

Iberia, France, W. Belgium, N.W. Italy

Surinam toad During amplexus, the
female releases eggs one at a time.
The male fertilizes and embeds each
egg in the skin of her back, where the
eggs sink in and form a honeycomb of
pockets. After 3–4 months, froglets
emerge from her back.

Up to 8 in (20 cm)
Aquatic
Spring
Common

N. South America

Mexican spadefoot toad Spadefoots
are nocturnal during the summer rainy
season, when they are breeding. The
rest of the year, they occupy burrows
that they dig in the soft earth.

Up to 2 in (5 cm)
Terrestrial
Summer
Common

S.C. USA, N. Mexico

Cape clawed frog Modification of the
acid, black-water ponds inhabited by
this species allowed the invasion of the
common clawed frog (*Xenopus laevis*).
The two are interbreeding, producing
sterile hybrids and further driving this
species toward extinction.

Up to 2 in (5 cm)
Aquatic
Winter
Vulnerable

S.W. South Africa

Mexican burrowing toad This toad
spends most of its life underground,
only emerging to breed after heavy
rains. Males' bodies are so inflated when
calling that they resemble balloons.

Up to 3½ in (9 cm)
Terrestrial
Summer
Common

Texas (USA) to Costa Rica

Turtle frog This frog burrows head-first with its strong forelimbs, often into termite nests to eat the inhabitants. Males call from the soil surface or with only their heads uncovered. Up to 40 large eggs are laid underground.

- Up to 2½ in (6 cm)
- Terrestrial, burrowing
- Rainy season
- Uncommon

S.W. Australia

Crucifix toad This fossorial toad spends most of its life underground and only emerges to breed after heavy rains in temporary pools. Males call while floating on the surface. Small eggs are deposited in the water.

- Up to 2¼ in (5.5 cm)
- Terrestrial, burrowing
- Rainy season
- Common

S.E. Australia

Giant banjo frog Adults spend daylight hours and drier months buried beneath the surface. Males call while floating on vegetation or concealed in burrows at the water's edge. Oviposition take place in flooded burrows.

- Up to 3½ in (9 cm)
- Aquatic
- Spring, summer
- Uncommon

S.E. Australia

GASTRIC BROODERS

Fertilized eggs or larvae are swallowed by the female gastric-brooding frog (*Rheobatrachus silus*) and develop in her stomach. The production of hydrochloric acid in the female's stomach ceases during this time. Tadpoles develop from the nutrients in the egg yolk, so the labial teeth are absent.

Up they come The young crawl out into the world after developing in their mother's stomach for 6–7 weeks.

Red-crowned toadlet
Pseudophryne australis

Skeleton ghost frog
Heleophryne rosei

Spatulate toes used for climbing rocks

Turtle frog
Myobatrachus gouldii

Thomasset's frog
Nesomantis thomasseti

Crucifix toad
Notaden bennettii

Natal ghost frog
Heleophryne natalensis

Giant banjo frog
Limnodynastes interioris

Differs from the giant burrowing frog (*Helioporus australicacus*) as lacks black spines on the back and throat

Western marsh frog
Heleioporus barycragus

Surinam horned frog
Ceratophrys cornuta

South American bullfrog
Leptodactylus pentadactylus

Active forager, feeding on small prey only

Ornate horned toad
Ceratophrys ornata

Vizcacheras' white-lipped frog
Leptodactylus bufonius

Budgett's frog
Lepidobatrachus laevis

Schmidt's forest frog
Hydrolaetare schmidti

Dumeril's striped frog
Leptodactylus gracilis

Weeping frog
Physalaemus biligonigerus

Sehuenca's water frog
Telmatobius yuracare

FACT FILE

Surinam horned frog When prey ventures nearby, this frog lurches forward, opening the mouth that dominates the entire top of its head, and swallowing the prey whole.

- Up to 4¾ in (12 cm)
- Terrestrial
- Fall rainy season
- Common

Amazonia (South America)

South American bullfrog The call is a single, loud, whistle-like hoot. Up to 3,000 eggs are laid in a depression in the forest floor. The cannibalistic tadpoles are dispersed to nearby streams or swamps by heavy rains.

- Up to 7 in (18 cm)
- Terrestrial
- Fall
- Common

Honduras to Bolivia

Budgett's frog This is a large, stout, aquatic frog with a flattened body. The head is large and robust, one-third of the total body length, and broad to accommodate its very wide jaws.

- Up to 4 in (10 cm)
- Aquatic
- Summer
- Common

Gran Chaco (Argentina, Bolivia, Paraguay)

DROUGHT RESISTANCE

During the dry winter months, ornate horned toads are inactive underground, encased in a hard shell composed of layers of unshed skin. This "cocoon" protects the animal from excessive water loss and allows it to survive until the rains arrive. These signal the beginning of the wet summer months in South America, which last from October to February. The heavy rains flood the Gran Chaco and create transient pools for foraging and breeding.

Digging in Ornate horned toads will remain buried until rains signal the beginning of the wet summer months.

FACT FILE

Coqui This species gets its name from its high-pitched chirp, which sounds like "co qui." Eggs are laid on land with direct development in the egg. Coquis have been introduced into Florida and Hawaii, United States.

- Up to 2¼ in (5.5 cm)
- Terrestrial, arboreal
- Year round
- Common

Puerto Rico (Caribbean)

Barking frog The breeding call of this species sounds like a dog barking when heard at a distance; close up, it is a guttural "whurr." Females make a screech when grasped. When captured, their bodies puff up immensely.

- Up to 3¾ in (9.5 cm)
- Terrestrial
- Spring
- Common

S.W. USA to C.W. Mexico

Peru robber frog This species has direct development. The eggs are deposited in moist areas in the leaf litter. The males, which are considerably smaller than the females, call day and night from the forest floor.

- Up to 1¼ in (3 cm)
- Terrestrial
- Fall rainy season
- Common

W. Amazonia (Brazil, Bolivia, Peru, Ecuador)

Lowland tropical frog Females deposit up to 20 unpigmented eggs in a foam nest. The tadpoles developing in the nest subsist entirely on the egg yolk. Males call from mudflats.

- Up to 1¼ in (3 cm)
- Terrestrial
- Spring
- Common

Amazonia (N. South America)

Gold-striped frog The flash coloration—bright red spots in the groin and on the rear of the thighs—is displayed when the frog moves. Its coloration mimics that of the spotted-thighed poison frog (*Epipedobates femoralis*). Eggs are deposited in foam nests.

- Up to 2 in (5 cm)
- Terrestrial
- Winter
- Common

N. South America

Calls can reach 100 decibels; recently introduced to Hawaii

Coqui
Eleutherodactylus coqui

Barking frog
Eleutherodactylus augusti

Seldom venture out from their limestone cave haunts

No webbing between the toes

Jimenez robber frog
Eleutherodactylus lacrimosus

Carabaya robber frog
Eleutherodactylus ockendeni

Peru robber frog
Eleutherodactylus peruvianus

Variable robber frog
Eleutherodactylus variabilis

Lowland tropical frog
Adenomera andreae

Red spots on thighs mimic those of a poisonous frog

Gold-striped frog
Lithodytes lineatus

Darwin's mouthbreeder
Rhinoderma darwinii

ADVANCE OF THE CANE TOAD

Successful stories of the cane toad (*Bufo marinos*) (also known as the marine toad) being introduced into the sugarcane fields of Puerto Rico to control insect pests convinced the sugarcane growers in Queensland, Australia, to import and breed 100 adult toads. In 1935, they released 62,000 subadults in Queensland to control the grayback cane beetle (*Dermolepida albohirtum*). Since the neotropical cane toad has no natural predators in Australia, populations have reached plague proportions. The toads adapted well to feeding on all animals smaller than themselves, even competing with dogs for the rations in their bowls. Studies in Brazil are yet to come up with a solution.

paratoid gland

Toad nightmare The cane fields did not have proper daytime cover so the introduced toads dispersed into the countryside. They are now so abundant that gardens become a moving mass of toads at night and the roads are slippery with splattered bodies.

Cane toad poison When cane toads are threatened, they inflate their bodies and begin sweating a milky, latex-like liquid from the paratoid glands. In extreme cases, the secretions can be projected up to 3 feet (92 cm) toward the aggressive attacker, but are not toxic unless ingested. The poison has been used as a hallucinogenic drug.

Breeding The cane toad breeds year-round in Australia in temporary pools, stock tanks, lakes, and streams. The prolific toads are capable of producing up to 13,000 eggs at a time. Their tadpoles transform rapidly and have minimal habitat requirements: algae and water. Although cane toads take several years to mature, they can live for over 20 years. Calling cane toads interfere with the breeding choruses of native frogs.

Indiscriminate eaters The cane toad grows up to 9 inches (23 cm) long and can weigh over 2¼ pounds (1 kg). It eats nearly anything smaller than itself, including many beneficial frogs. The cane toad above is swallowing a pygmy possum.

Fatal meal The cane toad's paratoid glands contain a secretion that is fatal to some animals. The cane toad pictured right has angled its paratoid glands toward the approaching snake. Populations of Australian snakes that normally consume native anurans are diminishing because they die from swallowing cane toads. This is also a problem for other indigenous animals. Birds, dingos, monitor lizards, and other anurans see the cane toad as possible prey. Fishes die from ingesting the toxic tadpoles. And the problem is not restricted to areas into which it has been introduced: in South America, a group of Peruvian Indians is believed to have perished after eating a soup made from cane toad eggs.

FACT FILE

Colorado river toad The skin glands of these toads produce a toxin that can cause intoxication and hallucination in humans, and is a controlled substance in the United States, where people have been arrested for milking toads.

▶ Up to 8 in (20 cm)
◯ Terrestrial
⇶ Summer
⚑ Common

S.W. USA & N.W. Mexico

Common Asian toad Once common, this species is declining due to habitat alteration and loss, caused by drought, deforestation, drainage of habitat, pesticides, fertilizers, and pollutants.

▶ Up to 6 in (15 cm)
◯ Terrestrial
⇶ Summer
⚑ Declining

S.E. Asia

AMPHIBIAN EGG

Amphibian embryos have gelatinous membranes around them, but lack the protective amnion present in reptiles. Since eggs also lack shells, they must be protected from desiccation. Eggs contain nutrients for the tadpoles to develop into free-swimming larvae. Eggs of some species have enough yolk to nourish the embryos until they hatch as miniature adults.

Tadpole developing in egg
Anurans must either deposit their eggs in water or in moist places to avoid desiccation.

⚑ CONSERVATION WATCH

The 18 species of Bufonidae on the IUCN Red List are categorized as follows:

    1   Critically endangered
    6   Endangered
    6   Vulnerable
    2   Near threatened
    3   Data deficient

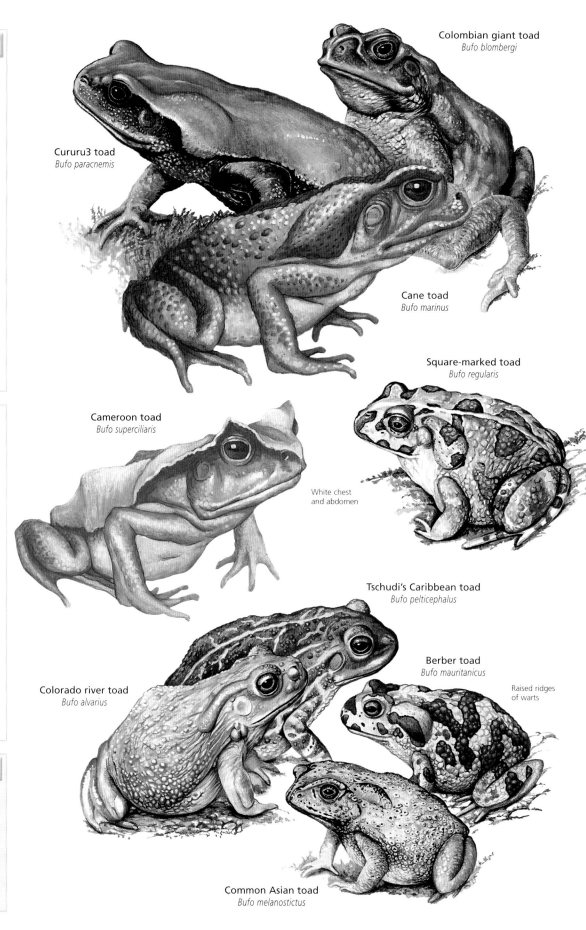

Colombian giant toad
Bufo blombergi

Cururu3 toad
Bufo paracnemis

Cane toad
Bufo marinus

Square-marked toad
Bufo regularis

Cameroon toad
Bufo superciliaris

White chest and abdomen

Tschudi's Caribbean toad
Bufo pelticephalus

Berber toad
Bufo mauritanicus

Raised ridges of warts

Colorado river toad
Bufo alvarius

Common Asian toad
Bufo melanostictus

Everett's Asian tree toad
Pedostibes everetti

Sonoran green toad
Bufo retiformis

Horned toad
Bufo ceratophrys

South American common toad
Bufo margaritifer

Red toad
Schismaderma carens

Oak toad
Bufo quercinus

Red-spotted toad
Bufo punctatus

Two color morphs
of harlequin frogs

Green toad
Bufo viridis

Harlequin frog
Atelopus varius

Horned toad This diurnal toad lives on the forest floor where it forages for termites and breeds in forest streams.

- Up to 3¼ in (8.2 cm)
- Terrestrial
- Unknown
- Common

N.W. Amazonia (South America)

Green toad Green toads form dense populations in areas altered by people, and these are often much higher than in adjacent natural habitats. They prefer burrows and live in the burrows of rodents. Abundance can reach more than 100 individuals per 1,075 square feet (100 sq. m).

- Up to 4¾ in (12 cm)
- Terrestrial
- Spring
- Common

Europe to Asia

Harlequin frog No courtship has been reported for this species. Amplexus is prolonged; females carry males on their backs from a few days to over a month until about 20 eggs are laid in water.

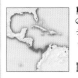

- Up to 2 in (5 cm)
- Terrestrial, aquatic
- Fall
- Declining

S. Costa Rica, Panama, N. Colombia

TOADS VERSUS FROGS

In Europe and North America, toads (family Bufonidae) have short legs for hopping, dry warty skin, and are terrestrial. Frogs (family Ranidae) have long, slender legs for leaping great distances, moist skin, and are aquatic. However, the use of the terms "frog" and "toad" depends on the region of the world you are in. In Africa, the smooth and moist-skinned aquatic Cape clawed frog (*Xenopus gilli*) is called a clawed toad.

To kiss a toad
Even though South Africans call Bufo
*pardalis (above) the leopard frog, it
belongs to the toad family Bufonidae.*

FACT FILE

Australian lace-lid frog This frog has huge eyes with vertically elliptical pupils and a lower eyelid with a golden reticulation. It is found on rocks and vegetation in fast-flowing rocky streams in rain forest up to 3,900 feet (1,200 m).

- Up to 2½ in (6 cm)
- Arboreal
- Spring, summer
- Endangered

N.E. Australia

Southern bell frog Males call while floating on the water. The call is a low growl lasting about a second. The eggs are deposited in a floating jelly that later sinks. They feed on other frogs and even their own species.

- Up to 4 in (10 cm)
- Terrestrial, aquatic
- Summer
- Locally common

S.E. Australia & Tasmania

Short-footed frog This is a robust, burrowing frog with striking and highly variable markings. The back is dark brown with silver-brown blotches. The frog usually also has a silver-brown stripe down the back and a white belly.

- Up to 2 in (5 cm)
- Terrestrial, burrowing
- Unknown
- Common

N.E. Australia

Paradox frog This frog has large webbed feet and extremely slippery skin. The tadpoles are three times as large as the adults, up to 10 inches (25 cm) in length.

- Up to 3 in (7.5 cm)
- Aquatic
- Rainy season
- Common

Amazonia (South America) to N. Argentina

Water-holding frog This species spends the long dry periods, which can be up to several years long, in burrows deep underground. It surrounds itself with a cocoon-like chamber, formed with sloughed dead layers of its skin.

- Up to 2½ in (6 cm)
- Terrestrial, burrowing
- Variable
- Common

Central Australia

Australian lace-lid frog
Nyctimystes dayi

Dainty green tree frog
Litoria gracilenta

Southern bell frog
Litoria raniformis

Blue Mountains tree frog
Litoria citropa

Green and golden bell frog
Litoria aurea

Short-footed frog
Cyclorana brevipes

White's tree frog
Litoria caerulea

Paradox frog
Pseudis paradoxa

Extensively webbed feet

Water-holding frog
Cyclorana platycephala

Fringed leaf frog
Agalychnis craspedopus

Painted-belly leaf frog
Phyllomedusa sauvagii

Shovel-headed tree frog
Triprion spatulatus

Jaguar leaf frog
Phyllomedusa palliate

Cayenne slender-legged
tree frog
Osteocephalus leprieurii

Map tree frog
Hyla geographica

Red-eyed tree frog
Agalychnis callidryas

Veined tree frog
Phrynohyas venulosa

Jordan's casque-headed
tree frog
Trachycephalus jordani

Rusty tree frog
Hyla boans

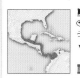
FROG FEET

Frogs have four digits on the forelimbs and five on the hindlimbs. The shapes vary depending on their habits: fully webbed for swimming, or toe pads for climbing, or modified claws with extra tubercules for digging.

***Frog toes** Parallel evolution has produced the same types of toes in unrelated families: tree frogs in Hylidae and Rhacophoridae both have rounded toe pads.*

FACT FILE

Nicaragua giant glass frog This species calls—using a three-note series of high-pitched "ticks"—from above streams. It attaches eggs to leaves that overhang the streams. Tadpoles attach to rocks with their suction mouth.

Up to 1 in (2.5 cm)
Arboreal
Summer
Common

N. Nicaragua to Colombia & Ecuador

Barking tree frog This frog gets its name from its loud raucous call of nine or ten notes from high in the treetops, possibly a territorial call. Its breeding call is a simple "doonk" or "toonk." The female deposits eggs singly on the bottom of the breeding pond.

Up to 2¾ in (7 cm)
Terrestrial, arboreal
Spring, summer
Common

S.E. USA

European tree frog This tree frog is declining in western and central Europe due to loss of habitat, habitat isolation, pollution, and climate change.

Up to 2 in (5 cm)
Terrestrial, arboreal
Spring
Common

Europe, W. Asia, N.W. Africa

Marsupial frog During amplexus, the male pushes the fertilized eggs into a pouch on the back of the female. Direct development takes place in the pouch without a tadpole stage.

Up to 2¾ in (7 cm)
Terrestrial, arboreal
Spring, summer
Common

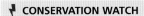

Amazonia (Peru, Bolivia)

⚡ CONSERVATION WATCH

The 72 species of Hylidae on the IUCN Red List are categorized as follows:

6	Critically endangered
5	Endangered
5	Vulnerable
5	Near threatened
8	Data deficient
43	Least concern

Nicaragua giant glass frog
Centrolene prosoblepon

Glass frogs named for their translucent undersides

Hourglass tree frog
Hyla ebraccata

Bereis' tree frog
Hyla leucophyllata

Barking tree frog
Hyla gratiosa

Green tree frog
Hyla cinera

Equally at home in treetops or underground burrows

Sumaco horned tree frog
Hemiphractus proboscideus

Mexican tree frog
Smilisca baudini

European tree frog
Hyla arborea

Marsupial frog
Gastrotheca marsupiata

Female frog without eggs in pouch

Ornate chorus frog
Pseudacris ornata

TREE FROGS

The family Hylidae—tree frogs—comprises 855 species in 42 genera, distributed primarily in North America, South America, and Australia, and to a lesser extent in Europe and Asia. Tree frogs range in size from the half an inch (12 mm) adult javelin frog (*Litoria microbelos*) to the 5½ inch (14 cm) Hispaniola tree frog (*Hyla vasta*). Most hylids are arboreal, but some are terrestrial, aquatic, or burrowing. Most possess adhesive toe pads, which allow them to cling to any surface. Almost all are very flattened and streamlined, with long legs that are useful for leaping from branch to branch. Tree frogs have horizontally elliptical pupils, with the exception of the Phyllomedusids, which have vertical pupils.

Striking skin The Bereis' tree frog has a variable color pattern resembling the markings of a giraffe; other tree frogs are less striking. Large toe pads and loose belly skin allow this frog to stick to leaves and other smooth surfaces when climbing and searching for prey.

Burrowing habits The burrowing tree frog (*Pternohyla fodiens*) is found in many habitats subject to seasonal inundation. They are well adapted for burrowing and spend the dry season in a dormant state beneath the surface. They will only breed after heavy rain.

Harlequin flying tree frog
The harlequin flying tree frog (*Rhacophorus pardalis*) is found from 650–5,575 feet (200–1,700 m) and has a 2½ inch (6.5 cm) snout–vent length. They lay up to 50 eggs in a foamy mass on leaves suspended in the trees above ponds between March and May and can be found in the Philippines, Borneo, and Sumatra.

Safe hands The brown-belly leaf frog (*Phyllomedusa tarsius*) is nocturnal and arboreal in primary and secondary rain-forests in the Amazon. The first digit on the front foot is opposable, so these frogs can grasp small branches like a primate as they crawl slowly through the canopy oblivious to wind and rain. They have rounded paratoid glands extending at least to mid-body.

Hanging on
Glass frogs typically call from the upper side of leaves overhanging streams and attach their eggs to the underside of the same leaves.

Reproduction in the trees Males have species-specific vocalizations that they use to attract gravid females. Amplexus stimulates the females to deposit eggs, usually in water, where they hatch into free-swimming tadpoles. Many species deposit their eggs in overhanging vegetation; when the eggs hatch, the tadpoles fall into the water to finish their development. Some species deposit their eggs in bromeliads and the tadpoles develop there. Casqueheaded tree frogs (*Osteocephalus oophagus*) have parental care. After fertilizing the eggs laid in bromeliads or tree holes, males guard their progeny from predators. Females join in by laying yolked unfertilized eggs at regular intervals in these nests to feed their tadpoles.

RAIN FROGS OF AFRICA

Rain frogs (genus *Breviceps*) have short heads and stout bodies. They appear above ground only during torrential rain. Males have loud, bellowing calls that can be heard from great distances, and sticky skin secretions that attach them to the females during amplexus. They lay their eggs underground, and the young frogs develop without any need for water.

Puffed up like a balloon
*Desert rain frog males (*Breviceps maacrops*) inflate their bodies enormously when calling for mates.*

Ornate rice frog
Microhyla ornata

Nosy Be giant tree frog
Platypelis milloti

Red rain frog
Scaphiophryne gottlebei

Dotted humming frog
Chiasmocleis ventrimaculata

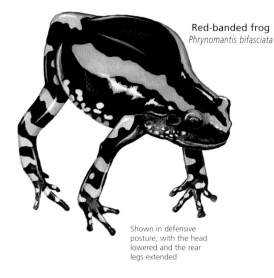

Red-banded frog
Phrynomantis bifasciata

Muller's termite frog
Dermatonotus muelleri

Shown in defensive posture, with the head lowered and the rear legs extended

Great Plains
narrow-mouthed toad
Gastrophryne olivacea

Tomato frog
Dyscophus antongilii

Malaysian
narrow-mouthed toad
Kaloula pulchra

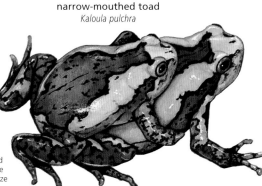

Males are patterned like females, but are slightly smaller in size

Brilliant-thighed poison frog
Allobates femoralis

Harlequin poison frog
Dendrobates histrionicus

Redback poison frog
Dendrobates reticulatus

Trinidad poison frog
Mannophryne trinitatis

Yellow-headed poison frog
Dendrobates leucomelas

Strawberry poison frog
Dendrobates pumilio

Lehmann's poison frog
Dendrobates lehmanni

Has enlarged toe pads for climbing to bromeliads

Green and black poison frog
Dendrobates auratus

Blue poison frog
Dendrobates azureus

Golden poison frog
Phyllobates terribilis

FACT FILE

Harlequin poison frog The male calls from branches up to 3 feet (92 cm) high. The male often sits on the back of the female on the way to the oviposition site. Their complex courtship ritual, which lasts for 2–3 hours, involves a sequence of sitting, bowing, crouching, touching, and circling behavior patterns.

- Up to 1½ in (4 cm)
- Terrestrial, arboreal
- Rainy season
- Common

Colombia, Ecuador

Redback poison frog Females lay either two or three eggs, ⅛ inch (2 mm) in diameter. Although they are primarily found on the forest floor, males hop up tree trunks carrying one or two tadpoles to deposit in bromeliads.

- Up to ¼ in (2 cm)
- Terrestrial, arboreal
- Rainy season
- Common

N.E. Peru, W. Brazil

Blue poison frog Females lay eggs in water for the males to fertilize. The males usually guard the eggs until the tadpoles develop after about 12 days. At 12 weeks, the tadpoles metamorphose into grown frogs.

- Up to 2 in (5 cm)
- Terrestrial
- Rainy season
- Uncommon

Suriname

POISON-ARROW FROGS

Indigenous tribes coat their dart tips with the secretions of dendrobatids, or poison-arrow frogs. This toxin blocks neural transmission at the acetylcholine receptor of the neuro-muscular junction, which causes paralysis or even death. To produce these skin toxins, the frogs need to consume ants that produce formic acid.

FACT FILE

Madagascar reed frog These frogs are common in dunes, savanna, and deforested habitats of the east coast of Madagascar. They are active at night in the vegetation above, or at the edge of, shallow ponds and swamps. During the day they take refuge near pools, submerging when disturbed by a potential predator. Eggs are laid in the water.

- Up to 1½ in (4 cm)
- Terrestrial
- Year round
- Common

Madagascar

Tulear golden frog The species was described from a series of specimens obtained via the pet trade, for which it is currently subject to intense collecting at the beginning of the rainy season (October to December). During the first rains, these frogs, which breed explosively, come out from their refuges and are very easy to capture.

- Up to 1¼ in (3.2 cm)
- Terrestrial
- Rainy season
- Uncommon

Madagascar

Weal's running frog Males call from elevated positions in vegetation, on the banks of, or partly submerged among, plants in a pond. The voice is a coarse, loud rattle, similar to the creak of a cork being removed from a wine bottle. One call, lasting about half a second, is emitted every 3–5 seconds.

- Up to 1¾ in (4.4 cm)
- Terrestrial
- Rainy season
- Common

E. & S.E. South Africa

⚡ CONSERVATION WATCH

In danger At least 27 species of anurans are listed on the IUCN Red List as critically endangered, many because of direct encroachment of humans, habitat destruction, water pollution, and use of herbicides and pesticides. But even populations of the golden toad (*Bufo periglenes*), which lives in protected reserves on mountain tops, have recently plummeted. This may be due to global warming and forest cutting, which affect the rainfall patterns that maintain the misty environment in montane cloud forests.

Madagascar reed frog
Heterixalus madagascariensis

Striped spiny reed frog
Afrixalus dorsalis

Distinctive yellow stripe on body, bordered on both sides with black

Yellow-striped reed frog
Hyperolius semidiscus

Natal forest tree frog
Leptopelis natalensis

Seychelles reed frog
Tachycnemis seychellensis

Marbled reed frog
Hyperolius marmoratus

Weal's running frog
Semnodactylus wealii

Tulear golden frog
Mantella expectata

Runs instead of hopping, jumping, or crawling

Red-legged kassina
Kassina maculata

Madagascar golden frog
Mantella madagascariensis

Red-eared frog
Rana erythraea

African bullfrog
Pyxicephalus adspersus

European common frog
Rana temporaria

Pickerel frog
Rana palustris

Malaysian frog
Rana luctuosa

Marsh frog
Rana ridibunda

Pig frog
Rana grylio

Dorsum has two rows of
square chocolate-colored
blotches, while the leopard
frog, for which it has been
mistaken, usually has
round blotches

Amazon river frog
Rana palmipes

Bullfrog
Rana catesbeiana

MASS SPAWNING

The European common frog mates en
masse in 3 days in spring, each laying
about 400 black eggs in gelatinous
clusters. The eggs absorb UV radiation,
which increases the water temperature
and thus the eggs' developmental rate.

Group sex
Mass breeding reduces the chance
of predation by swamping predators
with more than they could possibly eat.

FACT FILE

Singapore wart frog In the field, this frog can be distinguished from Blyth's giant frog (*Limnonectes blythii*) by the sharp angle of the dark line behind the eye, and by the clearly defined black patch on the upper tympanum.

- Up to 4 in (10 cm)
- Terrestrial
- Unknown
- Common

W. Malaysia, Singapore, Sumatra, Borneo, Java

Cape dainty frog This frog lives in inundated grasslands and depressions in dunes and on cultivated lands on poorly drained clays.

- Up to 1½ in (4 cm)
- Terrestrial
- Winter
- Near threatened

South Africa

ANURAN DEFORMITIES

Like the canaries in the coal mines, frogs are whistling a warning about chemical pollution in the environment when they begin appearing with grossly deformed bodies. Part of the chemical pollution is hormonal from the progesterone used in birth control pills not being filtered out at sewage-treatment plants.

Multi-legged frog
Notice how chemical pollution in the breeding ponds caused this frog to develop with extra legs.

⚡ CONSERVATION WATCH

The 49 species of Ranidae on the IUCN Red List are categorized as follows:

3	Extinct
7	Critically endangered
6	Endangered
15	Vulnerable
4	Near threatened
12	Data deficient
2	Least concern

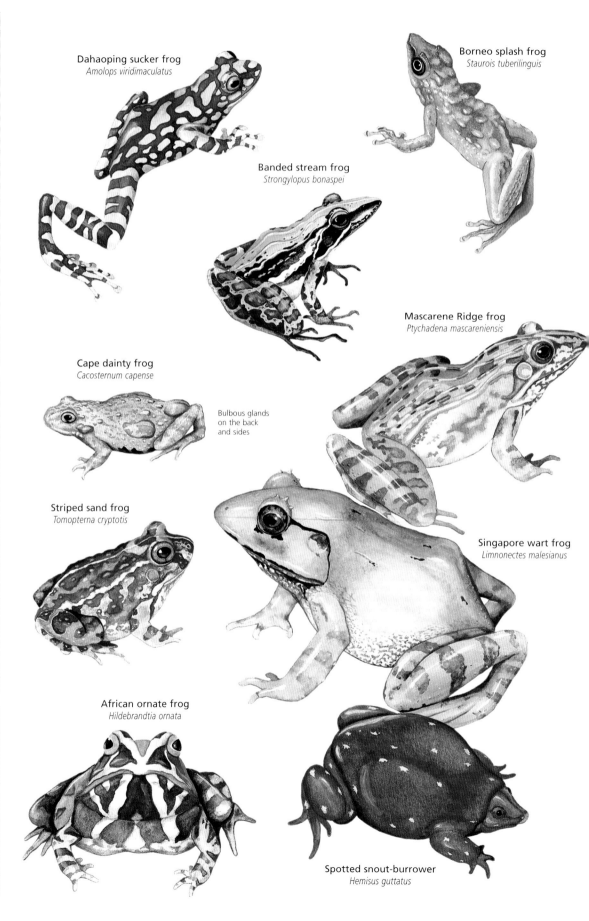

Dahaoping sucker frog
Amolops viridimaculatus

Borneo splash frog
Staurois tuberilinguis

Banded stream frog
Strongylopus bonaspei

Mascarene Ridge frog
Ptychadena mascareniensis

Cape dainty frog
Cacosternum capense

Bulbous glands on the back and sides

Striped sand frog
Tomopterna cryptotis

Singapore wart frog
Limnonectes malesianus

African ornate frog
Hildebrandtia ornata

Spotted snout-burrower
Hemisus guttatus

Bush squeaker
Arthroleptis wahlbergii

Painted Indonesian tree frog
Nyctixalus pictus

Java whipping frog
Polypedates leucomystax

Warty tree frog
Theloderma asperum

Distinctive
black membranes
between the heavily
webbed toes

Abah River flying frog
Rhacophorus nigropalmatus

Madagascar bright-eyed frog
Boophis madagascariensis

Hairy frog
Trichobatrachus robustus

African gray tree frog
Chiromantis xerampelina

Highly vascularized
papillae on the
hindlimbs

Bongon whipping frog
Polypedates otilophus

FACT FILE

Java whipping frog This is one of the more successful frogs of modern times, as it adapts well to human environments. Their foam nests are found inside bathrooms, water tanks, drains, or any damp spot.

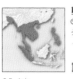

▶	Up to 3¼ in (8 cm)
⊕	Arboreal
⇌	April to December
⌇	Common

S.E. Asia

Abah River flying frog The female beats a body fluid into a foam in a nest of twigs and leaves above the water. When the fertilized embryos hatch into tadpoles, the nest deteriorates and they drop into the water.

▶	Up to 4 in (10 cm)
⊕	Arboreal
⇌	Rainy season
⌇	Common

Indonesia, Malaysia, Thailand

Hairy frog The dermal papillae of males increase the surface area for respiration. Males need an enlarged respiratory surface due to their small lungs and robust body. Tadpoles are carnivorous and possess teeth.

▶	Up to 4¼ in (11 cm)
◯	Terrestrial
⇌	Unknown
⌇	Common

Guinea, Cameroon, Congo, Nigeria

CONTROLLED FALLING

Frogs possessing expanded webs of the feet are able to fall in a controlled fashion to avoid predation or move about. They can adjust the impact and control the direction of their fall.

Expanded webbing *The Java flying frog* (Rhacophorus reinwardtii) *uses its expanded webbed feet to guide its leaps from tree to tree.*

INVERTEBRATES

INVERTEBRATES

Constituting more than 95 percent of all known animal species, invertebrates are not distinguished by any single positive characteristic. Instead, this group is characterized by what its members lack: they have no backbone, no bones, and no cartilage. Although the term invertebrate is in common use, it has little scientific validity. It is, in fact, a contrived category that arose in the 19th century to account for all the animal groups not clearly or seemingly directly related to the human species. Unlike vertebrates, which belong to a single phylum, invertebrates are a collection of more than 30 phyla.

INVERTEBRATES	
PHYLA	> 30
CLASSES	> 90
ORDERS	> 370
SPECIES	> 1.3 million

Exoskeleton

Hydroskeleton

DIVERSITY OF FORM

Invertebrates encompass such diverse forms as porous sponges, floating jellyfishes, parasitic flatworms, jet-propelled squids, hard-cased crabs, venomous spiders, and fluttering butterflies. They arose in the oceans and that is where their greatest diversity still occurs. But invertebrates are now found in virtually all land and water habitats, from air currents passing over Mount Everest to deep-sea thermal vents.

Most species are small and some are microscopic. However, a few invertebrates reach staggering proportions. The elusive giant squid—the stuff of sea monster legends—can grow up to 59 feet (18 m) in length and attain weights of up to 1,980 pounds (900 kg).

There are two basic invertebrate body plans. Species with radial symmetry, such as jellyfishes and sea anemones, have a circular body and a central mouth. Others, such as insects and worms, have bilateral symmetry with a distinct head and right and left sides.

Invertebrates lack bones but all are supported by some sort of skeleton. While many appear soft, they are held together by protein fibers, a feature of all animals. Many worms have a hydrostatic skeleton, with fluid held under pressure inside the body cavity. Sponges and echinoderms have endoskeletons, with hard elements made of substances such as silica and calcium carbonate providing support inside their tissues. Most mollusks and all arthropods have an exoskeleton, a tough external casing. A mollusk's exoskeleton is a hard shell, while an arthropod's tough external skeleton is jointed and flexible.

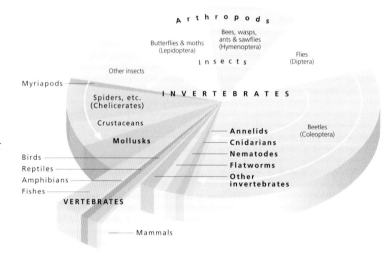

Most invertebrates reproduce sexually, releasing vast numbers of fertilized eggs that are usually left to hatch on their own. Some species, however, develop from unfertilized eggs, and others reproduce by fragmenting or budding, with parts of their own body becoming the offspring. While the young of some invertebrates are similar in body form to their parents, others produce offspring, called larvae, that are quite unlike them. These must go through a major transformation to become adults. This metamorphosis, as it is known, is a characteristic feature of many groups of insects.

Travel modes Portuguese men-of-war can cover great distances floating at the whim of oceanic currents and winds. Their close relatives, the sea anemones, do not move so easily. As adults they usually remain fixed in one spot and wave their tentacles. However, during the larval stage of their life-cycle they are dispersed by drifting with the currents.

Body support Invertebrate skeletons are not constructed from bones. An internal fluid-filled hydroskeleton supports the bodies of creatures such as worms, but is viable only in moist environments. An external skeleton (exoskeleton) helped arthropods, such as centipedes, colonize land.

Species scores Invertebrates (see chart at left) account for the overwhelming majority of animal species. So far, scientists have described about 1.75 million species of life-forms. But they estimate they have between 5 and 100 million still to discover. Most will be invertebrates, particularly insects. One million are already described but there may be as many as 30 million more that we are yet to find.

INVERTEBRATES THROUGH THE AGES

Tracks and burrows in ancient rocks indicate that the first invertebrate-like life had appeared on Earth by 1 billion years ago. The first body fossils of ancient multicellular life come from about 600 million years ago, toward the end of the Precambrian period. They belong to a group of soft-bodied marine organisms known as the Ediacaran fauna, the first evidence of which was found in ancient rocks in the Ediacara Hills, in South Australia's Flinders Ranges, in the 1940s. Since then, similar fossils have been found on all continents except Antarctica. They include some bizarre forms unlike anything known from other times. Others are reminiscent of modern invertebrates such as worms, jellyfishes, and arthropods. Their relationship to modern animals remains mysterious and is a subject of ongoing scientific debate.

CAMBRIAN EXPLOSION

During the Cambrian period, between 570 and 530 million years ago, life underwent an abrupt and massive rise in diversity, the scale of which has never been seen since. Ancestors of almost all major living invertebrate phyla—which account for the majority of modern animal species—appear in the fossil record for the first time in the Cambrian during a period spanning just 40 million years.

Of particular significance is the earliest evidence of hard shells and exoskeletons. Long-extinct trilobites, early arthropods with unusually well-developed eyes, proliferated. So too did sponges. Echinoderms were also plentiful and were represented by several large classes. Only one from that time, however, Class Crinoidea, survives. Both gastropod and cephalopod mollusks occurred in the Cambrian, but these groups did not reach their heyday until later. The earliest chordates, distant ancestors of our own species and all other vertebrates, appeared as well. There were also many strange life-forms that do not seem directly allied to any known group and may, perhaps, represent invertebrate evolutionary dead-ends.

Dominant creatures Trilobites (below) dominated the Cambrian seas but became extinct 250 million years ago. Their bodies consisted of three sections: a shield-like head with paired eyes and antennae, a hinged trunk, and a tail of fused segments.

Evolution in action Rapid life-cycles and high reproductive rates seem to expedite invertebrate evolution. The best-known example is the peppered moth (above), which became darker with successive generations to maintain camouflage in an increasingly dirty industrial environment.

Lichida   Agnostida   Proetida

Living fossils At 3.5 billion years of age, stromatolites are the world's oldest fossils. These ancient reef-building structures were formed mainly by colonial cyanobacteria, known also as blue-green algae, believed to have been Earth's dominant life-form for about 2 billion years. Oxygen, released as these organisms photosynthesized, built up in the atmosphere until there were sufficient amounts for the ancestors of the first recognizable invertebrates. Stromatolites survive in Shark Bay, Western Australia.

growth zone

older layers

base

CLASSIFICATION

Over 95 percent of all animals are invertebrates. They are characterized by a structure that they all lack: a backbone or vertebral column. Invertebrates are divided into about 30 phyla, each displaying a distinct body form. Features that define phyla include the organization of the body as a loose association of cells (Porifera), through tissue formation (Cnidaria) to the development of organs (Platyhelminthes). The acquisition of a fluid-filled body cavity was a defining point in animal evolution that allowed animals, such as Nematoda, Annelida, and many other phyla of worms, to move about by an hydraulic system driven by fluid pressure. The origin and form of these body cavities characterize different phyla. While these phyla are soft-bodied, others are protected and supported by various types of skeletons, such as shells in Mollusca and a jointed exoskeleton in Arthropoda.

Stinging phylum Anemones were originally classified as "zoophytes" or animal plants, in reference to their flower-like appearance. Modern classification groups anemones, corals, jellyfishes, and hydroids as the phylum Cnidaria. This phylum refers to microscopic stinging cells that members of this group use to harpoon and immobilize prey.

Widow family Known commonly as the red widow, this spider (top right) is a close relative of the notoriously deadly black widow. Widow spiders, in which females allegedly consume males, are included in the genus *Latrodectus*. This genus, in turn, is included in the family Theridiidae, known as comb-footed spiders due to small hairs on their hind feet.

KINGDOM
Animalia
red widow spider, seastar, dragonfly, sponge, kangaroo

PHYLUM
Arthropoda
red widow spider, butterfly, crab, scorpion, millipede

CLASS
Arachnida
red widow spider, black widow spider, harvestman, scorpion, tick

ORDER
Araneae
red widow spider, black widow spider, funnel-web spider, wolf spider

FAMILY
Theridiidae
red widow spider, black widow spider, tentweb spider, button spider

GENUS
Latrodectus
red widow spider, black widow spider

SPECIES
Latrodectus bishopi
red widow spider

INVERTEBRATES

Phylum Chordata
Invertebrate Chordates

    Subphylum Urochordata
    Sea squirts

    Subphylum Cephalochordata
    Lancelets

Phylum Porifera
Sponges

Phylum Cnidaria
Cnidarians (sea anemones, corals, jellyfishes, etc.)

Phylum Platyhelminthes
Flatworms

Phylum Nematoda
Roundworms

Phylum Mollusca
  Mollusks (bivalves, snails, squids, etc.)

    Phylum Annelida
    Segmented worms

    Phylum Arthropoda
    Arthropods

      Subphylum Chelicerata
      Chelicerates

        Class Arachnida
        Arachnids

        Class Merostomata
        Horseshoe crabs

        Class Pycnogonida
        Sea spiders

      Subphylum Myriapoda
      Myriapods (centipedes, etc.)

Phylum Cnidaria, page 132

Phylum Mollusca, page 137

Class Arachnida, page 148

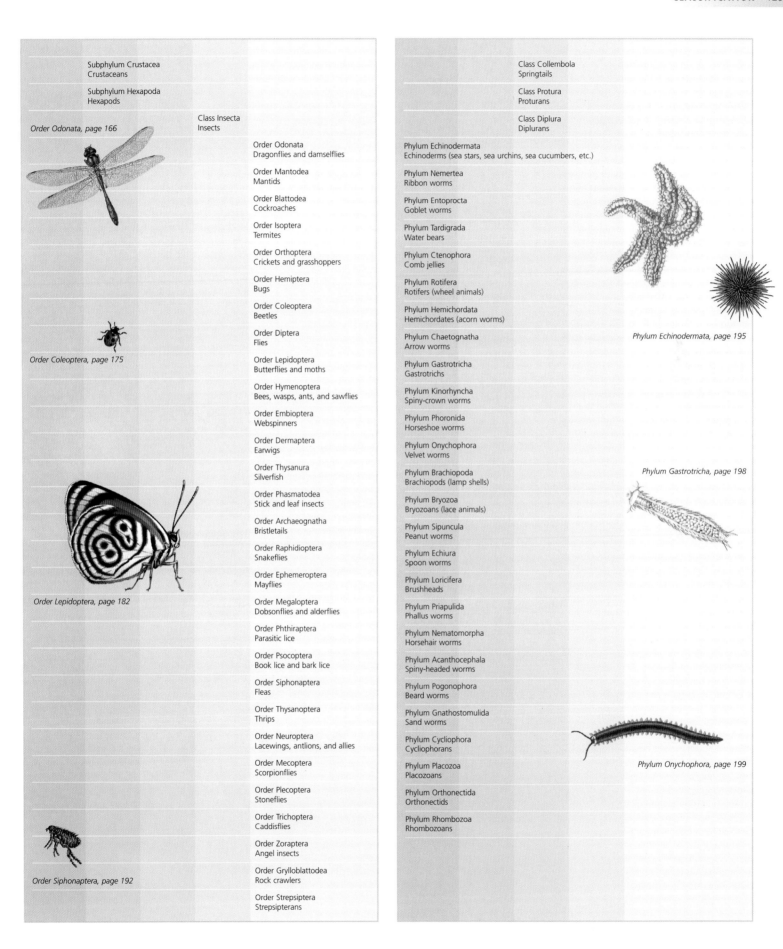

Subphylum Crustacea
Crustaceans

Subphylum Hexapoda
Hexapods

Class Insecta
Insects

Order Odonata, page 166

Order Odonata
Dragonflies and damselflies

Order Mantodea
Mantids

Order Blattodea
Cockroaches

Order Isoptera
Termites

Order Orthoptera
Crickets and grasshoppers

Order Hemiptera
Bugs

Order Coleoptera
Beetles

Order Coleoptera, page 175

Order Diptera
Flies

Order Lepidoptera
Butterflies and moths

Order Hymenoptera
Bees, wasps, ants, and sawflies

Order Embioptera
Webspinners

Order Dermaptera
Earwigs

Order Thysanura
Silverfish

Order Phasmatodea
Stick and leaf insects

Order Archaeognatha
Bristletails

Order Lepidoptera, page 182

Order Raphidioptera
Snakeflies

Order Ephemeroptera
Mayflies

Order Megaloptera
Dobsonflies and alderflies

Order Phthiraptera
Parasitic lice

Order Psocoptera
Book lice and bark lice

Order Siphonaptera
Fleas

Order Thysanoptera
Thrips

Order Neuroptera
Lacewings, antlions, and allies

Order Mecoptera
Scorpionflies

Order Plecoptera
Stoneflies

Order Trichoptera
Caddisflies

Order Zoraptera
Angel insects

Order Siphonaptera, page 192

Order Grylloblattodea
Rock crawlers

Order Strepsiptera
Strepsipterans

Class Collembola
Springtails

Class Protura
Proturans

Class Diplura
Diplurans

Phylum Echinodermata
Echinoderms (sea stars, sea urchins, sea cucumbers, etc.)

Phylum Nemertea
Ribbon worms

Phylum Entoprocta
Goblet worms

Phylum Tardigrada
Water bears

Phylum Ctenophora
Comb jellies

Phylum Rotifera
Rotifers (wheel animals)

Phylum Hemichordata
Hemichordates (acorn worms)

Phylum Chaetognatha
Arrow worms

Phylum Echinodermata, page 195

Phylum Gastrotricha
Gastrotrichs

Phylum Kinorhyncha
Spiny-crown worms

Phylum Phoronida
Horseshoe worms

Phylum Onychophora
Velvet worms

Phylum Brachiopoda
Brachiopods (lamp shells)

Phylum Bryozoa
Bryozoans (lace animals)

Phylum Gastrotricha, page 198

Phylum Sipuncula
Peanut worms

Phylum Echiura
Spoon worms

Phylum Loricifera
Brushheads

Phylum Priapulida
Phallus worms

Phylum Nematomorpha
Horsehair worms

Phylum Acanthocephala
Spiny-headed worms

Phylum Pogonophora
Beard worms

Phylum Gnathostomulida
Sand worms

Phylum Cycliophora
Cycliophorans

Phylum Placozoa
Placozoans

Phylum Onychophora, page 199

Phylum Orthonectida
Orthonectids

Phylum Rhombozoa
Rhombozoans

BIOLOGY AND BEHAVIOR

Most invertebrate behavior is highly instinctive and usually relates to gathering food, avoiding predators, and reproducing the species. Some of these innate behavioral responses are very complex, such as the social organization of honeybees. Many invertebrates are also capable of extensive behavioral modification. Octopus, for example, change their behavior by learning from previous experiences. Invertebrates have a diversity of sensory structures to facilitate sight, smell, taste, touch, and hearing. Many adopt a cryptic approach to life, hidden among vegetation, within leaf-litter or buried in sediment and soil. Some exhibit exquisite forms of camouflage, such as spiders that look and even smell like bird droppings or stick and leaf insects that mimic the vegetation on which they browse.

Communicating odors Like most moths, the African moon moth communicates with its own species using chemicals known as pheromones. Females release pheromones to attract males from afar while males do so only when close by, to sexually stimulate females.

Silk trappings Tarantulas do not spin the sorts of webs traditionally associated with spiders. This species—the Arizona blond tarantula—is a long-lived nocturnal ground hunter that dwells in a subterranean burrow. It uses its silk to plug the burrow in winter, when it survives on fat reserves.

Toxic warning Some invertebrates have poisons in their flesh or body parts to deter predators. Most, such as this nudibranch (below)—a sea slug that accumulates toxin by consuming other poisonous invertebrates—are brightly colored to warn would-be attackers.

EAT OR BE EATEN

Invertebrates play a crucial role in most food chains, which makes them essential to the health of ecosystems. Zooplankton feeding on phytoplankton in the oceans and invertebrates feeding on terrestrial plants provide the first link between the primary producers (plants) and the consumers (animals).

Invertebrates are also among the most active consumers of the dead bodies of plants and animals. Many invertebrates are parasites, feeding on the blood or other tissues of their animal hosts. In turn, invertebrates make up the diet of many species of vertebrates. The flesh of a number of invertebrates, including oysters, squid, prawns, crabs, and lobsters, is considered a delicacy by humans.

HABITATS AND ADAPTATIONS

Each generation of a species results in a slightly different range of genetic combinations. For this reason, animals with rapid reproductive rates—such as most invertebrates—are better equipped than less prolific breeders to deal with changing environments. This partly explains why invertebrates have managed to adapt to and exploit virtually every available habitat, from the deepest oceans to the highest mountains, polar ice caps, hot springs, and hypersaline lakes.

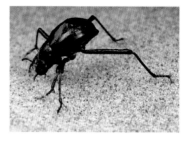

Fog catcher Early morning fog rolling in from the coast is the only regular moisture in Africa's Namib Desert. The darkling beetle (left) points its rear upward, the fog condenses on its back, and the water droplets trickle down dorsal grooves to its mouth.

Invertebrate builders Hard coral reefs are built by tiny invertebrates called polyps. Although sedentary, their larvae drift in oceanic currents before eventually settling out of the water column to form new reefs or re-seed old ones.

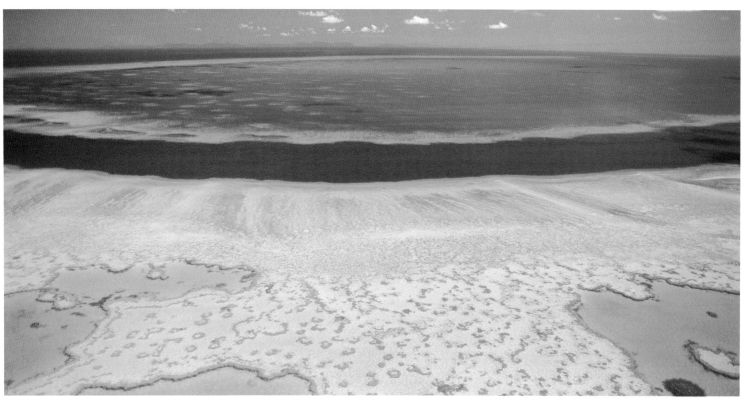

OCEANIC BEGINNINGS

Invertebrates are critical components of some of the planet's most productive habitats. All reef systems in the world are ultimately based on invertebrate life-forms. Animal life arose in the oceans and it is here that the greatest diversity of invertebrates is found. Many groups of invertebrates are predominately or exclusively marine, such as sponges, cnidarians, and echinoderms. Sponges, found in the fossil record from the Cambrian to the present, have barely changed during their 600 million years of existence. When found alongside other fossils in preserved reefs, sponge fossils enable scientists to piece together entire ancient ecosystems.

Arthropods were the first animals to emerge from the sea to lead a terrestrial existence and their extraordinary success on land has been due largely to their tough, waxy exoskeleton. Scorpions had ventured onto the land by about 350 million years ago and were soon followed by terrestrial insects. Now ubiquitous in land habitats, insects have also invaded fresh water but they are rare in oceans.

Underlying the success of insects is their life-cycle, which involves an extreme metamorphosis into adulthood. This ensures that juveniles and adults of a particular species are able to exploit different environments and do not have to compete for the same resources such as food or shelter.

AQUATIC INVERTEBRATES

Aquatic habitats include oceans, estuaries, rivers, streams, and freshwater and hypersaline lakes. Each is characterized by a particular salinity level. At the base of the food chain are single-celled algae, the phytoplankton, which are fed upon by small to microscopic zooplankton. Most invertebrate phyla have representatives that spend at least part of their life-cycle as zooplankton. Larger invertebrates also feed by filtering out the plankton. Others graze or browse on larger plants, prey upon each other, or scavenge in the sediments for decaying remains. Sunlight, and its abscence, has a direct impact on aquatic life.

DESERT INVERTEBRATES

The majority of the invertebrates in deserts are insects. They are among the most dominant of desert animals. Behavioral adaptations are as important as physiological specializations to desert survival. Invertebrates are rarely seen in deserts because most tend to be active only at night or in the milder conditions of early morning or late afternoon. During the day they shelter in small burrows in the sand. The tough, waterproofed external skeleton of arthropods is a particularly useful desert adaptation. It reduces evaporative water loss, allowing insects, spiders, centipedes, and scorpions to survive in arid habitats.

MANGROVE INVERTEBRATES

Mangroves stabilize shorelines in wave-protected river deltas, estuaries, and other vulnerable coastal areas. Almost three-quarters of tropical coastlines are narrowly fringed by this valuable habitat, once widely and mistakenly dismissed as unproductive and smelly. The dominant trees and shrubs in mangroves are salt-tolerant and shallow-rooted.

Because of their high nutrients and the protected havens they form for larvae and juveniles, mangroves are exploited by animals as nursery grounds. Nevertheless, they remain the domain of adult invertebrates. Crustaceans, worms, and mollusks occur in enormous numbers in these waters. Some burrow in the sediments, extracting nutrients in the way earthworms extract them from soil. Others come to the surface to feed on the algal film covering the sediment or on dead plants and animals stranded by the low tide. The mangrove invertebrates are themselves fed upon by fishes during the high tides and by wading birds that forage on the flats at low tide.

PARASITIC INVERTEBRATES

Animal parasites are exclusively invertebrate and range from worms, such as flukes, tapeworms, and round worms, to blood-sucking arthropods, such as fleas and lice. Parasites can feed on the skin or live within the body, feeding on the digested food or tissues of the host. To offset the hazards of locating a host, parasites have an enormous reproductive capacity that often includes both sexual and asexual strategies. Some remain dormant as resistant eggs or encysted stages, waiting to be accidentally ingested, while others actively seek a host and penetrate its skin. Still others use the bodies of other animals as intermediate hosts in which further bouts of reproduction may occur. Using this strategy, some parasites can pass from one host to another in the food chain.

POLAR INVERTEBRATES

Antarctica is the coldest, windiest, driest continent and the Arctic is

Grisly nursery Parasitic wasps often lay their eggs directly into still-living caterpillars that they have paralyzed with their stings. In this way, the grub-like larvae will have a source of fresh food readily available to them when they hatch.

almost as inhospitable. There is, however, a surprisingly high level of invertebrate life, mostly underwater, at the poles. It includes giant sponges, sea anemones, and a range of worms, many of which have a form of antifreeze in their body fluids. Tiny crustaceans known as krill occur in truly huge numbers at the poles and form the basis of critical food chains, including some that support commercially valuable fisheries.

Vertical life Sediments around the roots of mangroves lack oxygen. Extensions (called pneumatophores) grow beyond the surface to convey oxygen to the roots below. These provide habitats for a variety of invertebrates, such as this mangrove crab.

FOREST INVERTEBRATES

Invertebrates, particularly insects, are important to the health of all forests. Insects undoubtedly eat far more leaves, bark, sap, and fruits than large herbivorous mammals. A vast amount of dead vegetation is also consumed by invertebrates such as insects, millipedes, and burrowing earthworms. Insect larvae also play a significant role in the recycling of dead animals. Scavengers are critical to forests. Their actions eventually result in the release of minerals and nutrients by fungi and bacteria, making them available to plants. Many temperate-forest invertebrates lead a distinctly seasonal existence, bursting into a flurry of activity that coincides with springtime growth after spending cold winter months hidden away in a form of torpor.

Web builders Spiny spiders of the genus *Gasteracantha* (above) are renowned spinners of vertical orb-webs in forest environments worldwide. Bushwalkers invariably stumble into their tough, sticky webs that often look like the perfectly crafted wheels of a horse-drawn carriage.

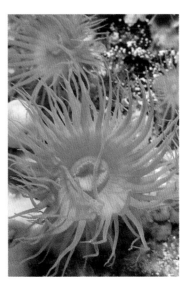

Under ice Seafloor-dwelling species such as sea anemones and sponges (left) are able to survive and flourish in relatively tranquil, unfrozen polar waters.

INVERTEBRATES IN DANGER

There are two main problems in assessing the conservation status of invertebrates. First, many biologists have estimated that we have described only a fraction of the total number of species. How can we assess invertebrates that have not even been identified? Second, because invertebrates are usually small and cryptic, estimates of their population density can be very difficult to measure. Consequently, invertebrates are significantly underrepresented in the IUCN Red List of Threatened Species, with only 600 species listed as endangered or critically endangered. The conservation status of most of the invertebrate world remains unknown. Extrapolation of data obtained from those invertebrates whose endangered status has been evaluated is sobering. Analysts predict that three-quarters of the roughly 1 million insect species so far described, 86 percent of crustaceans, and almost half of all known mollusk species are, in fact, endangered.

Big threat The giant clam (above and below), native to the Pacific and Indian oceans, is the world's largest bivalve mollusk, reaching lengths of more than 4 feet (1.2 m) and weights of around 500 pounds (227 kg). The species is listed as vulnerable due to extensive collecting for food, their shells, and the aquarium trade. They have been severely over-harvested across their range. Illegal collecting continues to be a threat to the species.

DISAPPEARING TREASURES

Many people can look at the exquisite forms and adaptations of mammals such as the cheetah, blue whale, or polar bear and feel passionate about securing them a future place on the planet. Unfortunately, far fewer people feel the same way about invertebrate animals. Arguments of altruism and responsible stewardship aside, there are two very good reasons why we should be as alarmed about invertebrate losses as we are about the decline of vertebrates.

First, Earth's invertebrate fauna harbors many unique genes, which means many unique substances, some of which may turn out to be safe and simple cures for human disease. There is particular interest among the world's pharmaceutical companies in marine invertebrates such as sponges, worms, and mollusks. Second, invertebrates are often highly sensitive to environmental change created by pollution, habitat clearing, and climate shifts. As a result, they can be excellent biological markers of the health of an ecosystem.

The current rate of invertebrate losses could be a warning about the tenuous hold we have on our own future as a species. It is not likely that the extinction of just one invertebrate species from an ecosystem would ever have as big an effect as that of a mammal or other large vertebrate. But invertebrates are being lost from the planet at a truly alarming rate and it is rare that just one invertebrate species disappears from a habitat. More often they topple like dominoes, so that several species disappear at once. It is then we see whole ecosystems suffering.

So what can we do? We must take responsibility for conserving habitats by preventing processes that threaten them, such as clearing land, draining wetlands, and polluting natural environments.

Collectable beauty The Rajah Brooke's birdwing butterfly is regarded as one of the most beautiful of all butterflies. That, however, could become its downfall. Birdwings are highly sought after by collectors and the trade has already forced several species onto the IUCN Red List of Threatened Species, although this species is still secure, for the moment.

INVERTEBRATE CHORDATES

PHYLUM	Chordata
SUBPHYLA	2
CLASSES	4
ORDERS	9
FAMILIES	47
SPECIES	> 2,000

The phylum Chordata is made up of three subphyla. The largest of these is Vertebrata, which includes all the vertebrates (mammals, birds, reptiles, amphibians, and fishes). The other two subphyla are marine invertebrate groups: Urochordata, which contains about 2,000 species of sea squirts and their relatives, and Cephalochordata, which has about 30 species of lancelets. These invertebrate chordates do not have a backbone made of vertebrae, but they do have a flexible skeletal rod known as a notochord. The notochord is present in vertebrate embryos, but is resorbed and replaced by the backbone. This strongly suggests that vertebrates have evolved from invertebrate chordates.

From the deep The predatory tunicate (*Megalodicopia hians*) lives on the floor of deep oceans. After a small animal such as a krill floats into its mouth-like hood, the hood quickly closes to capture the prey.

Colonies This photo shows several colonies of magnificent ascidians (*Botrylloides magnicoecum*). The dark spots represent individual inhalant openings; the sieve-like plates are communal exhalant openings.

FIXED AND FREE

Also known as tunicates, sea squirts hatch from eggs as a tadpole-shaped larva with a notochord in their tails. After dispersing to a new location, the tadpole usually attaches itself to the seafloor, resorbs the tail and notochord, and moves its mouth to its free end. This sessile sea squirt is a bag-like creature. Water enters through an inhalant opening and leaves via an exhalant opening. On the way, the water passes through a perforated pharynx (throat), which uses mucus to filter out particles of food. Sea squirts can be solitary or colonial. Most are fixed as adults, but a small number remain free-living throughout their lives. They are almost all hermaphrodites that release eggs and sperm into the water to produce their young.

Superficially resembling little eels, lancelets (or amphioxus) can swim well, but usually stay partly buried in sand or gravel in shallow waters, with only the head protruding. They filter-feed using the same method as sea squirts, with water entering one opening, passing through the pharnx, and exiting via a second opening. The sexes are separate and the eggs are fertilized externally.

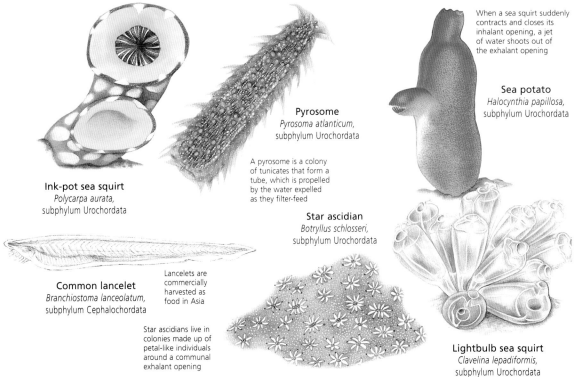

Ink-pot sea squirt
Polycarpa aurata,
subphylum Urochordata

Common lancelet
Branchiostoma lanceolatum,
subphylum Cephalochordata

Lancelets are commercially harvested as food in Asia

Pyrosome
Pyrosoma atlanticum,
subphylum Urochordata

A pyrosome is a colony of tunicates that form a tube, which is propelled by the water expelled as they filter-feed

Star ascidian
Botryllus schlosseri,
subphylum Urochordata

Star ascidians live in colonies made up of petal-like individuals around a communal exhalant opening

When a sea squirt suddenly contracts and closes its inhalant opening, a jet of water shoots out of the exhalant opening

Sea potato
Halocynthia papillosa,
subphylum Urochordata

Lightbulb sea squirt
Clavelina lepadiformis,
subphylum Urochordata

SPONGES

PHYLUM	Porifera
CLASSES	3
ORDERS	18
FAMILIES	80
SPECIES	about 9,000

More than 2,000 years ago, Aristotle considered sponges to be animals, but his claim remained without proof until 1765. In the interim, most scientists believed sponges, with their lack of movement and often branching form, to be plants. Sponges are unique in the animal kingdom. They do not possess a nervous system, muscles, or stomach. Their cells do not form tissues or organs, but are specialized for particular functions, such as food collection, digestion, defense, or skeleton formation. Able to migrate throughout a sponge, the cells can transform from one type to another, which allows the sponge to completely regenerate from a fragment or even from individual cells.

Electric sponge Although they lack nerves, glass sponges (class Hexactinellida) react to disturbances by sending electrical impulses through their body, which prompt their food-filtering system to shut down.

Supportive spicules A sponge's skeleton is made of units known as spicules, which can be scattered throughout the sponge or combined into fibers. This magnified view shows the needle-like and star-like spicules of a sponge at 100 times their actual size.

Budding young While most sponges reproduce sexually, many also use asexual reproduction. Some species fragment, while others grow buds (far right), which break away to become new sponges. Sponges may also expel collections of cells and food granules called gemmules which remain in a dormant state, growing into a sponge only when conditions are favorable.

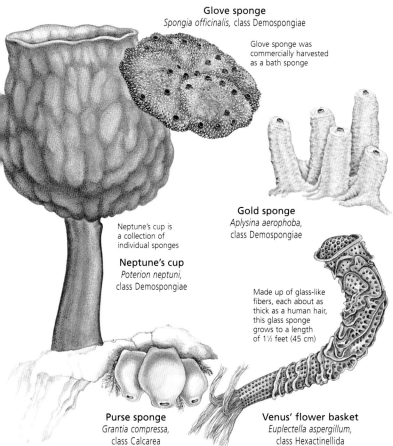

Glove sponge
Spongia officinalis, class Demospongiae

Glove sponge was commercially harvested as a bath sponge

Gold sponge
Aplysina aerophoba, class Demospongiae

Neptune's cup is a collection of individual sponges

Neptune's cup
Poterion neptuni, class Demospongiae

Made up of glass-like fibers, each about as thick as a human hair, this glass sponge grows to a length of 1½ feet (45 cm)

Purse sponge
Grantia compressa, class Calcarea

Venus' flower basket
Euplectella aspergillum, class Hexactinellida

POROUS FILTER-FEEDERS

Ranging in length from less than ½ inch to 6½ feet (1 cm to 2 m), sponges may be shaped like trees, bushes, vases, barrels, balls, cushions, or carpets, or they may simply form a shapeless mass. They are found in every marine habitat, from the shallows to the depths, and a small number of species have colonized freshwater lakes and rivers.

The skeletons of sponges are made of minerals, protein, or both. Species in the class Calcarea have skeletons of calcium carbonate and tend to be small and drab. Those in the class Hexactinellida are known as glass sponges and have skeletons made of silica. More than 90 percent of sponge species belong to the class Demospongiae. They have skeletons of silica and/or protein.

Sponges usually feed by filtering microorganisms from the water. After entering via tiny pores called ostia, the water travels through a system of canals, and is expelled via a large opening called the osculum. The collar cells that line the sponge's interior beat their whip-like flagella to maintain a constant current. A few carnivorous sponges use hook-like filaments to capture crustaceans.

Most sponges are hermaphrodites. Sperm are released into the water and carried to other sponges to fertilize their eggs. The larvae are free-swimming for a short period before attaching to a surface and developing into an adult sponge.

CNIDARIANS

PHYLUM Cnidaria	
CLASSES 4	
ORDERS 27	
FAMILIES 236	
SPECIES about 9,000	

The phylum Cnidaria is a diverse assortment of mostly marine invertebrates, including sea anemones, corals, jellyfishes, and hydroids. All members are carnivores and use cells containing stinging nematocysts to subdue prey and deter predators. The cnidarian body is organized around a gastrovascular cavity that digests food and acts as a hydroskeleton. Food enters and waste leaves via a single opening, the mouth, which is often surrounded by tentacles. Cnidarians occur in two forms: polyp and medusa. Polyps are cylindrical and attached to a surface, with the mouth and tentacles at the free end. Medusae are free-swimming and umbrella-shaped, with the mouth and tentacles hanging down.

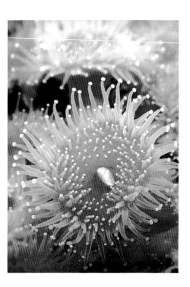

Fixed in position The jewel anemone (*Corynactis viridis*) has up to 100 tentacles arranged in three rings around its mouth. Attached to the substrate by a sucker-like disk, sea anemones rarely move but some are able to glide very slowly.

polyp   medusa

Jelly sandwich Between a cnidarian's two cell layers, the outer ectoderm and the inner endoderm, there is a jelly-like layer known as the mesoglea (shown as orange). In polyps, the mesoglea is thin, but in medusae, it forms the bulk of the animal.

Floating home At up to 1½ feet (45 cm) wide, the purple jellyfish (*Pelagia panopyra*) offers a temporary haven to fish and young crabs. Like other jellyfishes, it has only weak jet propulsion and relies mainly on ocean currents for transport.

POLYPS AND MEDUSAE

A small number of cnidarians live in fresh water, but most are marine, occupying all latitudes and levels of the ocean and reaching their greatest numbers in shallow tropical waters. They feed primarily on the fishes and crustaceans that swim past. Found mainly on the tentacles, a cnidarian's nematocysts (stingers) hold a coiled, barbed thread that can be ejected to spear and paralyze the prey. The tentacles then move the food to the mouth.

While corals and sea anemones exist only as polyps, many other cnidarians alternate between polyp and medusa during their life-cycle. Usually, the polyps asexually produce medusae, and the medusae sexually produce larvae that become polyps. Polyps and some medusae may grow buds or divide to create more of their own kind asexually. If the offspring detach from the parent they become clones, but if they remain attached they form colonies, such as the vast colonies that make up coral reefs. In some colonies, each member has a particular role and form, and may be specialized for feeding, defense, reproduction, or locomotion, for example.

Freshwater jellyfish
Craspedacusta sowerbyi, class Hydrozoa

Fire coral
Millepora dichotoma,
class Hydrozoa

Often mistaken for a true coral by divers, fire coral has a calcified exoskeleton that can scrape the skin, and nematocysts that can cause a burning or stinging rash

Colony made up of tightly packed branches resembling feathers

Yellow feathers
Gymnangium montagui,
class Hydrozoa

Green hydra
Chlorohydra viridis, class Hydrozoa

Oaten pipes hydroid
Tubularia indivisa, class Hydrozoa

Upside-down jellyfish
Cassiopeia andromeda,
class Scyphozoa

Attaches to sandy
ocean floor

Portuguese
man-of-war
Physalia physalis,
class Hydrozoa

The Portuguese man-of-war is a free-
floating colony, with a modified medusa
forming the gas-filled float, and some
polyps delivering a potent sting, some
digesting food, and others reproducing

Lion's mane jellyfish
Cyanea arctica,
class Scyphozoa

Hula skirt siphonophore
Physophora hydrostatica,
class Hydrozoa

Dead man's fingers
Alcyonium digitatum, class Anthozoa

Sea wasp
Chironex fleckeri,
class Cubozoa

A sea wasp
contains enough
venom to kill
60 people

By-the-wind sailor
Velella velella, class Hydrozoa

Phosphorescent sea pen
Pennatula phosphorea,
class Anthozoa

The stalked jellyfish
exists as a polyp
attached to algae
and does not occur
as a medusa

Stalked jellyfish
Haliclystus auricula,
class Scyphozoa

Formosan soft coral
Sarcophyton glaucum, class Anthozoa

Organ-pipe coral
Tubipora musica, class Anthozoa

FACT FILE

Class Scyphozoa True jellyfishes belong
to the class Scyphozoa. Generally, they
spend most of their lives as medusae,
but these medusae produce larvae that
settle on the seabed as minute polyps.
The polyps then divide horizontally
and break off to become medusae.
Most jellyfishes are free-swimming. By
pulsating their bell, they squirt out jets
of water that provide weak propulsion.

Species 200

Worldwide; marine

Common jelly
*Found worldwide
in coastal waters,
the moon jellyfish
(Aurelia aurita) is
often seen washed
up onto beaches.*

Class Hydrozoa This class contains
species that have both polyps and
medusae in the life-cycle, but the
medusae are often reduced to buds
on the polyp's surface. Many species
are colonial, often with the individuals
specialized for different functions.

Species 3,300

Worldwide

Freshwater hydra
*The brown hydra
(Pelmatohydra oligactis)
is found in lakes and
ponds. Its tentacles
can reach lengths of
10 inches (25 cm).*

Class Cubozoa Viewed from above,
the box jellies in this class have a square
shape, which distinguishes them from
true jellyfishes. They are also faster and
more agile swimmers, and include
some of the ocean's deadliest species.

Species 36

Worldwide; tropical & temperate seas

YOUNG CNIDARIANS

When cnidarians sexually reproduce,
they produce a microscopic planula
larva, which either swims using its
beating cilia (tiny hairs) or crawls along
the bottom. After a time, the planula
transforms into a polyp by attaching its
front end to a surface and developing
tentacles at its free end. For corals and
sea anemones, which do not become
medusae, the larval stage is the only
chance for the species to disperse.

GREAT BARRIER REEF

Stretching more than 1,400 miles (2,240 km) along the northeastern coast of Australia, the Great Barrier Reef is a collection of coral reefs that together form the largest natural feature on Earth. It was created over millions of years from the calcium carbonate exoskeletons of true corals. Symbiotic algae live inside the coral polyps, supplying most of the corals' energy. The corals are restricted to clear, shallow waters where the algae can photosynthesize.

Teeming with life *With 400 species of coral, 1,500 species of fish, and 4,000 species of mollusk, the Great Barrier Reef's biodiversity rivals that of tropical rain forests.*

CONSERVATION WATCH

Dying reefs Corals are extremely sensitive to environmental stress and can die from even small changes in the temperature, salinity, or nitrogen levels of the water. Consequently, they are particularly vulnerable to ocean pollution and global warming. Mass tourism, over-collecting, and introduced species have also taken their toll, and half of all the world's reefs could die in the next 50 years.

Red brain coral
Lobophyllia hemprichii, class Anthozoa

Individual polyps of brain coral fuse into wrinkled rows

Clubbed finger coral
Porites porites, class Anthozoa

Bubble coral
Plerogyra sinuosa, class Anthozoa

Red coral forms tree-like colonies

Red coral
Corallium rubrum, class Anthozoa

Black coral
Antipathes furcata, class Anthozoa

The tentacles of beadlet anemones retract when the tide goes out

Beadlet anemone
Actinia equina, class Anthozoa

Lophelia pertusa, class Anthozoa

West Indian sea fan
Gorgonia flabellum, class Anthozoa

Lophelia pertusa is a deep-water coral that forms reefs in the cold North Atlantic

Stalk is inserted into deep crevices or buried in mud or sand

Daisy anemone
Cereus pedunculatus, class Anthozoa

Mushroom coral
Fungia fungites, class Anthozoa

Caryophyllia smithi, class Anthozoa

FLATWORMS

PHYLUM	Platyhelminthes
CLASSES	4
ORDERS	35
FAMILIES	360
SPECIES	13,000

The flatworms that make up the phylum Platyhelminthes range from microscopic free-living species, to tapeworms up to 100 feet (30 m) long that live inside humans and other vertebrates. The simplest animals possessing bilateral symmetry, flatworms have no body cavity and lack respiratory and circulatory systems. A few parasitic species also do without a digestive system. In most species, the gut has a single opening to take in food and expel waste. The indistinct head contains a brain and many of the sense organs, including ocelli (simple eyes) that can perceive light and dark, and receptors that can detect chemicals, balance, gravity, and water movement.

A long colony A parasite of rats, the tapeworm *Hymenolepis diminuta* is shown here at 50 times its actual size and with its color enhanced, revealing its individual proglottids and the suckers at its tip.

A PARASITIC LIFE
While the flukes of Monogenea have a single host in their lifetime, most parasitic flatworms make use of different hosts at different stages in their life-cycle.

egg released in human feces and eaten by snail

final-stage larva emerges from snail

juvenile attaches to fish

adult matures inside a human's liver

Eggs of the Chinese liver fluke Opisthorchis sinensis *(class Trematoda) eggs are eaten by aquatic snails. The final-stage larvae emerge to attach to fish, which are eaten by humans. Once the flukes mature into adults, their eggs are passed out in the human host's feces.*

Crawling leaf Although some small species are cylindrical, most flatworms are flattened. Many marine species, such as *Pseudoceros dimidiatus*, are leaf-like.

DIFFERENT LIFESTYLES
Flatworms are divided into four classes. The first of these, Turbelleria, is predominantly free-living. Most species are marine, but many are found in lakes, ponds, and rivers, and a few can even tolerate both fresh and salt water. There are also a number of species that live on land in moist habitats. Turbellarians usually prey on invertebrates. They move along slime trails produced by special glands, beating cilia (tiny hairs) to propel themselves.

The other three flatworm classes are all parasitic during at least part of their often complex life-cycle. Members of Monogenea are small flukes. At the rear end, they have an opisthaptor, a bulb bearing suckers and/or hooks that attach to a fish's gills or a frog's bladder. Most flukes, however, belong to Trematoda. The adults are parasites of vertebrates, using suckers to attach to the gut and other organs. The class Cestoda contains the tapeworms, internal parasites that are long, flat colonies made up of individuals called proglottids. Almost all flatworms are hermaphrodites, and tapeworms have a set of male and female sex organs in each proglottid.

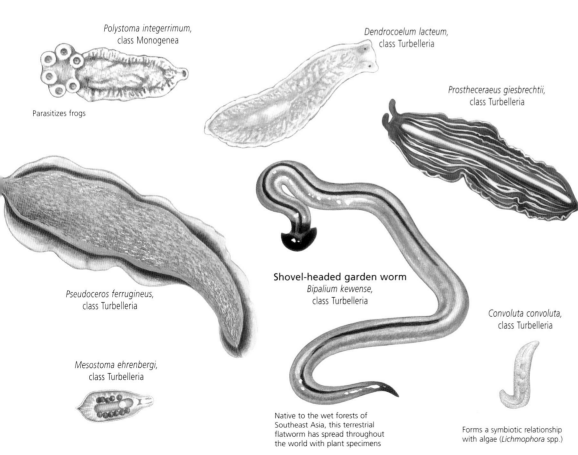

Polystoma integerrimum,
class Monogenea

Parasitizes frogs

Dendrocoelum lacteum,
class Turbelleria

Prostheceraeus giesbrechtii,
class Turbelleria

Pseudoceros ferrugineus,
class Turbelleria

Shovel-headed garden worm
Bipalium kewense,
class Turbelleria

Mesostoma ehrenbergi,
class Turbelleria

Native to the wet forests of Southeast Asia, this terrestrial flatworm has spread throughout the world with plant specimens

Convoluta convoluta,
class Turbelleria

Forms a symbiotic relationship with algae (*Lichmophora* spp.)

ROUNDWORMS

PHYLUM	Nematoda
CLASSES	4
ORDERS	20
FAMILIES	185
SPECIES	> 20,000

Although a species of roundworm that parasitizes sperm whales can grow to a length of 43 feet (13 m), most members of the phylum Nematoda are microscopic. Also known as nematodes, roundworms are among the most abundant of all animals—one rotting apple was found to contain about 90,000 individual roundworms. Free-living roundworms occur in virtually every aquatic and terrestrial habitat, and those living in soil play a crucial role in recycling detritus. Parasitic roundworms are found in most groups of plants and animals. Common roundworms, hookworms, pinworms, threadworms, and other roundworms infest more than half the world's human population.

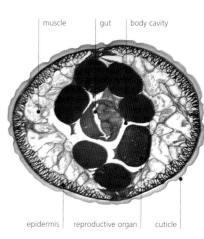

muscle | gut | body cavity

epidermis | reproductive organ | cuticle

Uncomplicated design The simple body plan of a roundworm, shown here in a magnified cross section, is not necessarily a sign of primitiveness, as it may have been derived from a more complex ancestor.

Growing up After hatching, this juvenile parasitic roundworm possesses all the features of an adult except for a mature reproductive system. It will molt four times before reaching adulthood.

Adaptable worms Free-living roundworms may be marine (right), freshwater, or terrestrial. Species occur in ice, hot springs, and even in acids, such as vinegar.

SIMPLE AND RESILIENT

Roundworms have long, slender, cylindrical bodies and often resemble tiny threads, a shape that allows them to live in tiny spaces between grains of soil, for example. They are bilaterally symmetrical and often tapered at both ends. The epidermis (skin) secretes a tough but flexible outer cuticle. As in arthropods such as insects, roundworms must molt as they grow. Most shed the cuticle four times before reaching maturity.

When a roundworm moves, it may appear to be thrashing aimlessly back and forth. Between the gut and the body wall, a body cavity known as a pseudocoel contains fluid under pressure. As the worm contracts its muscles, which run only lengthwise down its body, this pressure causes the body to flex from side to side—a method of locomotion that works well against soil particles or in water films.

After food enters a roundworm's mouth, it is pumped through the simple gut by a muscular pharynx (throat). Waste is released through an anus at the rear of the worm.

If they encounter unfavorable conditions, such as extreme heat or cold or drought, roundworms can enter a death-like state, known cryptobiosis, for months or even years. When conditions improve, they resume their life processes.

Although some roundworms are hermaphrodites, the sexes are more often separate. During copulation, the male holds onto the female with his hooked rear end. The young resemble miniature adults.

Of the more than 1 billion people who are infected with this roundworm, most have no symptoms but some experience wheezing and abdominal problems

Intestinal roundworm
Ascaris lumbricoides

Soil nematode
Caenorhabditis elegans

About 1/25 inch (1 mm) in length, this soil roundworm has been used extensively for research into the genetics of development and neurobiology

Wheat seed gall nematode
Anguina tritici

A plant parasite, the wheat seed gall nematode causes severe losses of rye and wheat crops in developing countries

Lives in the large intestine of about 400 million humans, and spreads to new hosts via eggs passed in feces

Human whipworm
Trichuris trichiura

MOLLUSKS

PHYLUM	Mollusca
CLASSES	8
ORDERS	35
FAMILIES	232
SPECIES	75,000

Abundant and adaptable, mollusks have diversified to fill most ecological niches. They are predominantly marine and are found in every level of the ocean, but have also colonized fresh water and land throughout the world. The diversity of their habitats is reflected in an immense variety of forms, from jet-propelled squid to creeping snails and fixed clams. Features shared by most mollusks include a well-developed head; a body cavity containing the internal organs; a specialized skin called the mantle that covers the body and secretes a shell of calcium carbonate; an intucking of the mantle to form a mantle cavity that houses the gills; and a muscular, often mucus-secreting foot.

Giants of the sea While many mollusks are small or even minute, some species reach great sizes. The largest bivalve, the giant clam (below), can measure almost 5 feet (1.5 m) across. It is dwarfed, however, by the giant squid, which grows to the astounding length of 59 feet (18 m).

Bottom-dweller Also known as sea slugs, nudibranchs are shell-less gastropods with external, feathery gills. *Chromodoris bullocki* is shown here feeding on coral.

Changing display Many cephalopods can change their colors and patterns, often for camouflage but also for communication. In a ritualized competition, male Caribbean reef squids (*Sepioteuthis sepioidea*) both try a zebra display to win the right to mate.

VARIED DESIGN

Mollusks are split into eight classes. The Aplacophora is a small class of worm-like mollusks that lack a shell. About 20 species that possess a low, rounded shell constitute the Monoplacophora. The chitons of Polyplacophora are protected by eight plates and creep on a sucker-like foot. Scaphopoda contains the burrowing tusk shells. The clams, oysters, mussels, and other bivalves of the class Bivalvia have a hinged, two-part shell and a tiny head. Gastropods such as snails and slugs (Gastropoda) sometimes have a spiral shell, but many have no shell at all. Octopuses, squids, and other cephalopods (Cephalopoda) have mobile arms and often lack a shell. They include the largest and most intelligent of all invertebrates.

Feeding habits among mollusks are varied. Species may feed on detritus, scrape algae from rocks, eat leaves, filter tiny organisms from the water, or actively pursue prey such as crustaceans and fishes. Food is taken in through the mouth, often with the help of a rasping, toothed organ called a radula, then passes through a complex digestive system terminating in an anus.

Most mollusks have separate sexes; some release eggs and sperm into the sea, while others copulate. Larvae tend to be free-swimming.

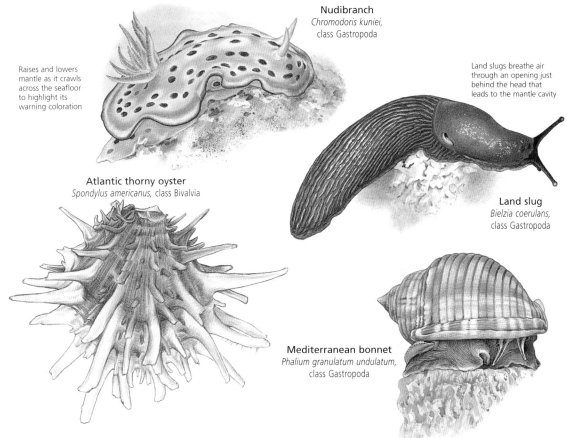

Nudibranch
Chromodoris kuniei,
class Gastropoda

Raises and lowers mantle as it crawls across the seafloor to highlight its warning coloration

Land slugs breathe air through an opening just behind the head that leads to the mantle cavity

Atlantic thorny oyster
Spondylus americanus, class Bivalvia

Land slug
Bielzia coerulans,
class Gastropoda

Mediterranean bonnet
Phalium granulatum undulatum,
class Gastropoda

FACT FILE

Class Monoplacophora Known only from fossil shells until 1952, this rare class is made up of small, limpet-like mollusks living at great depths, from roughly 660 feet (200 m) to ocean trenches at 23,000 feet (7,000 m). They are distinguished by the repetition of body parts: there are five or six pairs of gills, six pairs of kidneys, and eight pairs of retractor muscles.

Species 20

Atlantic, Pacific, Indian Ocean; on seafloor

Deep crawler
Monoplacophorans, such as Neopilina galatheae, are about 1 inch (2.5 cm) long and have a cap-like shell. They use a large flat foot to crawl across the seafloor.

Class Polyplacophora Ranging from ⅒ inch to 16 inches (3 mm to 40 cm) in length, the chitons in this class are long and flat and have a shell of eight overlapping plates. They creep slowly on their broad, flat foot, often using their long radula to scrape algae from rocks or shells. If disturbed, they will clamp down to create a vacuum that makes them very difficult to dislodge.

Species 500

Worldwide; intertidal zone to deeper seafloor

Shell clinger
As in other chitons, the shell of the common eastern chiton Chaetopleura apiculata of North America is surrounded by a girdle formed from its mantle. It uses this girdle and its foot to cling to rocks or shells.

Class Scaphopoda This class contains the tusk shells, burrowing mollusks with long, tubular shells that are open at both ends. A muscular foot and a small head bearing sticky, thread-like tentacles protrude from the large end of the shell. Tusk shells feed on tiny organisms that are collected by the tentacles and broken up by the radula.

Species 500

Worldwide; sandy or muddy seafloor

Burrowing foot
Scaphopods, such as this Entalina sp., use their well-developed foot to burrow into sand or mud on the seafloor.

Glistenworm
Chaetoderma canadense,
class Aplacophora

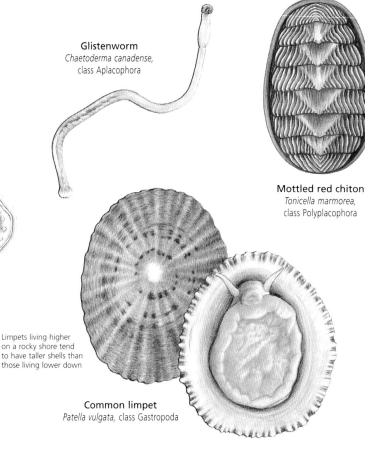

Browses on sedentary invertebrates such as sponges and bryozoans

Mottled red chiton
Tonicella marmorea,
class Polyplacophora

Stenochiton longicymba,
class Polyplacophora

Limpets living higher on a rocky shore tend to have taller shells than those living lower down

Common limpet
Patella vulgata, class Gastropoda

Chiton olivaceus,
class Polyplacophora

Formosan tusk
Pictodentalium formosum,
class Scaphopoda

Elephant tusk
Dentalium elephantinum,
class Scaphopoda

Unlike the jade-green *Dentalium elephantinum,* most tusk shells are white or yelllowish

Antalis tarentinum,
class Scaphopoda

Tusk shells range from ³⁄₁₆ inch to 6 inches (4 mm to 15 cm) in length

West Indian green chiton
Chiton tuberculatus,
class Polyplacophora

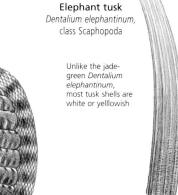

One of the most common chitons in the Caribbean

Spiny cockle
Acanthocardia aculeata, class Bivalvia

Common piddock
Pholas dactylus, class Bivalvia

Bores into soft rock,
clay, and peat

About 4 inches (10 cm) in length
and burrows up to 20 inches
(50 cm) into the sand

Corrugations
strengthen
cockle shell

Sand gaper
Mya arenaria,
class Bivalvia

Burrows in sand,
mud, or gravel

Grooved razor clam
Solen vagina, class Bivalvia

The pen shell
can reach more
than 3¼ feet
(1 m) in length

Pen shell
Pinna nobilis,
class Bivalvia

Nut shell
Nucula nucleus, class Bivalvia

Common mussel
Mytilus edulis, class Bivalvia

Shape, size, and
color of common
mussel's shell vary
according to the
local conditions

Watering-pot
shells secrete a
calcareous tube

File clam
Lima hians, class Bivalvia

Edge of mantle
bears many
small tentacles

Flat oyster
Ostrea edulis, class Bivalvia

Swan mussel
Anodonta cygnaea,
class Bivalvia

Greatly reduced
valves have
fused with tube

Freshwater pearl mussel
Margaritana margaritifera, class Bivalvia

Watering-pot shell
Penicillus javanus, class Bivalvia

FACT FILE

Class Bivalvia Clams, oysters, mussels, and other bivalves live inside a hinged two-valve shell. Most are burrowers, but some cement one valve to a firm surface or attach themselves with a byssus, sticky fibers secreted by the foot. Other bivalves live free on the sediment or in the water.

Species 10,000

Worldwide

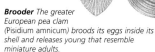

Brooder *The greater European pea clam* (Pisidium amnicum) *broods its eggs inside its shell and releases young that resemble miniature adults.*

GIANT CLAM

The largest bivalve of all lives on the tropical coral reefs of the Indian and Pacific oceans. Weighing up to 700 pounds (320 kg), giant clams (*Tridacna gigas*) remain embedded in the sediment, filtering plankton from the water. The bulk of their nutrition, however, comes from the algae that they host in the exposed thick lips of the mantle.

INSIDE A BIVALVE

A bivalve's mantle forms a sheet of tissue lining the two valves. The adductor muscles are used to close the shell, and the blade-like foot is often used for burrowing. Bivalves use their gills to filter particles from the water and their palps to sort them by size.

stomach | heart | kidney
adductor muscle | adductor muscle
mouth
gill
foot | palps | intestine | mantle edge

⚡ CONSERVATION WATCH

Unwelcome mussels First noticed in the Great Lakes in the 1980s, the European zebra mussels (*Dreissena* sp.) have now invaded many of the United States' major rivers and lakes. By filtering vast amounts of phytoplankton from the water, they are having a dramatic effect on aquatic food webs and endangering native mollusks and other species.

FACT FILE

Class Gastropoda This is the largest class of mollusks and includes snails, slugs, limpets, and nudibranchs. Some gastropods have lost their shells, but most have a spiral shell that contains a twisted body mass. Gastropods usually have a distinct head with eyes and tentacles. The mantle cavity lies over the head, allowing the head to retract into the shell. The muscular foot is used for creeping, swimming, or burrowing.

Species 60,000

Worldwide

Gastropod cannibal *The banded tulip (*Fasciolaria hunteria*) can be very aggressive and will eat other members of its species.*

RADULAS

A mollusk's mouth usually includes a tongue-like structure known as a radula. In some species, such as deep-sea limpets (*Neomphalus* sp.), a covering of hardened teeth makes the radula a rasping tool, able to scrape algae from rocks. In others, such as the slit shell mollusk (*Scissurella* sp.), the surface of the radula is feathery and is used to sweep detritus from sand. In a few carnivorous species, such as cone shells (*Conus* sp.), the radula has become a sharp, venom-injecting tooth.

THE GASTROPOD SHELL

While gastropod shells display immense variety in their details, the typical shell is a conical spire. The mantle adds new material to the inner and outer lips of the shell at slightly different rates, resulting in the spiral form.

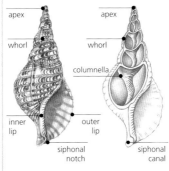

apex

whorl

inner lip

outer lip

siphonal notch

apex

whorl

columnella

outer lip

siphonal canal

Plain marginella
Marginella cornea,
class Gastropoda

Purple bubble-raft snail
Janthina janthina, class Gastropoda

Floats at the ocean's surface, buoyed by mucus-covered bubbles

Phyllidia ocellata,
class Gastropoda

Color of *Phyllidia ocellata* is variable, but it can be identified by its knobby tubercles and white-ringed black spots

Crown conch
Melongena corona, class Gastropoda

European edible abalone
Haliotis tuberculata,
class Gastropoda

The mucus of *Murex brandarius* was used by the ancient Greeks to produce a dye called Tyrian purple, which was so rare that it was used only for the clothes of royalty

Purple-dye murex
Murex brandarius, class Gastropoda

Trumpet triton
Charonia tritonis,
class Gastropoda

Ruffled flaps of tissue (parapodia) resemble lettuce leaves

Lettuce sea slug
Elysia crispata,
class Gastropoda

Floats upside down and feeds on Portuguese man-of-war, ingesting the host's nematocysts (stingers) to use in its own defense

Tiger cowry
Cypraea tigris, class Gastropoda

Blue sea slug
Glaucus atlanticus, class Gastropoda

Common egg cowrie
Ovula ovum, class Gastropoda

Queen conch
Strombus gigas, class Gastropoda

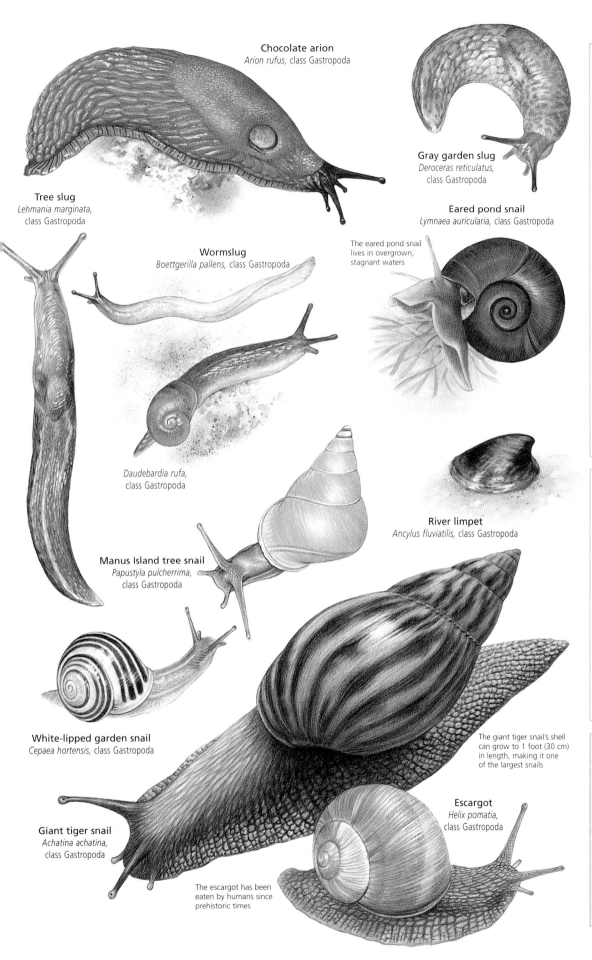

Chocolate arion
Arion rufus, class Gastropoda

Gray garden slug
Deroceras reticulatus,
class Gastropoda

Tree slug
Lehmania marginata,
class Gastropoda

Eared pond snail
Lymnaea auricularia, class Gastropoda

Wormslug
Boettgerilla pallens, class Gastropoda

The eared pond snail
lives in overgrown,
stagnant waters

Daudebardia rufa,
class Gastropoda

River limpet
Ancylus fluviatilis, class Gastropoda

Manus Island tree snail
Papustyla pulcherrima,
class Gastropoda

White-lipped garden snail
Cepaea hortensis, class Gastropoda

The giant tiger snail's shell
can grow to 1 foot (30 cm)
in length, making it one
of the largest snails

Escargot
Helix pomatia,
class Gastropoda

Giant tiger snail
Achatina achatina,
class Gastropoda

The escargot has been
eaten by humans since
prehistoric times

LIFE ON LAND

Several times during the course of evolution, gastropods have adapted to life on land. There are now roughly 20,000 land snail species. In most, gills have been lost and replaced by a lung. Some species, however, have both a gill chamber and a lung. Out of water, the shell has become lightweight and now protects against desiccation as well as against predators. The mantle and the mucus that cover the body also help to keep the snail moist. If conditions become too dry, a snail will attach itself to a plant or other surface and become dormant. Land slugs, which have lost the shell, live largely in crevices.

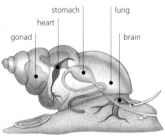

stomach   lung
heart
gonad   brain

Air breather *Most land snails lack gills. Instead, the mantle wall has become filled with blood vessels and acts as a lung.*

MATING HERMAPHRODITES

Land snails are hermaphrodites but do not self-fertilize. Before mating, two snails will usually circle each other, touch tentacles, intertwine bodies, and bite each other. In the copulation that follows, sperm are exchanged so that the eggs of both snails can be fertilized.

Love darts *The courtship of some land snails, such as Helix sp., is bizarre. When the snails are intertwined, one will shoot a chalky dart from its body into its mate. The dart appears to carry a chemical that helps the sperm reach the storage area in the female reproductive system.*

⚡ CONSERVATION WATCH

Mollusk losses Non-marine mollusks appear to be the most threatened of all animal groups. In the last 300 years, 284 species of non-marine mollusk are known to have become extinct—far more than in mammals (74 extinctions) or birds (129 extinctions). Although the oceans are by no means pristine, terrestrial and freshwater habitats have been drastically modified by human activities and their mollusk populations have suffered as a result.

FACT FILE

Class Cephalopoda The cephalopod foot lies close to the head and has been modified to form arms, tentacles, and a funnel. Nautiluses retain a large external shell; in squids and cuttlefishes the shell has been reduced and covered by tissue; and octopuses have lost their shell altogether. With the most developed brains of any invertebrates, cephalopods display complex behavior and are able to learn.

Species 600

Worldwide; marine

Predator *Like all cephalopods, the European common squid (Loligo subulata) is carnivorous. It captures prey with its tentacles and arms and breaks it up with its beak and radula.*

THE CHAMBERED NAUTILUS

The most primitive of the cephalopods, chambered nautiluses live in the last chamber of their large shell. The other chambers are filled with gas, and the nautilus controls its buoyancy by adding fluid to or removing fluid from them.

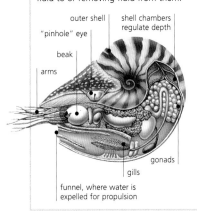

outer shell

"pinhole" eye

shell chambers regulate depth

beak

arms

gonads

gills

funnel, where water is expelled for propulsion

CEPHALOPOD SIGHT

Most cephalopods have excellent vision. Like the eyes of vertebrates, their eyes have a cornea, iris, lens, and retina. While humans bring objects into focus by changing the shape of the lens, cephalopods move the entire lens closer to or farther from the retina. Guided by the cephalopod's statocysts (balance organs), the slit-shaped pupils maintain a horizontal position no matter what the angle of the head.

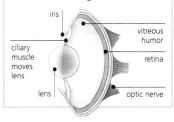

iris

vitreous humor

ciliary muscle moves lens

retina

lens

optic nerve

All squids have eight arms and two long tentacles, all with suckers

Long-finned squid
Loligo vulgaris, class Cephalopoda

Like many cephalopods, cuttlefishes react to danger by immediately changing color to camouflage themselves, and may also squirt a black ink called sepia to confuse a predator

To escape predators, flying squids can shoot out of the water and glide for a distance

Common cuttlefish
Sepia officinalis, class Cephalopoda

Flying squid
Ommastrephes sagittatus, class Cephalopoda

The ram's horn squid is the only surviving member of the family Spirulidae

Lesser cuttlefish (dwarf bobtail)
Sepiola rondeleti, class Cephalopoda

The internal shell, or pen, of the ram's horn squid acts as a buoyancy device

Chambered nautiluses have about 90 sticky tentacles without suckers

Ram's horn squid
Spirula spirula, class Cephalopoda

Has light-producing organs at the tip of its two tentacles and on the underside of its body

Abraliopsis morisii, class Cephalopoda

Common nautilus
Nautilus pompilius, class Cephalopoda

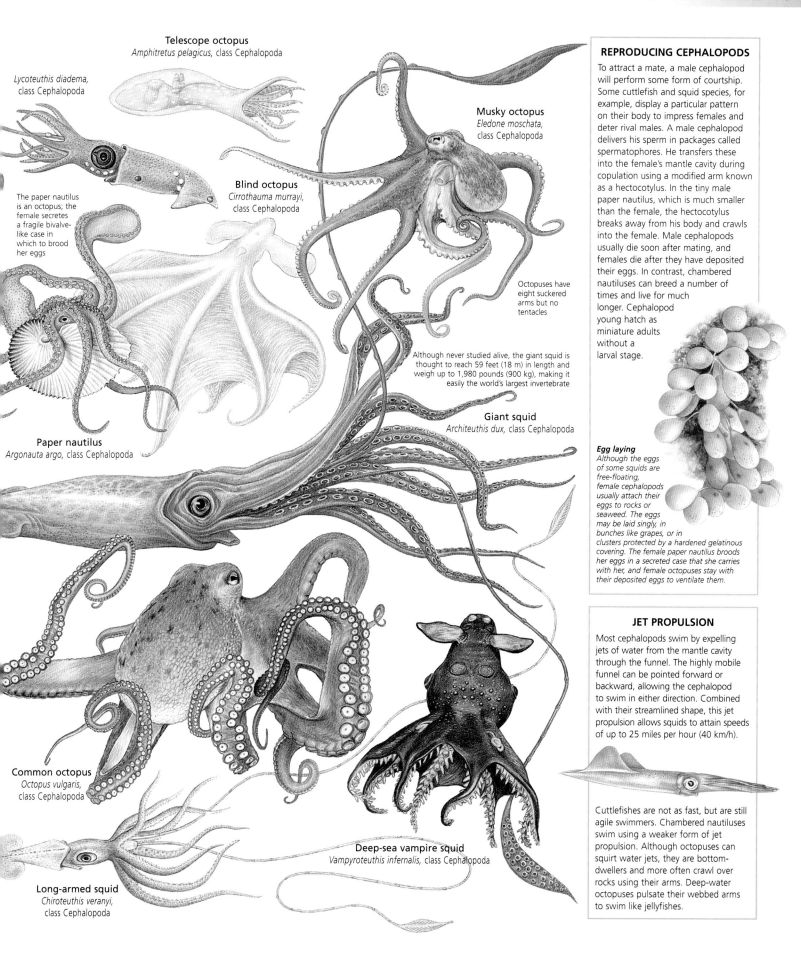

Telescope octopus
Amphitretus pelagicus, class Cephalopoda

Lycoteuthis diadema, class Cephalopoda

The paper nautilus is an octopus; the female secretes a fragile bivalve-like case in which to brood her eggs

Musky octopus
Eledone moschata, class Cephalopoda

Blind octopus
Cirrothauma murrayi, class Cephalopoda

Octopuses have eight suckered arms but no tentacles

Although never studied alive, the giant squid is thought to reach 59 feet (18 m) in length and weigh up to 1,980 pounds (900 kg), making it easily the world's largest invertebrate

Giant squid
Architeuthis dux, class Cephalopoda

Paper nautilus
Argonauta argo, class Cephalopoda

Common octopus
Octopus vulgaris, class Cephalopoda

Deep-sea vampire squid
Vampyroteuthis infernalis, class Cephalopoda

Long-armed squid
Chiroteuthis veranyi, class Cephalopoda

REPRODUCING CEPHALOPODS

To attract a mate, a male cephalopod will perform some form of courtship. Some cuttlefish and squid species, for example, display a particular pattern on their body to impress females and deter rival males. A male cephalopod delivers his sperm in packages called spermatophores. He transfers these into the female's mantle cavity during copulation using a modified arm known as a hectocotylus. In the tiny male paper nautilus, which is much smaller than the female, the hectocotylus breaks away from his body and crawls into the female. Male cephalopods usually die soon after mating, and females die after they have deposited their eggs. In contrast, chambered nautiluses can breed a number of times and live for much longer. Cephalopod young hatch as miniature adults without a larval stage.

Egg laying
Although the eggs of some squids are free-floating, female cephalopods usually attach their eggs to rocks or seaweed. The eggs may be laid singly, in bunches like grapes, or in clusters protected by a hardened gelatinous covering. The female paper nautilus broods her eggs in a secreted case that she carries with her, and female octopuses stay with their deposited eggs to ventilate them.

JET PROPULSION

Most cephalopods swim by expelling jets of water from the mantle cavity through the funnel. The highly mobile funnel can be pointed forward or backward, allowing the cephalopod to swim in either direction. Combined with their streamlined shape, this jet propulsion allows squids to attain speeds of up to 25 miles per hour (40 km/h).

Cuttlefishes are not as fast, but are still agile swimmers. Chambered nautiluses swim using a weaker form of jet propulsion. Although octopuses can squirt water jets, they are bottom-dwellers and more often crawl over rocks using their arms. Deep-water octopuses pulsate their webbed arms to swim like jellyfishes.

SEGMENTED WORMS

PHYLUM	Annelida
CLASSES	2
ORDERS	21
FAMILIES	130
SPECIES	12,000

Also known as annelids, segmented worms have a head and a long body made up of segments that look like rings from the outside. Each segment has its own fluid-filled body cavity that acts as a hydroskeleton and contains a separate set of excretory, locomotory, and respiratory organs. The segments are united, however, by common digestive, circulatory, and nervous systems. Segmented worms crawl or swim by wriggling from side to side, or burrow by waves of contractions that pass down the length of the body. Stiff bristles known as chetae protrude from each segment and provide traction. While many species are highly active, others live in burrows or tubes.

In the soil Long and thin with a small head, earthworms are shaped for burrowing. With up to 650 individuals per square yard (800 per sq. m), earthworms play a crucial role in aerating and fertilizing the soil.

Food-filtering fans
Fanworms are annelids that live attached to the seafloor. Most of their body is hidden inside a tube that they have secreted or built from sediment. A crown of fine tentacles, each covered in tiny beating hairs called cilia, filters particles of food from the water.

IN WATER AND ON LAND

Segmented worms are found in all levels of the ocean, in freshwater lakes and rivers, and on land. They include filter-feeders, predators, and blood-suckers, as well as deposit-feeders such as earthworms, which eat sediment to extract nutrients.

Commonly called bristleworms, the species in the class Polychaeta are almost entirely marine and usually swim or crawl using paddle-like appendages known as parapodia. The parapodia are often lost in tube-living forms, which have a modified head region for food-gathering. Typically, the sexes are separate and release eggs and sperm into the water for fertilization.

The class Clitellata includes many terrestrial and freshwater species such as earthworms and leeches, as well as some marine species. Most are hermaphrodites that exchange sperm by copulation. They all bear a clitellum, a ring of glandular skin that secretes a cocoon for the eggs.

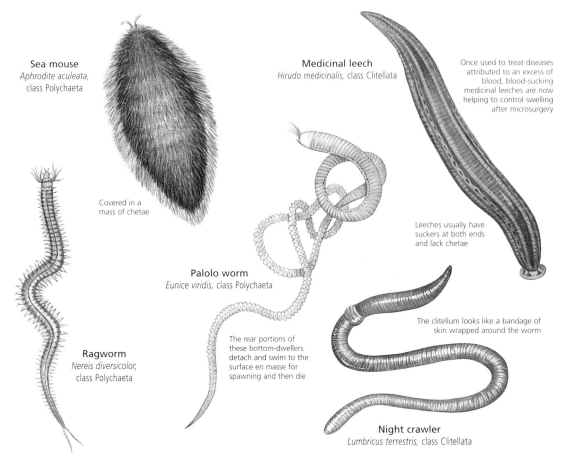

Sea mouse
Aphrodite aculeata,
class Polychaeta

Covered in a mass of chetae

Ragworm
Nereis diversicolor,
class Polychaeta

Palolo worm
Eunice viridis, class Polychaeta

The rear portions of these bottom-dwellers detach and swim to the surface en masse for spawning and then die

Medicinal leech
Hirudo medicinalis, class Clitellata

Once used to treat diseases attributed to an excess of blood, blood-sucking medicinal leeches are now helping to control swelling after microsurgery

Leeches usually have suckers at both ends and lack chetae

The clitellum looks like a bandage of skin wrapped around the worm

Night crawler
Lumbricus terrestris, class Clitellata

Instantly withdraws its feathery crown if disturbed

Red feather duster
Spirographis spallanzanii,
class Polychaeta

METAMORPHOSIS

While some newly hatched invertebrates resemble little adults, most look quite distinct from their parents and have a very different lifestyle. To become adults, these young must go through a transformation known as metamorphosis. Corals, clams, many crustaceans, and most other invertebrates metamorphose into adults after a brief larval stage. For most insects, the larval stage is prolonged. In some insect groups, such as crickets and bugs, metamorphosis is incomplete. The hatched form, called a nymph, is structured like the adult, but lacks wings and full sex organs until it emerges from the final molt. Other insects, such as butterflies and bees, have complete metamorphosis. The young, called larvae, differ so much from their parents that they must go through a pupal stage, in which their bodies break down and are built up again as adults.

Veliger larva Marine gastropods such as sea snails have a free-swimming veliger larva, which feeds and propels itself using tiny hairs known as cilia. The larva gradually develops a shell, mantle cavity, and foot (above), then metamorphoses into an adult (below).

Zoea larva Decapods such as squat lobsters often hatch as a zoea, a free-swimming, spiny larva (above). The zoea metamorphoses into a postlarval megalopa, with adult appendages. This sinks to the seafloor and becomes a bottom-dwelling adult (below).

Egg to nymph to adult A dragonfly develops through incomplete metamorphosis. **1.** Male and female mate. **2.** Female lays eggs in water or in stem of water plant. **3.** Aquatic nymph hatches. **4.** Nymph feeds on tadpoles and worms and grows through a series of molts. **5.** Nymph emerges from the water for its final molt. **6.** Adult bursts from the nymphal skin. **7.** Adult rests while its wings dry out. **8.** Feeding on flying insects, adult flies to a new location to find a mate.

ARTHROPODS

PHYLUM	Arthropoda
CLASSES	22
ORDERS	110
FAMILIES	2,120
SPECIES	> 1.1 million

The insects, spiders, crustaceans, centipedes, and other invertebrates in the phylum Arthropoda account for three-quarters of all known animal species, and millions more remain to be discovered. Arthropods have adapted to fill virtually every ecological niche on land, in fresh water, and in the oceans. Consequently, their anatomy and lifestyles are extraordinarily diverse, but they share a number of defining features. The name arthropod means "jointed feet," and arthropods do have jointed appendages and segmented bodies. They are distinguished from other invertebrates by their tough but flexible exoskeleton, which provides both protection and support.

Fossilized marine class Arthropods called trilobites dominate marine fossil beds from about 500 million years ago, and include more than 15,000 known species. They disappeared about 250 million years ago.

Insects everywhere Insects account for about 90 percent of all arthropod species. Ubiquitous on land and in fresh water, but rare in the ocean, insects include predators such as the praying mantis, and nectar-feeders such as the swallowtail butterfly.

EARLY ARRIVALS

The first arthropods appeared in the oceans about 530 million years ago and included crustaceans; ancestors of horseshoe crabs; and the now-extinct trilobites. These early species tended to have numerous body segments, each bearing a similar pair of appendages. Over time, the appendages became specialized for particular tasks, such as locomotion, food collection, sensory perception, and copulation. Furthermore, the segments became arranged into distinct regions of the body called tagma, such as the head, thorax, and abdomen of insects.

Arthropods were the first animals to leave the sea and the first to take to the sky. Scorpions had ventured onto land by 350 million years ago and were soon followed by the first terrestrial insects. Before long, winged insects had emerged. The success of arthropods on land rests in part on their waxy exoskeleton, which stops them from drying out. Jointed legs also make arthropods highly mobile, thus enhancing their ability to find food and mates, evade predators, and colonize new places. In insects, the development of wings increases the advantage.

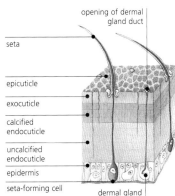

opening of dermal gland duct

seta

epicuticle

exocuticle

calcified endocuticle

uncalcified endocuticle

epidermis

seta-forming cell

dermal gland

Arthropod armor Secreted by epidermal cells, the arthropod exoskeleton has thin layers of wax and protein, known as the epicuticle, overlying various layers of chitin and protein. Tanning of proteins in the exocuticle, and often calcification in the endocuticle, hardens exoskeleton. This coral crab (*Hoplophrys oatesii*) (right) discards its old exoskeleton as it grows.

Legs and bodies Tarantulas (left) and other spiders have eight legs and a body divided into two parts: the cephalothorax (fused head and thorax) and the abdomen. Insects have six legs and a three-part body made up of a head, thorax, and abdomen.

Deadly bites While some arthropods are venomous, few deliver a bite that is fatal to humans. Far more deadly are the diseases transmitted by blood-sucking arthropods such as mosquitoes (below), which transfer malaria and other illnesses from one vertebrate host to another.

WAYS OF BREATHING

The arthropod exoskeleton offers great protection, but it is also usually too impermeable to allow gas exchange. While some tiny arthropods can breathe directly through the body wall, most have developed specialized structures. Aquatic arthropods tend to have gills. Derived from gills are book lungs, found in many arachnids. Terrestrial arthropods often rely on minute air ducts known as tracheae, which deliver air to all parts of the body.

Gills Oxygen is absorbed from water by the gills (above), which also help to maintain salt balance. In crustaceans, the gills are external and often positioned on the legs, but are protected by the exoskeleton. Horseshoe crabs have unique structures called book gills, with flaps like the pages of a book.

Limbs in motion By modifying their jointed limbs for walking, running, leaping, pushing, burrowing, and swimming, arthropods have been able to occupy diverse habitats. In some, such as grasshoppers (right), the legs also hold their hearing organs.

While many arthropods are themselves predators, almost all are prey to vertebrates or to other invertebrates. The compound eyes found on many arthropod species are made up of multiple lenses and are extremely effective at detecting motion. Simple eyes, with a single lens, detect light intensity. Hairs (known as setae), projections, and slits on the antennae, mouthparts, and legs detect subtle vibrations. A cerebral ganglion (brain) connects via a nerve cord to ganglia (clusters of nerve cells) in each body segment. In arthropods' open circulatory system, a heart pumps hemolymph (blood) to bathe the organs.

The sexes are separate in most arthropod species, and reproduction usually involves the male's sperm fertilizing the female's eggs. Often, the sperm is transferred in packages known as spermatophores, which the female can use when she is ready. The life stages of arthropods vary greatly. Some species are like small adults when they hatch, while others add segments as they grow. Many insect larvae look nothing like their parents and must go through a pupal stage to transform into a winged adult.

Book lungs Most likely derived from the book gills attached to the under surface of the abdomen of horseshoe crabs, book lungs have become internalised within the abdominal cavity. A small opening allows air to flow into the cavity of the book lung, whose 'pages' form the respiratory surface. Book lungs are found in many arachnids either as the only respiratory organ, such as in scorpions, or in combination with tracheae, as in most spiders. Oxygen from the air diffuses across the respiratory surface and is taken into the blood for distribution to the tissues. Carbon dioxide diffuses in the opposite direction.

Tracheae Found in insects, arachnids, and centipedes and millipedes, tracheae (above) are tubes that collect air through minute openings in the exoskeleton called spiracles, and transport it to the tissues or blood. The spiracles can be closed to minimize moisture loss.

ARACHNIDS

Including some of the most feared and fascinating of all invertebrates, the class Arachnida encompasses spiders, scorpions, harvestmen (or daddy-longlegs), and mites and ticks, along with several lesser known groups. Apart from some families of aquatic mites and a few species of water spiders, all arachnids are terrestrial, and the majority are predators of other invertebrates. Many spiders use silk webs to snare prey, and both scorpions and spiders inject their prey with venom to paralyze or kill it. Most arachnids are unable to swallow solid food and must squirt digestive enzymes into the prey and then suck the liquefied meal into their mouth.

PHYLUM	Arthropoda
SUBPHYLUM	Chelicerata
CLASS	Arachnida
ORDERS	17
FAMILIES	450
SPECIES	80,000

Diurnal vision Most arachnid species are nocturnal and their simple eyes detect only variations in light. In daytime hunters, such as jumping spiders (family Salticidae), the two primary simple eyes provide very sharp vision at close range.

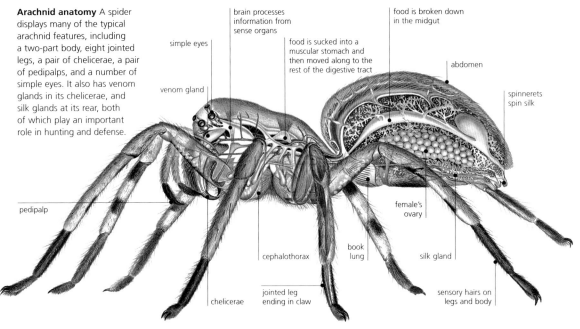

Arachnid anatomy A spider displays many of the typical arachnid features, including a two-part body, eight jointed legs, a pair of chelicerae, a pair of pedipalps, and a number of simple eyes. It also has venom glands in its chelicerae, and silk glands at its rear, both of which play an important role in hunting and defense.

simple eyes

brain processes information from sense organs

food is sucked into a muscular stomach and then moved along to the rest of the digestive tract

food is broken down in the midgut

venom gland

abdomen

spinnerets spin silk

pedipalp

female's ovary

book lung

silk gland

cephalothorax

sensory hairs on legs and body

chelicerae

jointed leg ending in claw

EIGHT-LEGGED PREDATORS

Like other arthropods, arachnids have a segmented body, a tough but flexible exoskeleton, and jointed limbs. Mites and ticks have rounded bodies made up of a single region, but other arachnids have two-part bodies, with a cephalothorax holding the eyes, mouthparts, and limbs, and an abdomen containing many of the internal organs.

Arachnids have eight legs, unlike insects, which have six. They also have two pairs of appendages near the mouth. The first pair, known as chelicerae, may be pincer-like or can form fangs that inject venom. They are used for subduing prey. The second pair, the pedipalps, are often used like antennae to sense the surroundings. Scorpions and some other arachnids use pedipalps to seize prey, while male spiders use them to transfer sperm to females.

To find prey and avoid danger, arachnids rely on the fine sensory hairs on their body and legs. They also have a number of simple eyes. Fine slits in the cuticle may detect odors, gravity, or vibrations.

Arachnids breathe using book lungs or a tracheal system, or both. Book lungs probably developed from gills and are made up of stacked leaves of tissue. The tracheal system takes air in through tiny pores called spiracles and distributes it to tissues via a network of tubes.

Development of arachnids is direct, with the young hatching as small versions of their parents and growing through a series of molts. Most arachnids are solitary.

Blood-sucking parasite While most arachnids hunt live prey, ticks and some mites are parasites. A tick uses its hooked mouthparts to pierce the skin of a mammal, then feed on its blood. Once engorged, the tick drops off the host and molts.

Stinging defense While arachnids such as spiders and scorpions are widely feared, only a tiny minority of species deliver a bite or sting that can be fatal to humans. The giant desert hairy scorpion (*Hadrurus arizonensis*) has a painful sting, but the effect of its venom on humans is mild.

Whip-spider
Phrynichus sp.,
order Amblypygi

Members of the order Amblypygi are known as whip-spiders or tailless whip-scorpions

Book scorpion
Chelifer cancroides, order Pseudoscorpiones

Book scorpions are often found living in books and furniture

Hooded tick spider
Ricinoides sjoestedti,
order Ricinulei

Hood can be lowered over the mouth

European buthid
Buthus occitanus,
order Scorpiones

Extremely long front legs act as tactile organs

Whip-spider
Charinus milloti, order Amblypygi

Venom glands in claw-like pedipalps

Fat-tailed scorpion
Androctonus australis,
order Scorpiones

Moss neobisid
Neobisium carcinoides,
order Pseudoscorpiones

The first pair of legs on a whip-scorpion is used as feelers

Whip-scorpion
Thelyphonus caudatus, order Uropygi

Short-tailed whip-scorpion
Schizomus crassicaudatus,
order Schizomida

Emperor scorpion
Pandinus imperator, order Scorpiones

Can weigh more than 2 ounces (60 g) and will hunt small vertebrates such as mice and lizards, crushing them in its large pedipalps

FACT FILE

Order Scorpiones Scorpions are distinguished from other arachnids by two large clawed pedipalps and a segmented abdomen. The tip of the tail holds a prominent stinger, which is sometimes used to subdue prey but more often plays a defensive role. Scorpions shelter in crevices or burrows by day, and hunt by night.

Species 1,400

Warmer regions; under rocks & bark

Houseguest
*The slender-brown scorpion (*Centruroides gracilis*) usually lives in tropical forests, but may dwell in houses in regions where it has been introduced.*

Order Uropygi Known as whip-scorpions or vinegaroons, the arachnids in this order resemble scorpions but their pedipalps are stouter, and their tails are long and thin. If threatened, a whip-scorpion will spray acid from glands at the base of its whip-like tail.

Species 100

Mainly tropical regions; under rocks

Takeaway meals *The giant whip-scorpion (*Mastigoproctus giganteus*) seizes and crushes its invertebrate prey with its pedipalps, then carries the meal back to its burrow.*

PARENTAL CARE

Most female arachnids lay their eggs in soil or another safe location and leave them to hatch on their own. In *Euscorpius carpathicus* (left) and other scorpions, however, the fertilized eggs develop inside the mother and she produces live young. The mother catches them in her first or first and second pairs of legs. At this stage, the larval young are rather helpless as they lack pedipalps and cannot sting. They crawl onto the mother's back and are carried around until after their first molt, about 3 to 14 days later. Now equipped with their pedipalps and a functioning stinger, they are able to hunt. They quickly scatter and establish their own territories to escape their mother eating them.

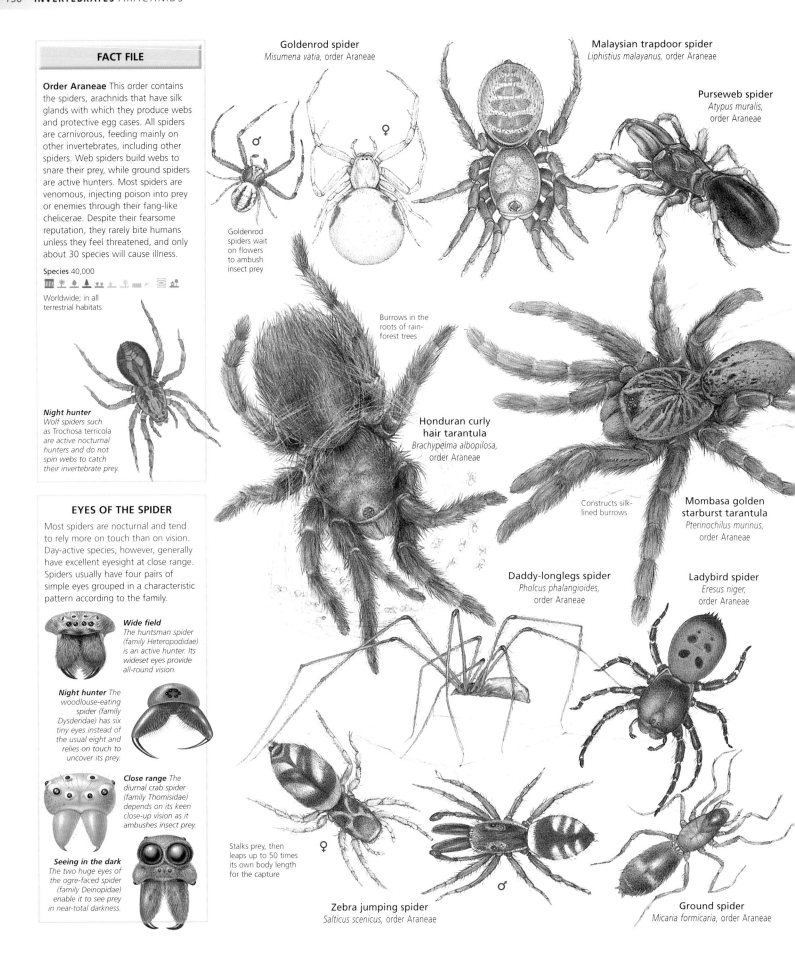

Order Araneae This order contains the spiders, arachnids that have silk glands with which they produce webs and protective egg cases. All spiders are carnivorous, feeding mainly on other invertebrates, including other spiders. Web spiders build webs to snare their prey, while ground spiders are active hunters. Most spiders are venomous, injecting poison into prey or enemies through their fang-like chelicerae. Despite their fearsome reputation, they rarely bite humans unless they feel threatened, and only about 30 species will cause illness.

Species 40,000

Worldwide; in all terrestrial habitats

Night hunter
Wolf spiders such as Trochosa terricola are active nocturnal hunters and do not spin webs to catch their invertebrate prey.

EYES OF THE SPIDER

Most spiders are nocturnal and tend to rely more on touch than on vision. Day-active species, however, generally have excellent eyesight at close range. Spiders usually have four pairs of simple eyes grouped in a characteristic pattern according to the family.

Wide field
The huntsman spider (family Heteropodidae) is an active hunter. Its wideset eyes provide all-round vision.

Night hunter *The woodlouse-eating spider (family Dysderidae) has six tiny eyes instead of the usual eight and relies on touch to uncover its prey.*

Close range *The diurnal crab spider (family Thomisidae) depends on its keen close-up vision as it ambushes insect prey.*

Seeing in the dark
The two huge eyes of the ogre-faced spider (family Deinopidae) enable it to see prey in near-total darkness.

Goldenrod spider
Misumena vatia, order Araneae

Goldenrod spiders wait on flowers to ambush insect prey

Malaysian trapdoor spider
Liphistius malayanus, order Araneae

Purseweb spider
Atypus muralis, order Araneae

Burrows in the roots of rain-forest trees

Honduran curly hair tarantula
Brachypelma albopilosa, order Araneae

Constructs silk-lined burrows

Mombasa golden starburst tarantula
Pterinochilus murinus, order Araneae

Daddy-longlegs spider
Pholcus phalangioides, order Araneae

Ladybird spider
Eresus niger, order Araneae

Stalks prey, then leaps up to 50 times its own body length for the capture

Zebra jumping spider
Salticus scenicus, order Araneae

Ground spider
Micaria formicaria, order Araneae

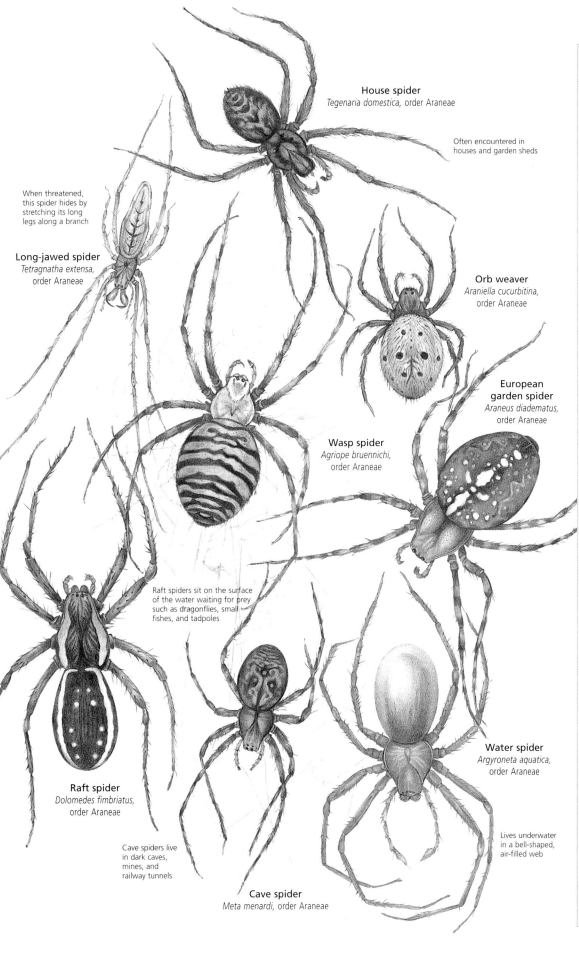

House spider
Tegenaria domestica, order Araneae

Often encountered in houses and garden sheds

When threatened, this spider hides by stretching its long legs along a branch

Long-jawed spider
Tetragnatha extensa, order Araneae

Orb weaver
Araniella cucurbitina, order Araneae

European garden spider
Araneus diadematus, order Araneae

Wasp spider
Agriope bruennichi, order Araneae

Raft spiders sit on the surface of the water waiting for prey such as dragonflies, small fishes, and tadpoles

Raft spider
Dolomedes fimbriatus, order Araneae

Cave spiders live in dark caves, mines, and railway tunnels

Water spider
Argyroneta aquatica, order Araneae

Lives underwater in a bell-shaped, air-filled web

Cave spider
Meta menardi, order Araneae

CAPTURE METHODS

Not all spiders sit waiting for prey to fall into their webs. The spitting spider (*Scytodes thoracica*) has an enlarged cephalothorax that houses linked venom and silk glands. It hunts its prey by night, stealthily approaching until it is within spitting distance. The spider then ejects two poisonous silk threads, covering the prey in a zig-zag pattern. The prey is glued to the ground by the silk and paralyzed by the venom.

Spitting spider With only six small eyes, the spitting spider has poor vision and uses the sensory hairs on its front legs to find prey such as flies and moths.

Bolas spiders belong to the orb-weaver family, Araneidae, but they do not build orb webs. Instead, they "fish" for their prey, suspending a single strand of silk tipped with a sticky globule known as a bolas. The bolas seems to be laced with pheromones that mimic those of particular female noctuid moths. When male moths are attracted to the bolas and become stuck, the spider reels them in.

Bolas spider When it senses a moth approaching, a bolas spider will start swinging its fishing line in a circle.

Spiders in various families have adapted their anatomy to convincingly mimic ants. They are even thought to produce pheromones that allow them to infiltrate ant colonies. Some ant-mimics use their disguise to prey on the unsuspecting ants. Others may merely be protecting themselves from predators such as wasps and birds that avoid ants because of the formic acid ants produce when threatened.

Brazilian ant-mimicking spider Like other ant-mimics, Aphantochilus rogersi has a long waist and the abdomen is partially divided into segments to give the impression of an insect body. The first pair of legs is held in front like antennae.

SILK AND WEBS

Scaffold web *A scaffold web has stretched traplines with sticky ends attached to the ground. If a crawling insect walks into a trapline, the line snaps back, with the victim dangling in the air.*

While only some species build webs, almost all spiders produce silk. Made of the protein fibroin, spider silk is as strong as nylon thread but has greater elasticity. A spider may have up to eight silk glands in its abdomen, each yielding a different kind of silk. One kind of silk is used for the dragline a spider usually spins after itself like a mountain climber's safety line. Other types are used for cocooning fertilized eggs or wrapping up captured prey. Male spiders may use silk to hold their packages of sperm. Some spiderlings use threads of silk like balloons to carry them aloft so they can disperse. The best known use of silk is among the webspinning spiders, which build a remarkable variety of webs to snare their prey.

Captured prey A net-casting spider (*Deinopus* sp.) prepares a little snare net each night and holds it in its legs as it awaits prey. When a potential victim passes by, the spider flings the net over it, quickly wraps the catch in extra silk, and then bites it.

Hammock web *The hammock web spun by a money spider over low bushes may look messy, but any insect caught in its fine lattice weave usually falls into another web suspended below.*

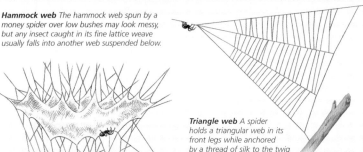

Triangle web *A spider holds a triangular web in its front legs while anchored by a thread of silk to the twig behind it. When an insect hits the web, the spider releases its grip and the web collapses, entangling the prey.*

Orb web *The most elaborate of all webs, the orb web covers a large area using a minimum of silk. An outer framework supports a continuous spiral and a series of spokes. The web is suspended between tree branches to capture flying insects.*

Lace-sheet web *The trap spun by a lace-web weaver is made of fine, woolly silk. It may not be sticky, but insects soon get tangled up in its many fibers, and remain trapped until the spider is ready for food.*

No sticky feet Spiders such as this orb weaver (*Argiope* sp.) (right) avoid getting trapped in their own webs because only some of the threads are sticky and they know where to tread.

Shared nest While most spiders are solitary, some share communal nests. Some species are truly colonial, and hunt and feed together. In others, such as *Cryptophora* sp., each spider guards its own orb web and feeds alone, but the webs share frame lines, creating a vast network of silk (below).

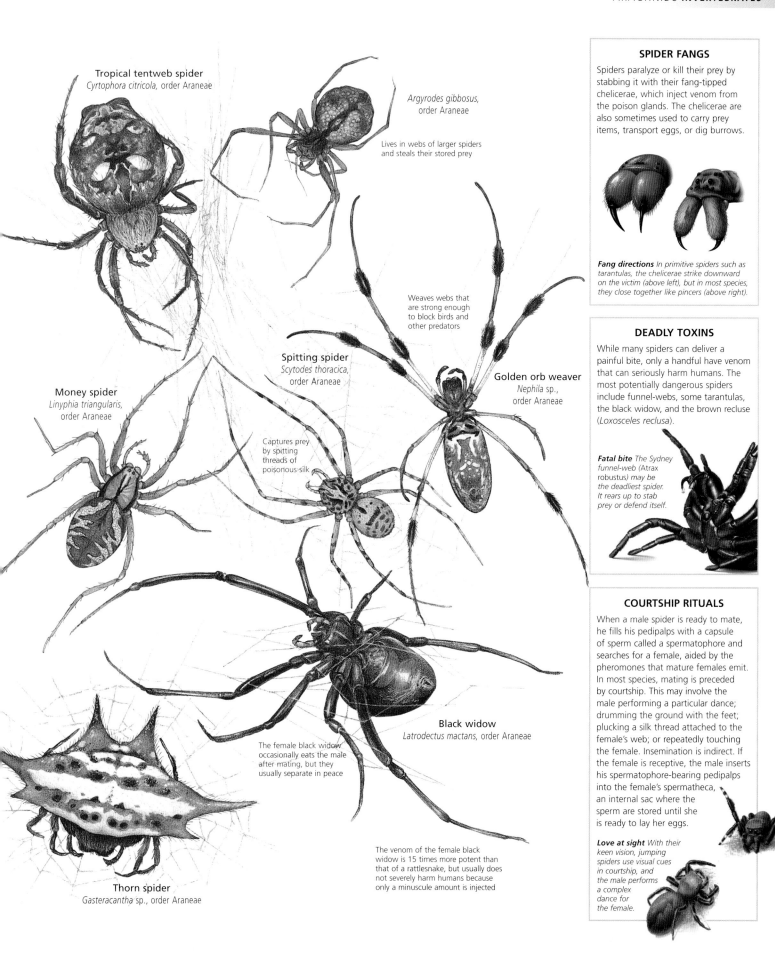

Tropical tentweb spider
Cyrtophora citricola, order Araneae

Argyrodes gibbosus,
order Araneae

Lives in webs of larger spiders
and steals their stored prey

Weaves webs that
are strong enough
to block birds and
other predators

Spitting spider
Scytodes thoracica,
order Araneae

Golden orb weaver
Nephila sp.,
order Araneae

Money spider
Linyphia triangularis,
order Araneae

Captures prey
by spitting
threads of
poisonous silk

Black widow
Latrodectus mactans, order Araneae

The female black widow
occasionally eats the male
after mating, but they
usually separate in peace

The venom of the female black
widow is 15 times more potent than
that of a rattlesnake, but usually does
not severely harm humans because
only a minuscule amount is injected

Thorn spider
Gasteracantha sp., order Araneae

SPIDER FANGS

Spiders paralyze or kill their prey by
stabbing it with their fang-tipped
chelicerae, which inject venom from
the poison glands. The chelicerae are
also sometimes used to carry prey
items, transport eggs, or dig burrows.

Fang directions *In primitive spiders such as
tarantulas, the chelicerae strike downward
on the victim (above left), but in most species,
they close together like pincers (above right).*

DEADLY TOXINS

While many spiders can deliver a
painful bite, only a handful have venom
that can seriously harm humans. The
most potentially dangerous spiders
include funnel-webs, some tarantulas,
the black widow, and the brown recluse
(*Loxosceles recluse*).

Fatal bite *The Sydney
funnel-web (Atrax
robustus) may be
the deadliest spider.
It rears up to stab
prey or defend itself.*

COURTSHIP RITUALS

When a male spider is ready to mate,
he fills his pedipalps with a capsule
of sperm called a spermatophore and
searches for a female, aided by the
pheromones that mature females emit.
In most species, mating is preceded
by courtship. This may involve the
male performing a particular dance;
drumming the ground with the feet;
plucking a silk thread attached to the
female's web; or repeatedly touching
the female. Insemination is indirect. If
the female is receptive, the male inserts
his spermatophore-bearing pedipalps
into the female's spermatheca,
an internal sac where the
sperm are stored until she
is ready to lay her eggs.

Love at sight *With their
keen vision, jumping
spiders use visual cues
in courtship, and
the male performs
a complex
dance
for
the female.*

FACT FILE

Order Opiliones The harvestmen, or daddy-longlegs, in this order differ from spiders in that they lack venom glands, silk glands, and a waist. Most species have very long, fine legs. Unlike most other arthropods, fertilization is direct, with the male using a penis to deposit sperm in the female.

Species 5,000

Worldwide; in leaf litter & under stones

Bringing in the harvest *The harvestman* Phalangium opilio *looks for small arthropods in the leaf litter. It is also common in crops, where it feeds on pests such as aphids.*

Subclass Acari Classified in seven orders in the subclass Acari, mites and ticks are the most varied and abundant arachnids. They flourish in almost every kind of habitat, from polar caps to deserts, thermal springs to ocean trenches. With some species small enough to live inside a human hair follicle, mites are so tiny that they are rarely noticed. Ticks tend to be larger, but rarely exceed ½ inch (1 cm) in length. Mites and ticks have only six legs when they hatch as larvae and acquire an extra pair as nymphs before becoming adults.

Species 30,000

Worldwide

Dust to dust *Flour mites (Acarus siro) are found living in the dust of grain crops, in animal cages, and in food stores.*

DISEASE SPREADERS

While most members of Acari are free-living inhabitants of soil, leaf litter, and water, some are parasites of other animals or plants. Those mites and ticks that feed on vertebrates often transmit bacteria that cause potentially fatal diseases in humans. Several species of ticks also commonly trigger acute paralysis in humans and domestic animals.

Sick tick *The European castor bean tick (Ixodes ricinus) infests livestock, dogs, and humans, and can spread Lyme disease and other illnesses.*

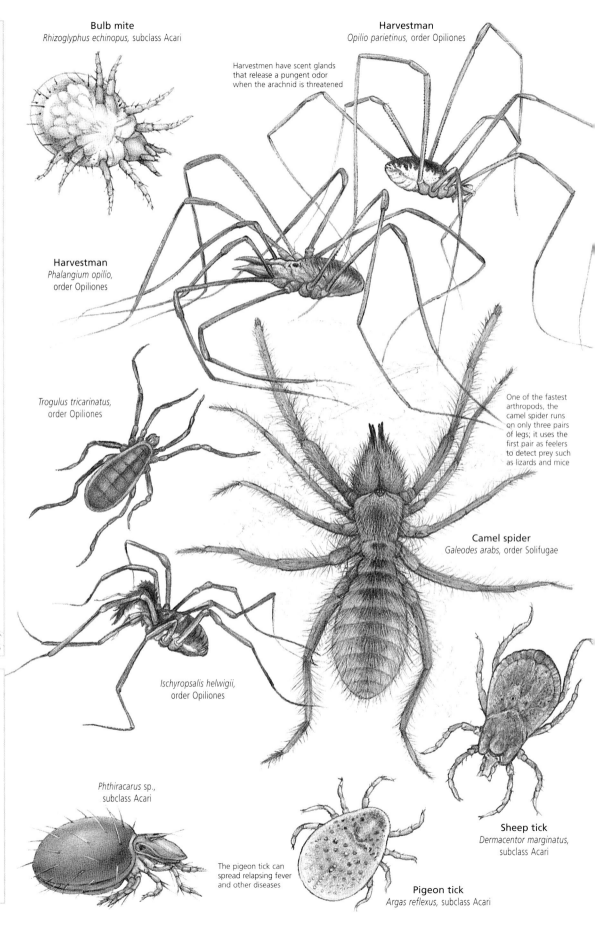

Bulb mite
Rhizoglyphus echinopus, subclass Acari

Harvestman
Opilio parietinus, order Opiliones

Harvestmen have scent glands that release a pungent odor when the arachnid is threatened

Harvestman
Phalangium opilio,
order Opiliones

Trogulus tricarinatus,
order Opiliones

One of the fastest arthropods, the camel spider runs on only three pairs of legs; it uses the first pair as feelers to detect prey such as lizards and mice

Camel spider
Galeodes arabs, order Solifugae

Ischyropsalis helwigii,
order Opiliones

Sheep tick
Dermacentor marginatus,
subclass Acari

Phthiracarus sp.,
subclass Acari

The pigeon tick can spread relapsing fever and other diseases

Pigeon tick
Argas reflexus, subclass Acari

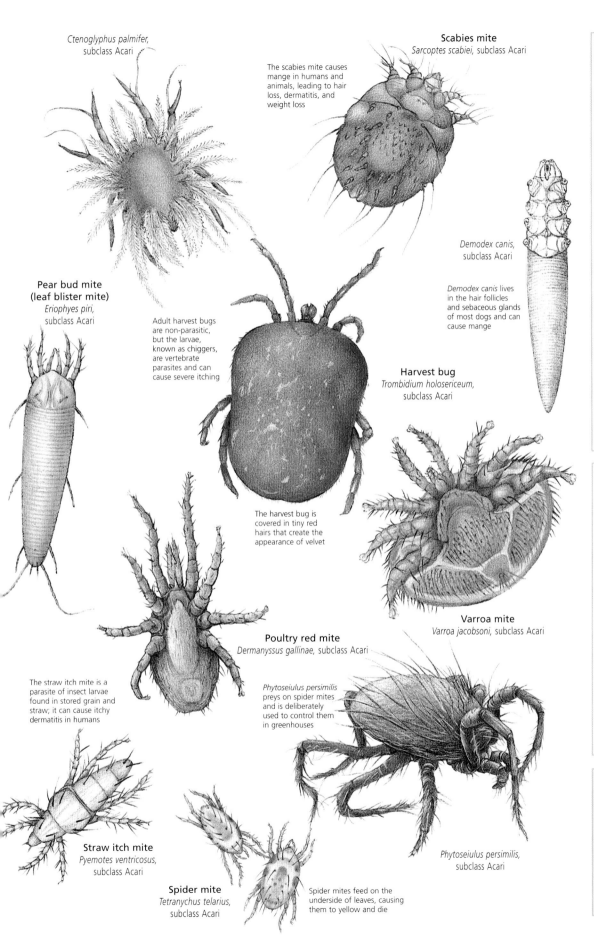

Ctenoglyphus palmifer,
subclass Acari

Scabies mite
Sarcoptes scabiei, subclass Acari

The scabies mite causes mange in humans and animals, leading to hair loss, dermatitis, and weight loss

Demodex canis,
subclass Acari

Demodex canis lives in the hair follicles and sebaceous glands of most dogs and can cause mange

**Pear bud mite
(leaf blister mite)**
Eriophyes piri,
subclass Acari

Adult harvest bugs are non-parasitic, but the larvae, known as chiggers, are vertebrate parasites and can cause severe itching

Harvest bug
Trombidium holosericeum,
subclass Acari

The harvest bug is covered in tiny red hairs that create the appearance of velvet

Poultry red mite
Dermanyssus gallinae, subclass Acari

Phytoseiulus persimilis preys on spider mites and is deliberately used to control them in greenhouses

Varroa mite
Varroa jacobsoni, subclass Acari

The straw itch mite is a parasite of insect larvae found in stored grain and straw; it can cause itchy dermatitis in humans

Straw itch mite
Pyemotes ventricosus,
subclass Acari

Spider mite
Tetranychus telarius,
subclass Acari

Spider mites feed on the underside of leaves, causing them to yellow and die

Phytoseiulus persimilis,
subclass Acari

AQUATIC MITES

Some mites have adapted to a life in water. They are found in every kind of freshwater habitat, from puddles to deep lakes, hot springs to raging rivers. Some have also colonized the ocean, where they live on mudflats, coral reefs, and the seafloor, absent only from open waters. While semiaquatic mites are found in many groups within Acari, more than 40 families of fully aquatic mites are gathered in the subcohort Hydracarina. These mites lay their eggs underwater on stones or plants or in sponges or mussels. The larvae are parasitic and quickly attach themselves to an invertebrate host. As the host is often a flying insect such as a dragonfly, it not only provides the mite larva with food, but also disperses it to a new body of water. As nymphs and adults, water mites are predators and feed on other mites, aquatic insects, and crustaceans.

Bright warning
Water mites such as Brachypoda versicolor often display bright colors, possibly to warn fishes and other predators that they are distasteful.

HONEYBEE THREAT

A honeybee colony can be severely harmed or even killed by the varroa mite (*Varroa jacobsoni*). An adult female mite moves into a honeybee's brood cell to lay her eggs. Both the mite and her hatched offspring then feed on the bee larva as it matures. The mite offspring mate while still in the brood cell. The males then die, but the females emerge attached to the young adult bee. The female mites then find another brood cell where they can deposit their eggs. Parasitized honeybee pupae tend to emerge as weak, deformed adults.

Snug fit *The varroa mite usually inserts itself between the honeybee's body segments, making it difficult to see.*

⚡ CONSERVATION WATCH

Arachnid alert The conservation movement has paid little attention to arachnids. Only 18 species have been assessed by the IUCN, but all of these are on the Red List. Further research is needed, but arachnid diversity is no doubt threatened by habitat loss, pollution, pesticide use, and invasive exotic species.

HORSESHOE CRABS

PHYLUM Arthropoda

SUBPHYLUM Chelicerata

CLASS Merostomata

ORDER Xiphosura

FAMILY Limulidae

SPECIES 4

More closely related to arachnids than to crustaceans, the horseshoe crabs of the class Merostomata have changed little in the past 200 million years. The four living species, found off the east coasts of North America and Asia, are marine. Their body is made up of a cephalothorax and abdomen, each protected by a hard shell. The horseshoe-shaped cephalothorax bears the pincer-like chelicerae, which are used for seizing worms and other prey from the muddy seafloor, and five pairs of legs, used for both walking and handling food. The formidable tail spine, or telson, does not act as a weapon but helps the horseshoe crab to right itself and to plow through mud.

Can grow 2 feet (60 cm) long

Horseshoe crab
Limulus polyphemus

SEA AND SHORE

Horseshoe crabs spend most of their time on the seafloor at depths of about 100 feet (30 m), breathing through book gills on the abdomen. They push through mud, and can also swim on their back and walk.

In spring, horseshoe crabs come ashore to breed. A male will cling onto a female's back as she makes her way over the tidal zone. The female scoops out holes in the sand and lays up to 300 eggs in each, and the male then covers the eggs with sperm to fertilize them. The larvae reach adulthood after about 16 molts over 9 to 12 years.

Time to breed
Breeding horseshoe crabs gather on beaches in spring. The eggs are buried in the sand just below the high-tide mark, where they stay moist but are warmed by the sun.

SEA SPIDERS

PHYLUM Arthropoda

SUBPHYLUM Chelicerata

CLASS Pycnogonida

ORDER Pantopoda

FAMILIES 9

SPECIES 1,000

With their long legs, sea spiders bear a superficial resemblance to spiders, but they evolved separately and have many unique features. A sea spider's body is greatly reduced. The small head region, known as the cephalon, holds a long proboscis with the mouth; four simple eyes on a stalk; and, usually, two chelicerae (to grasp prey) and two pedipalps (used as sensors). It also bears the first pair of walking legs and a pair of appendages called ovigers, used for grooming and egg-carrying. A segmented trunk holds another three pairs of legs, and leads to a tiny abdomen at the rear. Because the abdomen is so small, the digestive and reproductive organs extend into the legs.

Antarctic forms Both the red sea spider (*Pycnogonum decalopoda*) and the smaller spider (*P. nymphon*) live under the sea ice.

BOTTOM-DWELLERS

Sea spiders live in every ocean, from warm, shallow waters to icy depths of 23,000 feet (7,000 m). Most are small, but some deep-sea species have a leg-span of up to 28 inches (70 cm). Although some sea spiders can swim, most are bottom-dwellers and feed on soft-bodied invertebrates such as sponges and corals.

To breed, a female sea spider releases her eggs into the water and the male covers them with sperm. The male then carries the fertilized eggs on his ovigers until they hatch.

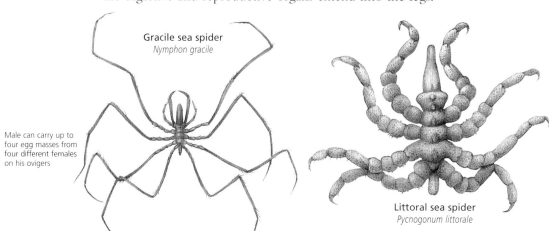

Gracile sea spider
Nymphon gracile

Male can carry up to four egg masses from four different females on his ovigers

Littoral sea spider
Pycnogonum littorale

MYRIAPODS

PHYLUM	Arthropoda
SUBPHYLUM	Myriapoda
CLASSES	4
ORDERS	20
FAMILIES	140
SPECIES	13,500

Centipedes (class Chilopoda), millipedes (class Diplopoda), symphylids (class Symphyla), and pauropods (class Pauropoda) are all myriapods with long, segmented bodies; simple eyes; a pair of jointed antennae; and numerous pairs of legs. Most centipedes are carnivores and hunt through leaf litter for other small invertebrates. They paralyze prey with a pair of venomous fangs on the underside of the head that can deliver a nasty bite even to humans. Millipedes are plant-feeders and do not bite, but many react to danger by curling into a coil and emitting a toxic substance. Resembling tiny centipedes, symphylids and pauropods live in leaf litter and soil and feed on decaying plant matter.

Tropical species Centipedes are most diverse in tropical forests. Their many legs can be short and hooked, or long and slender. The final pair may be antenna-like (as in the *Scutigera* sp. above) or pincer-like.

Coiled defense A forest log millipede (*Narceus americanus*) has curled into the typical millipede defensive posture that leaves only the tough, calcareous plates of its exoskeleton exposed. It may also squirt out a pungent, irritating liquid.

MANY LEGS

Centipedes have flattened, worm-like bodies, with one pair of legs attached to each body segment except the last. They have at least 15 and as many as 191 pairs of legs. The largest centipede, *Scolopendra gigantea* of the American tropics, can grow to 11 inches (28 cm) long. It is strong enough to prey on mice, frogs, and other small vertebrates.

A millipede's body is rounded and made up of doubled segments known as diplosomites, most of which bear double pairs of legs. Millipedes range from ¹⁄₁₂ inch to 11 inches (2 mm to 28 cm) long, and have up to 200 pairs of legs.

Measuring no more than ½ inch (1 cm) in length, symphylids have 12 pairs of legs. Pauropods are even smaller, at less than ¹⁄₁₂ inch (2 mm) long, and bear nine pairs of legs.

Most myriapods are nocturnal, live in moist forests, and tend to be hidden in leaf litter or soil or under rocks or logs. Some species, however, are found in grasslands or deserts. Millipedes usually lay their eggs in a soil nest, while some centipedes curl around their eggs and young to protect them.

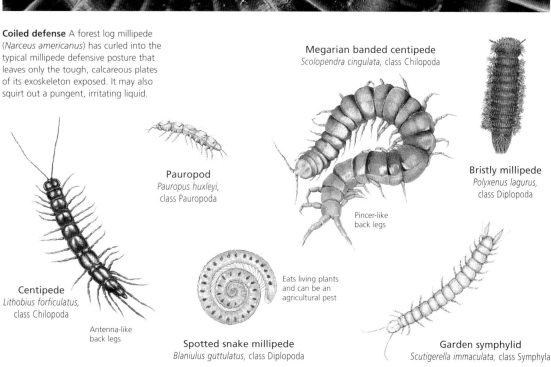

Pauropod
Pauropus huxleyi,
class Pauropoda

Megarian banded centipede
Scolopendra cingulata, class Chilopoda

Pincer-like
back legs

Bristly millipede
Polyxenus lagurus,
class Diplopoda

Centipede
Lithobius forficulatus,
class Chilopoda

Antenna-like
back legs

Eats living plants
and can be an
agricultural pest

Spotted snake millipede
Blaniulus guttulatus, class Diplopoda

Garden symphylid
Scutigerella immaculata, class Symphyla

CRUSTACEANS

PHYLUM	Arthropoda
SUBPHYLUM	Crustacea
CLASSES	11
ORDERS	37
FAMILIES	540
SPECIES	42,000

From water fleas less than ¹⁄₁₀₀ inch (0.25 mm) long, to giant spider crabs with legs spanning 12 feet (3.7 m), crustaceans are an extraordinarily diverse group. Although some species have adopted a terrestrial lifestyle, it is in aquatic environments that crustaceans have flourished, gradually evolving to exploit every marine and freshwater niche. Free-swimming planktonic species, such as krill, form the basis of vast aquatic food webs. Crabs and other bottom-dwellers may burrow into or crawl over the sediment. Barnacles remain cemented in place, filtering food from the water. There are also parasitic crustaceans, some of which exist in their adult form as a collection of cells inside the host.

LAND INVADERS

While crustaceans are abundant in water, only a minority have adapted to life on land. These tend to live in damp places and some return to water to breed. Sometimes known as pill bugs or sow bugs, the wood lice of family Oniscoidea are the most terrestrial crustaceans and even include a few desert species. Some wood lice curl into a tight ball when threatened (below). The limited exploitation by crustaceans of land habitats can be attributed to the lack of a waxy, watertight cuticle and the reliance on gills for breathing.

Attractive claw In many crustaceans, the first pair of limbs has been modified to form claws known as chelipeds. As a male fiddler crab (*Uca* sp.) (above) matures, the right cheliped grows disproportionately, until it accounts for 65 percent of the crab's total weight. The crab waves this huge claw to attract mates and intimidate rival males. It may also use it to make sounds that entice females into its burrow.

CRUSTACEAN ANATOMY

Like other arthropods, crustaceans have a segmented body, jointed legs, and an exoskeleton, and grow by molting. The exoskeleton can be thin and flexible, as in water fleas, or rigid and calcified, as in crabs. The body usually has three regions—head, thorax, and abdomen—but in many of the larger species, the head and thorax form a cephalothorax, which is protected by a shield-like carapace. The abdomen often has a tail-like extension called a telson.

A typical crustacean's head holds two pairs of antennae; a pair of compound eyes, often on stalks; and three pairs of biting mouthparts. The thorax and sometimes the abdomen carry the limbs, each of which usually has two branches. In many species, particular limbs have become specialized for walking, swimming, food collection, or defense. Crabs, for example, have modified their first pair into claws called chelipeds.

While some female crustaceans lay eggs in water, many brood eggs on their body. The eggs of some species hatch into free-swimming nauplius larvae, with two pairs of antennae, a pair of mandibles, and a single simple eye. In most species, the eggs hatch at a more advanced stage or even as miniature adults.

Shrimp design Like most crustaceans, shrimps have two pairs of antennae, the second of which is highly mobile; a pair of compound eyes, each with as many as 30,000 lenses; and specialized limbs. A shrimp's blood is pumped by a heart, and it breathes through gills attached to its legs.

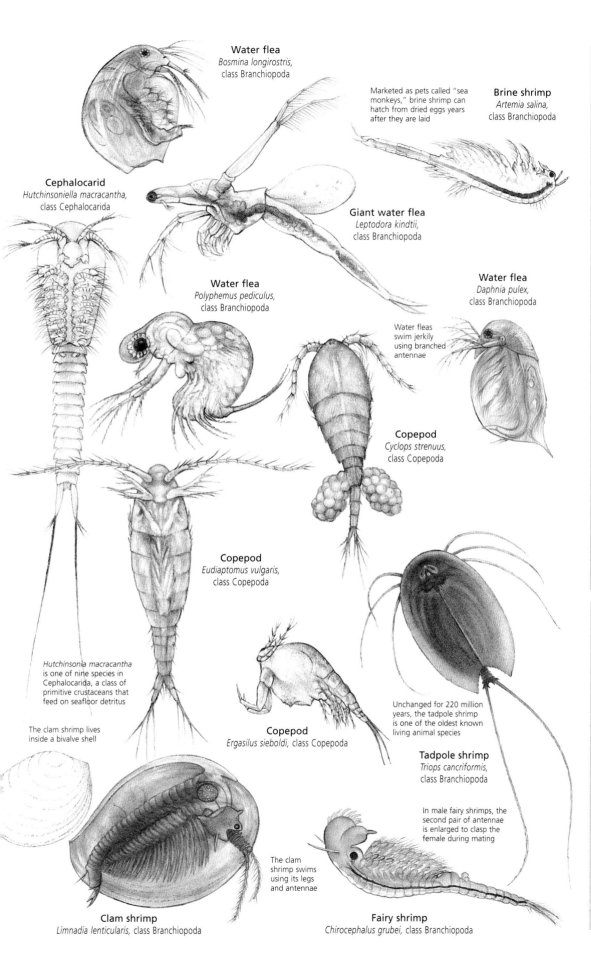

Water flea
Bosmina longirostris,
class Branchiopoda

Marketed as pets called "sea monkeys," brine shrimp can hatch from dried eggs years after they are laid

Brine shrimp
Artemia salina,
class Branchiopoda

Cephalocarid
Hutchinsoniella macrantha,
class Cephalocarida

Giant water flea
Leptodora kindtii,
class Branchiopoda

Water flea
Polyphemus pediculus,
class Branchiopoda

Water flea
Daphnia pulex,
class Branchiopoda

Water fleas swim jerkily using branched antennae

Copepod
Cyclops strenuus,
class Copepoda

Copepod
Eudiaptomus vulgaris,
class Copepoda

Hutchinsonia macrantha is one of nine species in Cephalocarida, a class of primitive crustaceans that feed on seafloor detritus

The clam shrimp lives inside a bivalve shell

Copepod
Ergasilus sieboldi, class Copepoda

Unchanged for 220 million years, the tadpole shrimp is one of the oldest known living animal species

Tadpole shrimp
Triops cancriformis,
class Branchiopoda

In male fairy shrimps, the second pair of antennae is enlarged to clasp the female during mating

The clam shrimp swims using its legs and antennae

Clam shrimp
Limnadia lenticularis, class Branchiopoda

Fairy shrimp
Chirocephalus grubei, class Branchiopoda

FACT FILE

Class Branchiopoda The tadpole shrimps, water fleas, clam shrimps, and fairy or brine shrimps in this class are all small, ranging from 1/100 inch to 4 inches (0.25 mm to 10 cm) in length. They have leaf-like legs, which they use to gather food, swim, and breathe. Found in almost every freshwater body in the world, branchiopods include species that live in temporary pools and survive dry spells as dormant eggs.

Species 800

Worldwide; mainly fresh water

Backstroker
Fairy shrimps such as Branchipus stagnalis swim on their back, using their legs to filter organic particles from the water.

Class Copepoda Found in vast numbers in the oceans, copepods are a crucial link in the marine food web. The body tends to be cylindrical. They lack compound eyes, but have a single simple eye retained from the nauplius larval stage. Some species are parasitic on fish and other aquatic animals.

Species 8,500

Worldwide; mainly marine

Forked tail
Canthocamptus staphylinus displays the branched telson (tail-like projection) typical of copepods.

RECENT DISCOVERY

When *Speleonectes lucayensis* was discovered in a sea cave in the Bahamas in 1981, it prompted the description of a new class of crustacean, Remipedia. Since then, several more species, all found in Caribbean or Australian caves connected to the sea, have been added to the class. These primitive forms have long, worm-like bodies with up to 32 segments, each bearing a pair of legs. They are carnivorous.

Swimming blind *Like other members of Remipedia, Speleonectes lucayensis lacks eyes. It swims on its back using its many legs as oars.*

TOTAL INVASION

The parasite *Sacculina carcini* can only be recognized as a barnacle by its free-swimming nauplius larvae. When a female larva has matured, it invades a host, usually the green crab (*Carcinus maenas*). The larva metamorphoses into a needle-like form that injects cells into the host. The cells form a root-like system, called an interna, throughout the crab's body. The interna eventually develops a reproductive body, an externa, outside the crab. Male larvae attach to the externa, into which they release cells that develop into sperm. Fertilization results in nauplius larvae.

Freshwater fish louse
Argulus foliaceus, class Branchiura

Adult fish lice parasitize freshwater fish, feeding on the skin or in the gills of the host and causing tissue damage

Acorn barnacle
Balanus tintinnabulum,
class Cirripedia

Acorn barnacles use their feathery cirri to sweep plankton from the water, but can retract them behind a trapdoor when the tide is out

Ostracod
Cypris pubera, class Ostracoda

Ostracod
Candona suburbana,
class Ostracoda

Like other members of the small class Mystacocarida, *Derocheilocaris remanei* lives among sand grains in the intertidal zone

Primitive barnacle that parasitizes brittle stars

Conchoderma auritum attaches to the skin of a whale, but does not feed on the host's body, filtering food from the water instead

Barnacle
Ascothorax ophioctenis, class Cirripedia

Barnacle
Conchoderma auritum,
class Cirripedia

Goose barnacles live in large clusters attached by flexible stalks to objects floating on the surface of deep oceans.

Mystarocarid
Derocheilocaris remanei,
class Mystacocarida

Goose barnacle
Lepas anatifera, class Cirripedia

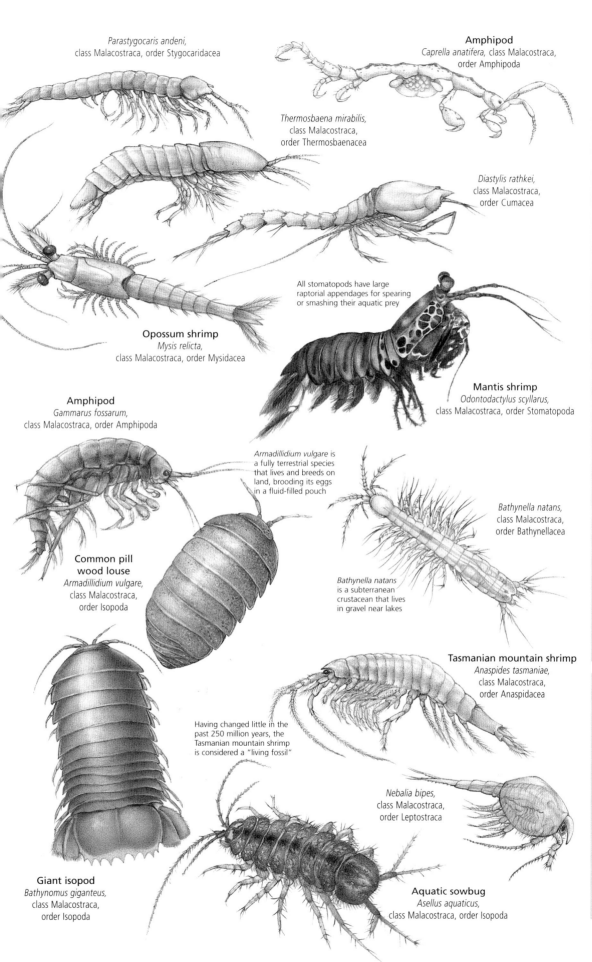

Parastygocaris andeni,
class Malacostraca, order Stygocaridacea

Amphipod
Caprella anatifera, class Malacostraca,
order Amphipoda

Thermosbaena mirabilis,
class Malacostraca,
order Thermosbaenacea

Diastylis rathkei,
class Malacostraca,
order Cumacea

All stomatopods have large
raptorial appendages for spearing
or smashing their aquatic prey

Opossum shrimp
Mysis relicta,
class Malacostraca, order Mysidacea

Mantis shrimp
Odontodactylus scyllarus,
class Malacostraca, order Stomatopoda

Amphipod
Gammarus fossarum,
class Malacostraca, order Amphipoda

Armadillidium vulgare is
a fully terrestrial species
that lives and breeds on
land, brooding its eggs
in a fluid-filled pouch

Bathynella natans,
class Malacostraca,
order Bathynellacea

**Common pill
wood louse**
Armadillidium vulgare,
class Malacostraca,
order Isopoda

Bathynella natans
is a subterranean
crustacean that lives
in gravel near lakes

Tasmanian mountain shrimp
Anaspides tasmaniae,
class Malacostraca,
order Anaspidacea

Having changed little in the
past 250 million years, the
Tasmanian mountain shrimp
is considered a "living fossil"

Nebalia bipes,
class Malacostraca,
order Leptostraca

Giant isopod
Bathynomus giganteus,
class Malacostraca,
order Isopoda

Aquatic sowbug
Asellus aquaticus,
class Malacostraca, order Isopoda

FACT FILE

Class Malacostraca By far the largest
class of crustaceans, Malacostraca
contains 13 orders. Almost all species
have six head segments, eight thoracic
segments, and six abdominal segments.
Except for the first head segment, each
segment usually bears two appendages.

Species 25,000

Worldwide; mainly aquatic

*Familiar crustaceans The
class Malacostraca includes
Daum's reef lobster (Enoplometopus
daumi), which joins other lobsters,
crabs, and shrimps in the order Decapoda.*

Order Amphipoda These small,
widespread members of the class
Malacostraca are found in marine,
freshwater, and moist terrestrial
habitats. An amphipod's
body is usually flattened
laterally, often creating
a shrimp-like appearance.

Species 6,000

Worldwide; mainly aquatic

*Varied salinities The amphipod Corophium
volutator lives in U-shaped burrows in
saltwater, brackish, and freshwater habitats.*

Order Isopoda Like amphipods,
isopods belong to Malacostraca. Their
bodies are flattened dorsoventrally
(from the back to the belly). They
include the truly terrestrial wood lice,
but most species crawl along the
bottom of aquatic habitats.

Species 4,000

Worldwide; mainly marine

*Aquatic isopod Like amphipods,
isopods such as Astacilla pusilla
lack a carapace. Most are
aquatic and can crawl and
swim. They tend to be omnivorous scavengers.*

PREDACIOUS EYES

The Stomatopoda is a highly specialized
order in the class Malacostraca. Known
as mantis shrimp, its members actively
prey on fish, crabs, and mollusks. Their
success as predators depends not only
on their raptorial appendages, but also
on their complex compound eyes.

*Stomatopod vision Each compound eye is
divided by a band that provides color vision
and also sees polarized light (contrast). The
rest of the eye provides monochromatic
vision and depth perception (perspective).*

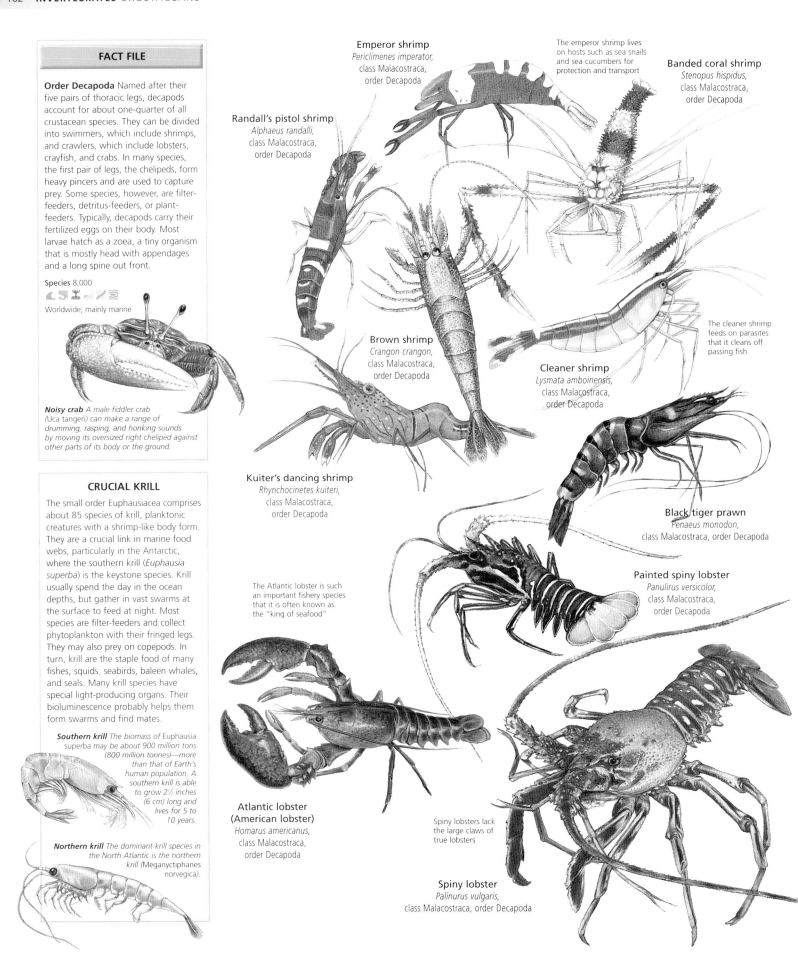

Emperor shrimp
Periclimenes imperator,
class Malacostraca,
order Decapoda

The emperor shrimp lives on hosts such as sea snails and sea cucumbers for protection and transport

Banded coral shrimp
Stenopus hispidus,
class Malacostraca,
order Decapoda

Randall's pistol shrimp
Alphaeus randalli,
class Malacostraca,
order Decapoda

Brown shrimp
Crangon crangon,
class Malacostraca,
order Decapoda

The cleaner shrimp feeds on parasites that it cleans off passing fish

Cleaner shrimp
Lysmata amboinensis,
class Malacostraca,
order Decapoda

Kuiter's dancing shrimp
Rhynchocinetes kuiteri,
class Malacostraca,
order Decapoda

Black tiger prawn
Penaeus monodon,
class Malacostraca, order Decapoda

The Atlantic lobster is such an important fishery species that it is often known as the "king of seafood"

Painted spiny lobster
Panulirus versicolor,
class Malacostraca,
order Decapoda

**Atlantic lobster
(American lobster)**
Homarus americanus,
class Malacostraca,
order Decapoda

Spiny lobsters lack the large claws of true lobsters

Spiny lobster
Palinurus vulgaris,
class Malacostraca, order Decapoda

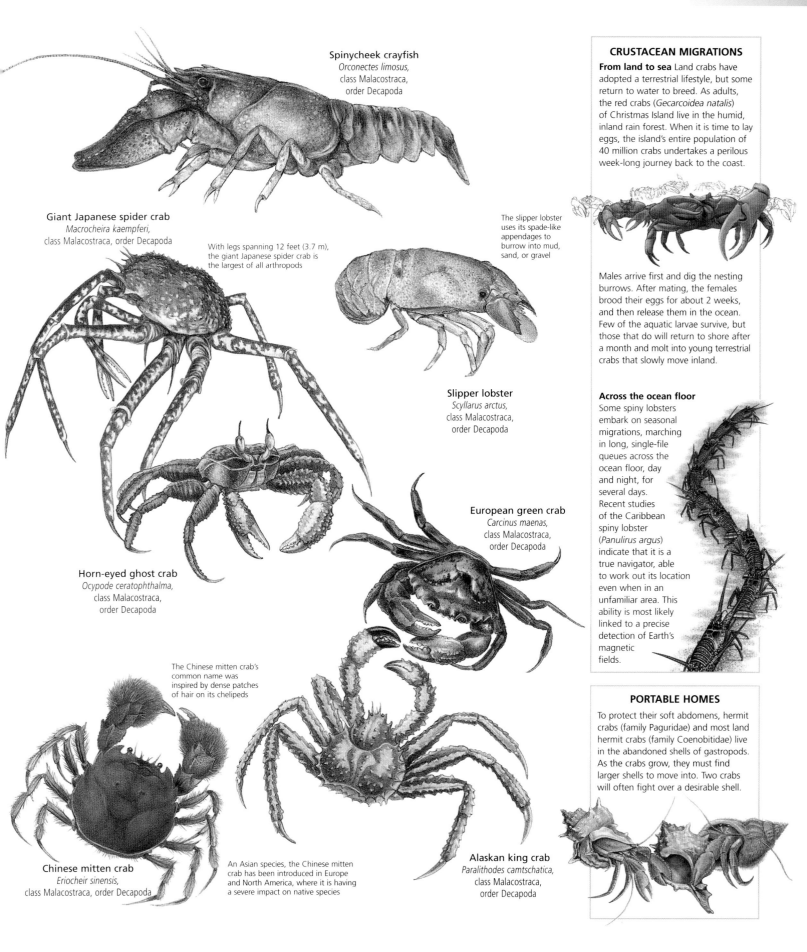

Spinycheek crayfish
Orconectes limosus,
class Malacostraca,
order Decapoda

Giant Japanese spider crab
Macrocheira kaempferi,
class Malacostraca, order Decapoda

With legs spanning 12 feet (3.7 m), the giant Japanese spider crab is the largest of all arthropods

The slipper lobster uses its spade-like appendages to burrow into mud, sand, or gravel

Slipper lobster
Scyllarus arctus,
class Malacostraca,
order Decapoda

Horn-eyed ghost crab
Ocypode ceratophthalma,
class Malacostraca,
order Decapoda

European green crab
Carcinus maenas,
class Malacostraca,
order Decapoda

The Chinese mitten crab's common name was inspired by dense patches of hair on its chelipeds

Chinese mitten crab
Eriocheir sinensis,
class Malacostraca, order Decapoda

An Asian species, the Chinese mitten crab has been introduced in Europe and North America, where it is having a severe impact on native species

Alaskan king crab
Paralithodes camtschatica,
class Malacostraca,
order Decapoda

CRUSTACEAN MIGRATIONS
From land to sea Land crabs have adopted a terrestrial lifestyle, but some return to water to breed. As adults, the red crabs (*Gecarcoidea natalis*) of Christmas Island live in the humid, inland rain forest. When it is time to lay eggs, the island's entire population of 40 million crabs undertakes a perilous week-long journey back to the coast.

Males arrive first and dig the nesting burrows. After mating, the females brood their eggs for about 2 weeks, and then release them in the ocean. Few of the aquatic larvae survive, but those that do will return to shore after a month and molt into young terrestrial crabs that slowly move inland.

Across the ocean floor Some spiny lobsters embark on seasonal migrations, marching in long, single-file queues across the ocean floor, day and night, for several days. Recent studies of the Caribbean spiny lobster (*Panulirus argus*) indicate that it is a true navigator, able to work out its location even when in an unfamiliar area. This ability is most likely linked to a precise detection of Earth's magnetic fields.

PORTABLE HOMES
To protect their soft abdomens, hermit crabs (family Paguridae) and most land hermit crabs (family Coenobitidae) live in the abandoned shells of gastropods. As the crabs grow, they must find larger shells to move into. Two crabs will often fight over a desirable shell.

INSECTS

PHYLUM	Arthropoda
SUBPHYLUM	Hexapoda
CLASS	Insecta
ORDERS	29
FAMILIES	949
SPECIES	>1 million

By most measures, insects are the most successful animals ever to have lived on Earth. With about a million described species, they account for more than half of all known animal species, and many more insects are still to be discovered, with estimates of the total number of insect species ranging from 2 million to 30 million. In terms of sheer numbers, insects overwhelm all other animal forms: some scientists believe that ants and termites alone make up 20 percent of the world's animal biomass. Some form of insect has managed to colonize the hottest deserts and the coldest polar zones, as well as virtually every land and freshwater habitat in between, and a handful live in the sea.

Extreme habitats Brine flies (family Ephydridae) are found along the shores of California's salty Mono Lake, where their larvae feed on algae. Other insects have been found living in pools of crude oil, in hot springs, and in the ice of Antarctica.

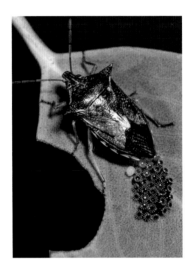

Parental guard Most insects display little parental care, depositing large numbers of eggs and then leaving them to hatch by themselves. Some shield bugs, however, will guard their eggs and then stay with the nymphs until at least their first molt.

Pollinators Pollen sticks to a honeybee as it drinks nectar from a flower. When the bee visits the next flower, some pollen will be dislodged. Most flowering plants rely on insects for pollination and have evolved flowers with different shapes, colors, and odors to attract particular species and force them to collect pollen as they feed.

CONSERVATION WATCH

Of the 1 million known species of insects, only 768 have been assessed by the IUCN. Of these, 97% are listed on the Red List, as follows:

70	Extinct, or extinct in wild
46	Critically endangered
118	Endangered
389	Vulnerable
3	Conservation dependent
76	Near threatened
42	Data deficient

SUCCESS STORY

Insects owe their incredible success to various aspects of their biology. Their tough, flexible exoskeleton provides protection without overly restricting movement. It is covered in a waxy coating that minimizes moisture loss, enabling insects to survive in dry conditions.

As the first creatures and the only invertebrates ever to develop powered flight, insects were able to find both food and mates, evade their predators, and colonize new areas with great efficiency. In most species, the wings can be folded over the body when at rest, so that the insect can exploit confined spaces inside bark, dung, leaf litter, or soil, for example.

Insects breathe through spiracles, small openings in the sides of their body that can be closed to prevent moisture loss. Rather than being transported around the body in the blood, oxygen is distributed directly into the body tissues by a series of tiny pipes known as tracheae. This method of gas diffusion works well only over short distances, which may be the main reason insects have remained small. Most insects are no more than an inch or two (a few centimeters) long. Their small size allowed insects to take advantage of a wide range of microhabitats, a major factor in their great diversity.

Sensory organs are scattered over an insect's body. The head usually has two compound eyes as well as three simple eyes, or ocelli. The two antennae can detect scent, taste, touch, and sound. Hearing organs

Spontaneous young Scarab beetles (family Scarabaeidae) use their sturdy front legs to roll dung into a large ball that may be taken underground as food, or used by the female as a nest for her eggs. Possibly because the young seemed to suddenly erupt from the dung, scarab beetles were revered by the ancient Egyptians.

INSECT FLIGHT
While some insects are wingless, the vast majority are winged as adults. Beetles and grasshoppers fly with a slow wing beat of 4–20 beats per second (bps) and limited maneuverability. Bees and true flies, with wing beats of about 190 bps, can hover and dart. Some midges have wing beats of 1,000 bps. The fastest sustained fliers are dragonflies, which can maintain speeds of 31 miles per hour (50 km/h).

Folding wings
The hindwings of a mantis fold up like fans when not in use. This protects the wings and allows the mantis to squeeze into tight spaces.

Stabilizers
True flies appear to have only one pair of wings. In fact, the second pair has been reduced to knob-like structures called halteres that provide stability in flight.

Purpose-built mouthparts The highly varied feeding habits of insects are reflected by the shape of their mouthparts. A moth (above) has a long, coiled tube, or proboscis, that can be unfurled to collect nectar. Mosquitoes have beaks that can pierce the skin of prey and suck up the body fluids, while aphids have piercing mouthparts for gathering plant juices. The mandibles, or jaws, of carnivorous insects such as ground beetles are sharp for cutting, while those of herbivores such as grasshoppers are adapted for grinding.

Insect anatomy While insects display a staggering diversity of shapes and forms, they follow the same basic body plan. Like other arthropods, insects have segmented bodies made up of a head, thorax, and abdomen; segmented limbs; and a tough exoskeleton. They are distinguished by having three pairs of legs and, usually, two sets of wings, a single pair of antennae, and a pair of compound eyes.

three ocelli (simple eyes) detect light variations

one pair of compound eyes, each made up of 100–30,000 lenses

two pairs of wings supported by thickened veins

head carries eyes, a pair of antennae, and mouthparts

abdomen contains digestive and reproductive organs

antennae help insect smell, taste, feel, and hear

thorax carries wings and legs

three pairs of segmented legs

Plumed wings
In thrips and plume moths, the wings look like tiny feathers and are made up of fine hairs supported by a midrib.

Hooked wings
Connected by tiny hooks, a wasp's forewings and hindwings move up and down in unison.

can also be on the body or legs. Other sensors detect changes in air pressure, humidity, and temperature.

The life-cycles of many insects allow for very rapid reproduction, enabling populations to respond quickly to favorable conditions and recover from catastrophes. Most insects use internal fertilization, but the female is able to store the male's sperm and use it over time. Some insects, such as aphids, can reproduce without fertilization to rapidly increase their numbers, but also use sexual reproduction to ensure genetic diversity. Insect eggs are protected by a shell-like membrane called the chorion that prevents them from drying out, another factor in the successful

colonization of dry habitats. While some insects resemble small versions of their parents when they hatch, most do not and must go through some form of metamorphosis. The juveniles and adults often occupy different ecological niches and eat different foods, which helps to avoid competition between them.

Because some species can cause human discomfort, spread disease, and destroy food stores and crops, insects are often regarded as pests. This ignores the fact that the vast majority of insects cause little harm and play a crucial role in the world's environments. About three-quarters of all flowering plants rely on insects for pollination, and many animals depend on insects for food.

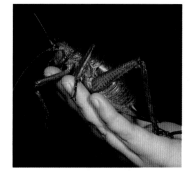

Giant insect About the size of a small rat, New Zealand's giant weta (*Deinacrida heteracantha*) can weigh up to 2½ ounces (70 g), making it among the heaviest of all insect species. The smallest insect species is probably the parasitic wasp *Dicopomorpha echmepterygis,* at ⅟₂₀₀ inch (0.14 mm) long.

Separate wings
A dragonfly's forewings and hindwings can beat in unison or independently. As in early flying insects, the wings do not fold back over the body.

Protective wings
In lady beetles and other beetles, the forewings have been modified to form protective cases known as elytra. The hindwings are used for flying.

DRAGONFLIES AND DAMSELFLIES

PHYLUM	Arthropoda
SUBPHYLUM	Hexapoda
CLASS	Insecta
ORDER	Odonata
FAMILIES	30
SPECIES	5,500

The first members of the order Odonata emerged more than 300 million years ago—100 million years before dinosaurs appeared—and included the largest insect that has ever lived, a dragonfly with a wingspan of 28 inches (70 cm). Today's dragonflies and damselflies are much smaller, with wingspans from ¾ inch to 7½ inches (18 mm to 19 cm). Often seen flying near water, these voracious aerial predators are most abundant in the tropics, but can be found worldwide except for the polar zones. Damselflies have a fluttery flight and usually rest with the wings near the body, while dragonflies are strong, agile flyers and always rest with the wings held out from the body.

Sharp sight A dragonfly's large compound eyes may be made up of 30,000 lenses, providing superb vision and a wide field of view. Strong, biting mouthparts indicate the insect's carnivorous diet.

Odonate aerobatics With two pairs of large, veined wings that can beat together or independently, a dragonfly has great maneuverability and can hover and fly backward. Some species reach speeds of 20 miles per hour (30 km/h).

Mating position To mate, a male odonate grasps a female's head with claspers at the tip of his abdomen (below). The female will then bend her abdomen under the male to collect sperm from his sperm pouch.

AQUATIC BEGINNINGS

A dragonfly or damselfly spends most of its life as a wingless aquatic nymph. The nymph breathes via gills and feeds on other insect larvae, tadpoles, and small fishes. It has a specialized lower mouthpart known as a mask that usually rests under its head but can shoot out to snatch prey in its pincers. Over a period of a few weeks to 8 years, depending on the species, the nymph may molt up to 17 times. For the final molt, it climbs out of the water and sheds its nymphal skin to reveal an adult with prominent eyes, sharp mouthparts, two pairs of transparent wings, a sloping thorax, and a long, slender abdomen.

A newly emerged adult dragonfly or damselfly flies away from water and starts to feed, snatching flying insects on the wing. To find mates, dragonflies will gather along a body of water, and males may engage in aerial contests. After mating, the male usually guards the female as she lays her eggs in the water. Most adults live for only several weeks.

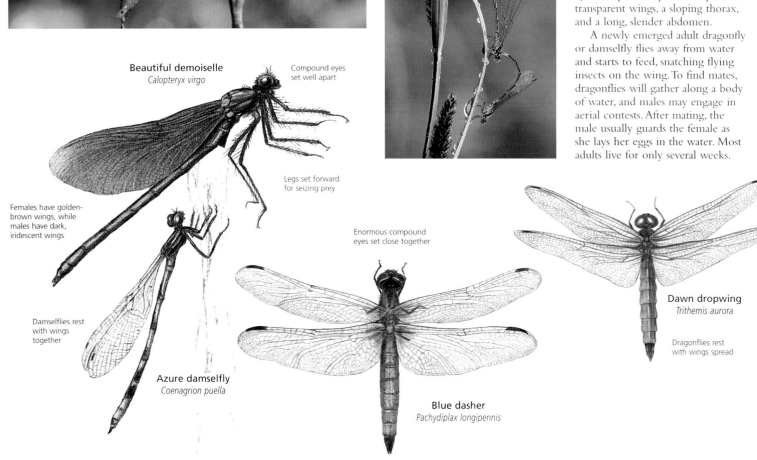

Beautiful demoiselle
Calopteryx virgo

Compound eyes set well apart

Legs set forward for seizing prey

Females have golden-brown wings, while males have dark, iridescent wings

Damselflies rest with wings together

Azure damselfly
Coenagrion puella

Enormous compound eyes set close together

Blue dasher
Pachydiplax longipennis

Dawn dropwing
Trithemis aurora

Dragonflies rest with wings spread

MANTIDS

PHYLUM	Arthropoda
SUBPHYLUM	Hexapoda
CLASS	Insecta
ORDER	Mantodea
FAMILIES	8
SPECIES	2,000

Waiting to ambush prey, a mantid will sit perfectly still, holding its large forelegs folded up before it—a posture that inspired the common name of praying mantis for some species. With lightning-quick reflexes, the raptorial forelegs will shoot out to snatch insect prey. Most mantids are medium-sized, measuring about 2 inches (5 cm) long, but some tropical species reach lengths of 10 inches (25 cm). These giant mantids may add small birds and reptiles to their primarily insectivorous diet. While the majority of mantids live in the tropics or subtropics, some are found in the warm temperate areas of southern Europe, North America, South Africa, and Australia.

Precision hunting With its forward-facing eyes supplying binocular vision, a praying mantis has used its spiky, hooked forelimbs to impale a passing wasp. The mantis's strong mandibles quickly devour the meal.

Foaming protection A female lays her eggs in a gummy fluid that she whips into a foam. When the foam hardens, it forms a case, or ootheca, that protects the eggs.

Cannibalistic mating In some mantid species, the transfer of sperm is more rapid if the female bites off the male's head. The male's self-sacrifice makes ecological sense as he is providing nourishment that will help his offspring survive.

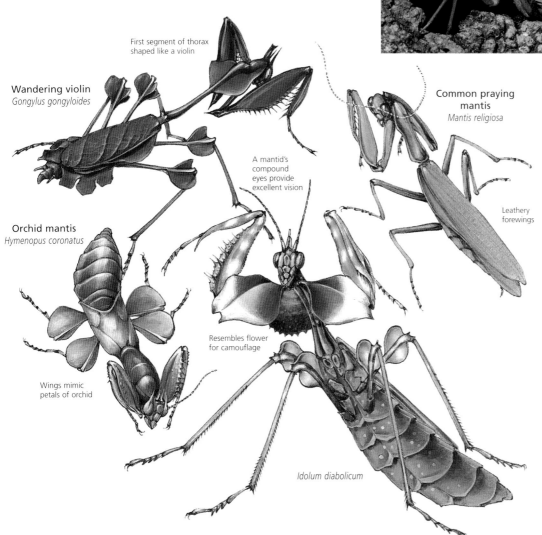

First segment of thorax shaped like a violin

Wandering violin
Gongylus gongyloides

A mantid's compound eyes provide excellent vision

Common praying mantis
Mantis religiosa

Leathery forewings

Orchid mantis
Hymenopus coronatus

Resembles flower for camouflage

Wings mimic petals of orchid

Idolum diabolicum

SILENT HUNTERS

Mantids are masters at hiding from both predators and prey. They are the only insects that can turn their head without moving other parts of the body, allowing them to silently observe potential victims. Most species also have cryptic coloration that helps them blend in with the grass, leaves, twigs, or flowers of their environment. An alarmed mantid will adopt a threat posture, raising and rustling its wings and rearing up to show off its vivid warning coloration. Mantids that are targeted by bats at night possess a single "ear" on their thorax that can detect a bat's ultrasonic signals.

In some species, and especially in captivity, the female mantid will devour the male during copulation. Females mate only once, but from that single mating, they can produce up to 20 ootheca, or egg cases, each containing from 30 to 300 eggs. The young emerge from the ootheca as highly active nymphs, looking like miniature, wingless versions of their parents. Ready to hunt, they may even eat each other. The survivors disperse. After a series of molts, the nymphs mature and develop wings and adult coloration.

COCKROACHES

PHYLUM	Arthropoda
SUBPHYLUM	Hexapoda
CLASS	Insecta
ORDER	Blattodea
FAMILIES	6
SPECIES	4,000

As scavenging insects willing to feed on almost any plant or animal product, including stored food, trash, paper, and clothing, some cockroaches thrive in human environments and are widely regarded as repulsive pests. In fact, less than 1 percent of all cockroach species are pests—the remainder perform an important ecological role by recycling leaf litter and animal excrement in forests and other habitats. While most cockroaches are found in warm tropical zones, about 25 species have spread worldwide, accidentally transported on ships. Cockroaches are among the most primitive of all living insects, with an anatomy that has changed little in more than 300 million years.

Safe eggs Female cockroaches deposit their eggs in an ootheca, or egg case. The nymphs emerge soft and white, but soon harden and turn brown. They eat the ootheca as their first food.

Maternal care Weighing up to 1¾ ounces (50 g), the giant burrowing cockroach (*Macropanesthia rhinoceros*) of Australia is the heaviest of all cockroaches. As many as 30 young are born alive and are fed by the mother in her burrow for up to 9 months.

SENSITIVE INSECTS

A range of sensors helps cockroaches to detect minute changes in their surroundings. Their long antennae can find minuscule amounts of food and moisture. Sensors on the legs and abdomen can pick up tiny air movements, prompting the insect to flee danger in a split second. With its oval, flattened shape, a cockroach can scuttle into tiny crevices. Not all cockroaches have wings, but in those that do the forewings are usually hardened and opaque, and the hindwings are translucent.

Mating between cockroaches may be initiated when a female emits a pheromone to attract males. Females usually lay 14–32 eggs in a hardened case known as an ootheca. The ootheca may then be left to hatch alone; carried at the base of the mother's abdomen; or incubated inside the mother's body so that she produces live young. Nymphs molt up to 13 times before emerging as adults. A cockroach usually lives for 2–4 years.

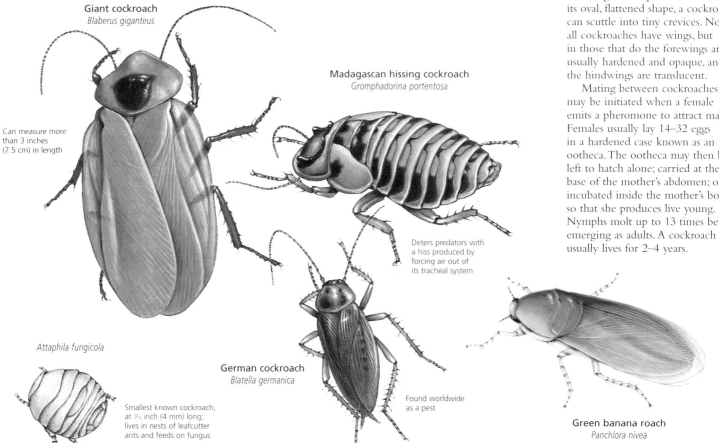

Giant cockroach *Blaberus giganteus*

Can measure more than 3 inches (7.5 cm) in length

Madagascan hissing cockroach *Gromphadorina portentosa*

Deters predators with a hiss produced by forcing air out of its tracheal system

Attaphila fungicola

Smallest known cockroach, at ⅙ inch (4 mm) long; lives in nests of leafcutter ants and feeds on fungus

German cockroach *Blatella germanica*

Found worldwide as a pest

Green banana roach *Panchlora nivea*

TERMITES

PHYLUM	Arthropoda
SUBPHYLUM	Hexapoda
CLASS	Insecta
ORDER	Isoptera
FAMILIES	7
SPECIES	2,750

Termites may be the world's most monogamous animals. A king and queen mate for life, producing thousands or millions of offspring that operate together as a highly structured colony. These small insects are often referred to as white ants, but although their social system and anatomy resemble those of ants, they evolved independently and are most closely related to cockroaches. Found throughout much of the world, termites are most abundant in tropical rain forests, where there can be as many as 25,000 individuals per square mile (10,000 per sq km). By feeding on dead wood, they recycle nutrients in their natural habitats but can severely damage buildings in urban environments.

Wood-eaters With saw-toothed jaws that can shear through wood, termites cause costly damage to buildings. Infestations often involve introduced species that never found a niche in the natural environment.

Egg-laying machine A termite queen, shown here attended by other colony members, can grow 4½ inches (11 cm) long and produces 36,000 eggs a day from her enormous abdomen.

CASTE SOCIETY

A mature termite colony has three castes: reproductives, workers, and soldiers. The main reproductives are the king and queen, who produce all the colony's other members and can live for 25 years. There may also be secondary reproductives ready to take over if the king or queen dies.

Workers and soldiers can be male or female. They are wingless, usually lack eyes and mature reproductive organs, and may live for 5 years. The pale and soft-bodied workers feed all other colony members and maintain the nest. Soldiers defend the colony, usually using powerful mandibles. Termite nymphs can develop into any caste, depending on the needs of the colony.

At a particular time each year, a swarm of winged males and females will emerge from a termite nest and disperse. They then shed their wings and form pairs, becoming the kings and queens of new colonies.

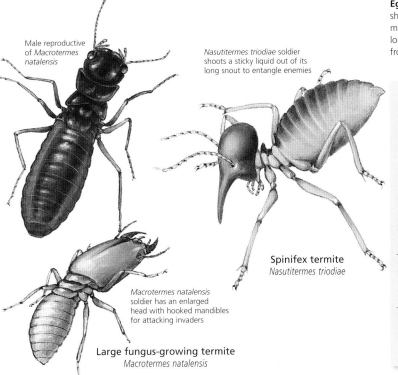

Male reproductive of *Macrotermes natalensis*

Nasutitermes triodiae soldier shoots a sticky liquid out of its long snout to entangle enemies

Spinifex termite
Nasutitermes triodiae

Macrotermes natalensis soldier has an enlarged head with hooked mandibles for attacking invaders

Large fungus-growing termite
Macrotermes natalensis

INSIDE A NEST

Termite nests create a stable, humid microclimate sealed from the elements. While some termites nest inside wood, most construct subterranean nests that may rise partly above ground as mounds. Worker termites use saliva or feces to glue together particles of soil or wood, building a hard outer wall to protect the softer internal network of chambers.

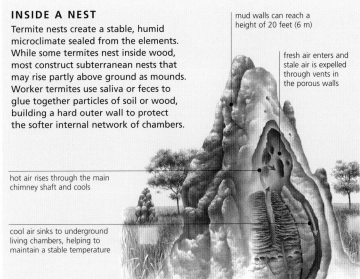

mud walls can reach a height of 20 feet (6 m)

fresh air enters and stale air is expelled through vents in the porous walls

hot air rises through the main chimney shaft and cools

cool air sinks to underground living chambers, helping to maintain a stable temperature

CRICKETS AND GRASSHOPPERS

PHYLUM	Arthropoda
SUBPHYLUM	Hexapoda
CLASS	Insecta
ORDER	Orthoptera
FAMILIES	28
SPECIES	> 20,000

Renowned for their songs and leaping ability, the members of the order Orthoptera include grasshoppers, locusts, crickets, katydids (or bush-crickets), and their kin. They are distinguished by elongated hindlegs that allow them to jump. Most species are winged, with slender, toughened forewings protecting the membranous, fan-shaped hindwings. While most orthopterans are ground-dwellers in grasslands and forests, some are arboreal, burrowing, or semiaquatic, and species can be found in deserts, caves, bogs and marshes, and seashores. Grasshoppers, groundhoppers, and a few katydids are herbivores, while most other orthopterans are omnivorous.

Threat display Colored to match the vegetation of its Amazon rain-forest home, a spiky-headed katydid (*Copiphora* sp.) is covered in sharp spines and will rear up in a threat display to deter predators.

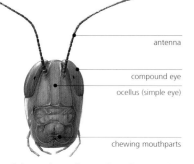

antenna
compound eye
ocellus (simple eye)
chewing mouthparts

Information collector An orthopteran's head features two fine, sensitive antennae, two large compound eyes, and mouthparts adapted for chewing vegetation.

Warning colors While many crickets and grasshoppers have cryptic coloration that helps them blend in with the background, others, such as this rain-forest grasshopper, are vividly colored as a warning to potential predators that they are unpalatable.

SINGING INSECTS

Most male orthopterans can make sounds by rubbing two parts of the body together, a technique known as stridulation. Crickets and long-horned grasshoppers move a scraper on one forewing along a row of teeth on the other forewing, while short-horned grasshoppers rub a ridged surface on the hindleg against a forewing. The sounds can be heard by tympanal organs located on the legs or abdomen.

There are three kinds of song: a calling song, to attract females from a distance; a courtship song, to entice a nearby female to mate; and a battle call, to deter rival males. The songs, some of which are too high-pitched to be heard by human ears, are unique to each species. Cricket songs tend to be affected by the weather, with the rate of chirps increasing with the temperature.

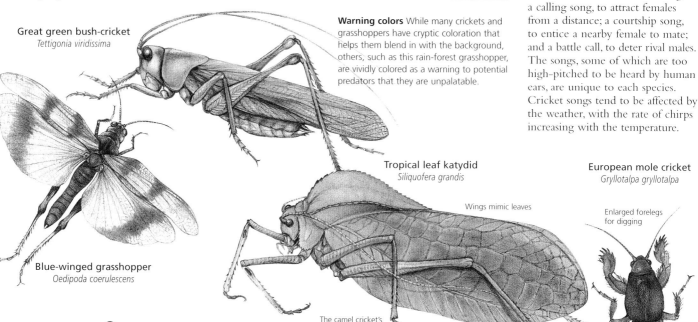

Great green bush-cricket
Tettigonia viridissima

Blue-winged grasshopper
Oedipoda coerulescens

Tropical leaf katydid
Siliquofera grandis

Wings mimic leaves

European mole cricket
Gryllotalpa gryllotalpa

Enlarged forelegs for digging

In response to overcrowding, many millions of locusts may form swarms that devastate crops as they migrate

The camel cricket's humped back inspired its common name

Migratory locust
Locusta migratoria

Camel cricket
Tachycines asynamorus

BUGS

PHYLUM	Arthropoda
SUBPHYLUM	Hexapoda
CLASS	Insecta
ORDER	Hemiptera
FAMILIES	134
SPECIES	> 80,000

Ranging from minute wingless aphids to giant frog-catching water bugs, the members of the order Hemiptera are extremely diverse. The name *Hemiptera* means "half wing," a reference to the fact that many, but not all, species have forewings that are leathery at the base and membranous at the tip. The one feature that all bugs have in common is their piercing and sucking mouthparts. With these, they pierce the surface of a plant or animal and inject saliva to start digesting the food, which they then suck into their mouth. Most bug species feed on plant sap, and some of these are significant agricultural pests. Other bugs suck the blood of vertebrates, or prey on other insects.

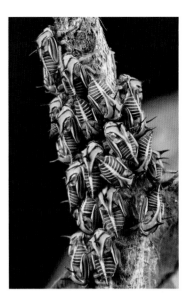

Malodorous defense The bright colors of many shield bugs serve to warn predators of the noxious odor produced when the insect is disturbed. Shield bugs are usually sap suckers, but a few are predatory.

Mimicry In thornbugs, or treehoppers, the first plate of the thorax forms a thorn-shaped spine. This camouflages the insect as it sucks sap, and, even if an enemy does spot the insect, the spine deters an attack.

Predator bugs While many bugs use their sucking mouthparts to feed on plant juices, others employ them to snare live prey. This assassin bug lies in wait, ready to ambush an unwitting insect victim.

DIFFERENT BUGS

Distributed throughout the world, bugs can be found in almost all terrestrial habitats. Some species have specialized for an aquatic life—these include sea skaters (*Halobates* sp.), the only insects on the open ocean. Bugs range from ⅟₂₅ inch to 4½ inches (1 mm to 11 cm) in length. They undergo incomplete metamorphosis, with nymphs that usually resemble small, wingless versions of the adults. In cicadas and some other species, however, the burrowing nymphs and the adults look quite different.

The order Hemiptera is divided into three suborders. In the true bugs (suborder Heteroptera), the forewings are toughened at the base and sit flat, concealing membranous hindwings. True bugs can flex their head and mouthparts forward, and many have stink glands. Cicadas and hoppers (Auchenorrhyncha) hold their uniform forewings over the abdomen like a tent. The head and mouthparts point down and back. Aphids, scale insects, mealy bugs, whiteflies, and their kin all belong to the suborder Sternorrhyncha. Most have soft bodies kept moist by a covering of wax or froth. Wings are often absent or reduced in adults.

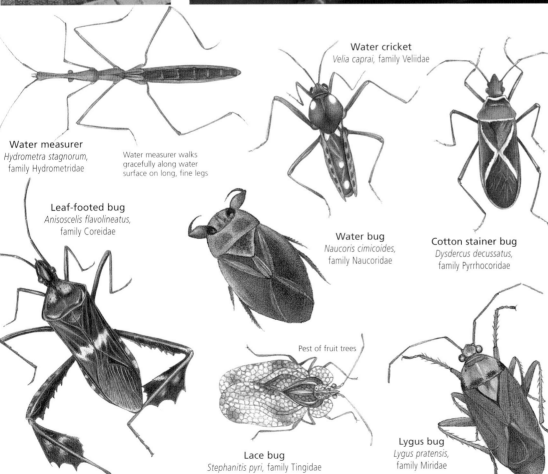

Water measurer
Hydrometra stagnorum,
family Hydrometridae

Water measurer walks gracefully along water surface on long, fine legs

Water cricket
Velia caprai, family Veliidae

Leaf-footed bug
Anisoscelis flavolineatus,
family Coreidae

Water bug
Naucoris cimicoides,
family Naucoridae

Cotton stainer bug
Dysdercus decussatus,
family Pyrrhocoridae

Pest of fruit trees

Lace bug
Stephanitis pyri, family Tingidae

Lygus bug
Lygus pratensis,
family Miridae

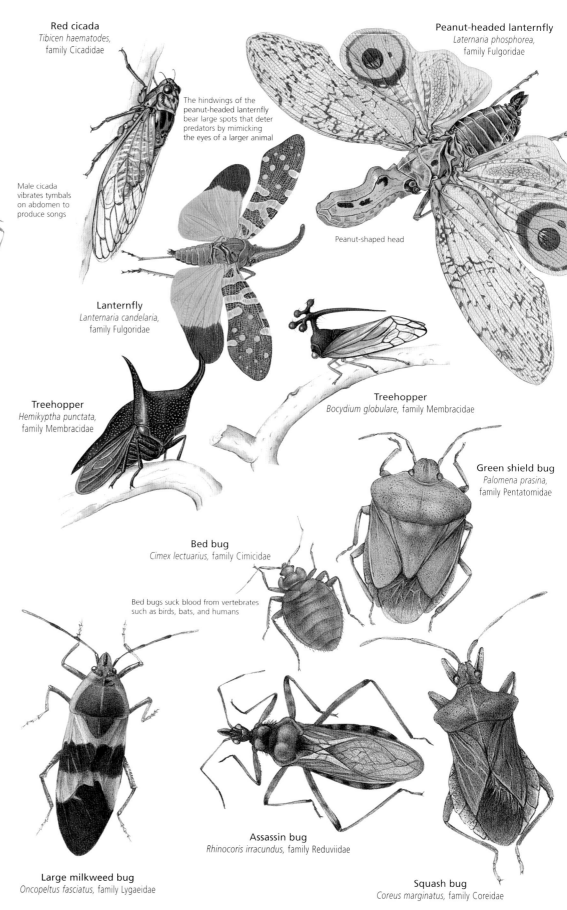

Red cicada *Tibicen haematodes,* family Cicadidae

Male cicada vibrates tymbals on abdomen to produce songs

Peanut-headed lanternfly *Laternaria phosphorea,* family Fulgoridae

The hindwings of the peanut-headed lanternfly bear large spots that deter predators by mimicking the eyes of a larger animal

Peanut-shaped head

Lanternfly *Lanternaria candelaria,* family Fulgoridae

Treehopper *Bocydium globulare,* family Membracidae

Treehopper *Hemikyptha punctata,* family Membracidae

Green shield bug *Palomena prasina,* family Pentatomidae

Bed bug *Cimex lectuarius,* family Cimicidae

Bed bugs suck blood from vertebrates such as birds, bats, and humans

Large milkweed bug *Oncopeltus fasciatus,* family Lygaeidae

Assassin bug *Rhinocoris irracundus,* family Reduviidae

Squash bug *Coreus marginatus,* family Coreidae

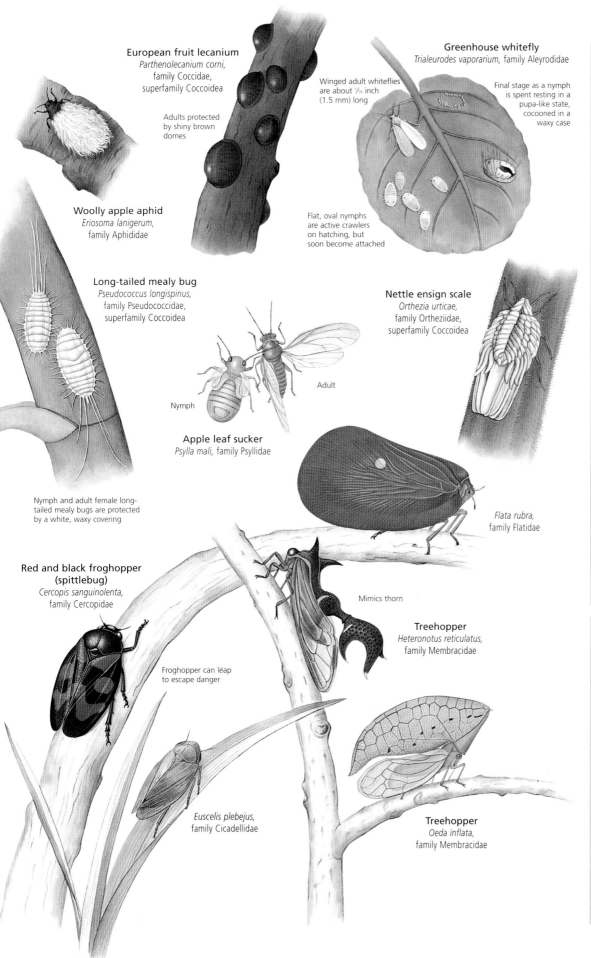

European fruit lecanium
Parthenolecanium corni,
family Coccidae,
superfamily Coccoidea

Adults protected
by shiny brown
domes

Woolly apple aphid
Eriosoma lanigerum,
family Aphididae

Greenhouse whitefly
Trialeurodes vaporarium, family Aleyrodidae

Winged adult whiteflies
are about ¹/₁₆ inch
(1.5 mm) long

Final stage as a nymph
is spent resting in a
pupa-like state,
cocooned in a
waxy case

Flat, oval nymphs
are active crawlers
on hatching, but
soon become attached

Long-tailed mealy bug
Pseudococcus longispinus,
family Pseudococcidae,
superfamily Coccoidea

Nettle ensign scale
Orthezia urticae,
family Ortheziidae,
superfamily Coccoidea

Nymph

Adult

Apple leaf sucker
Psylla mali, family Psyllidae

Nymph and adult female long-
tailed mealy bugs are protected
by a white, waxy covering

Flata rubra,
family Flatidae

**Red and black froghopper
(spittlebug)**
Cercopis sanguinolenta,
family Cercopidae

Mimics thorn

Treehopper
Heteronotus reticulatus,
family Membracidae

Froghopper can leap
to escape danger

Euscelis plebejus,
family Cicadellidae

Treehopper
Oeda inflata,
family Membracidae

FACT FILE

Family Aphididae Aphids are tiny,
soft-bodied plant-suckers that cause
great damage to crops. They are able
to rapidly increase their numbers by
producing wingless or winged females
from unfertilized eggs. In autumn, the
winged females produce males and
females that mate. The fertilized eggs
lay dormant through winter and hatch
in spring as females to begin
the cycle again.

Species 2,250

Worldwide; on plants

Cabbage lover
Native to Europe,
the cabbage aphid
(Bravicoryne brassicae)
has spread to many
parts of the world. It
feeds on both wild and
cultivated plants, causing
particular damage to cabbage crops.

Superfamily Coccoidea Spending
most of their life protected by a waxy
secretion, the scale insects collected in
this superfamily barely resemble insects
at all. Adult females have sack-like,
wingless bodies and often lack
legs and eyes. Adult males
usually have wings and a
more defined head, thorax,
and abdomen, but, lacking
mouthparts, they cannot
feed and are short-lived.

Species 7,300

Worldwide; on plants

Well protected
The oyster-shell scale
(Lepidosaphes ulmi) usually
overwinters as eggs.

APHIDS AS FOOD

Aphids provide food for many other
insects. They are prey for many lady
beetles (family Coccinellidae), hover
flies (family Syrphidae), and lacewings
(order Neuroptera). They also have a
happier relationship with some species
of ants, which protect them from
predators and the elements. In return,
the ants stroke, or "milk,"
the aphids to feed on
honeydew, the sweet
waste product
of the aphids'
plant-sap diet.

Aphid predator
In its lifespan of
1–2 months, a lady
beetle can consume
more than 2,000 aphids.

WATER INSECTS

Only about 3 percent, or 30,000, insect species are truly aquatic for at least part of their life-cycle. Water insects have had to adapt to the low oxygen content of water, as well as to the difficulty of moving about in still water or staying put in flowing water. Some insects, such as water striders, live only on the surface. Many, such as backswimmers, breathe air but carry it with them when they swim underwater. Others, such as dragonfly nymphs, spend all their time submerged, using gills to absorb oxygen from the water. The vast majority of aquatic insects live in fresh water, and only 300 or so species live in saltwater habitats, possibly because crustaceans evolved in the sea first and offer too much competition.

Spinning swimmers Whirligig beetles (family Gyrinidae) swim in small circles on the surface, using their flattened hindlegs like oars. They carry bubbles of air when they dive. Their eyes are split into two parts so they can see both above and below the water.

Bubble breather Predaceous diving beetles (family Dytiscidae) spend virtually their entire lives in water. The adults come to the surface to collect air, which they store in a bubble under their elytra (forewings). They swim using their hindlegs, which are fringed in thick hairs.

Aquatic locomotion Aquatic insects have evolved various strategies for moving around. Water scorpions (family Nepidae) can swim but often crawl along the bottom of a pond and spend much of their time hanging from pond weeds, waiting to ambush prey. They breathe air through a tube that sticks out above the surface. Water boatmen (family Corixidae) have long, hairy hindlegs that can "row" powerfully through the water. Water striders (family Gerridae) have fine hairs on their feet that allow them to make small jumps along the surface.

Snorkelers Mosquito larvae hang from the surface and filter plant matter from the water. While most aquatic larvae breathe through gills, mosquito larvae breathe air through a snorkel-like tube. This allows them to survive in pools of stagnant, oxygen-poor water.

Aquatic predators While many water insects are omnivores or plant-feeders, some, such as the predaceous diving beetles, are highly carnivorous. Even as larvae, diving beetles will tackle tadpoles, small fishes, and other prey larger than themselves. The adults use their powerful mandibles on substantial prey such as salamanders.

water scorpion hangs from pond weeds as it attacks a tadpole

water strider uses surface tension to "walk" on water

water boatman swims by using its legs as oars

BEETLES

PHYLUM	Arthropoda
SUBPHYLUM	Hexapoda
CLASS	Insecta
ORDER	Coleoptera
FAMILIES	166
SPECIES	> 370,000

When asked what his study of the natural world had revealed about its Creator, the scientist J. B. S. Haldane replied, "an inordinate fondness for beetles." Of all known animal species, about one in four is a beetle. Members of the order Coleoptera have colonized almost all of Earth's habitats, from Arctic tundra and exposed mountaintops to deserts, grasslands, woodlands, and lakes. They reach their greatest diversity, however, in the lush rain forests of the tropics. Most beetles are distinguished by their hardened, leathery forewings, known as elytra, which protect the membranous, flying hindwings and allow the insect to live in tight spaces under bark or in leaf litter.

Pollinating beetle Although considered pests by many gardeners, spotted cucumber beetles (*Diabrotica undecimpunctata*) and many other beetles that eat pollen and foliage play an important role in helping to pollinate the plants on which they feed.

Competing males The huge, branched mandibles of male stag beetles resemble a stag's antlers and perform a similar function, being used in competitions with rival males to win the right to mate. In some species, the mandibles are as long as the beetle.

DIVERSE FORMS

From lady beetles to diving beetles, scarab beetles to fireflies, the order Coleoptera encompasses enormous diversity. The feather-winged beetle (*Nanosella fungi*) is just 1/100 inch (0.25 mm) long, while the South American longhorn beetle (*Titanus giganteus*) can exceed 6½ inches (16 cm) in length. Adult beetles can be oval and flattened, long and slender, or squat and domed. While a few beetles are strong fliers, most are clumsy in flight, and some lack wings and cannot fly at all.

The mouthparts of beetles are all adapted for biting, but they have been put to many purposes. Plant-eating beetles may eat roots, stems, leaves, flowers, fruit, seeds, or wood. Carnivorous beetles usually attack invertebrate prey. A key ecological role is filled by scavenging beetles, which recycle dead animals and plants, excrement, and other waste.

Most beetles live on the ground, but some have specialized to live in trees, in water, and underground—a few even make their home in the nests of ants and termites.

Beetles develop by complete metamorphosis, with larvae looking markedly different from the parents and going through a non-feeding, pupal stage before becoming adults.

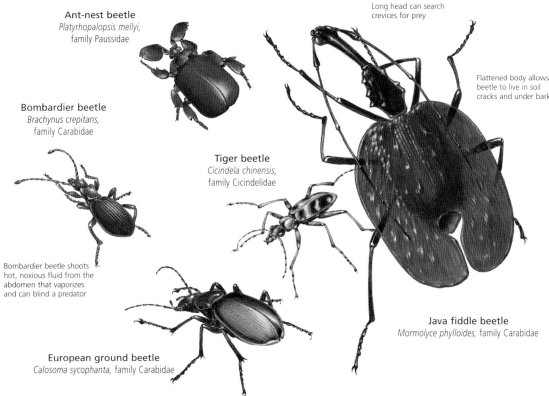

Ant-nest beetle
Platyrhopalopsis mellyi,
family Paussidae

Bombardier beetle
Brachynus crepitans,
family Carabidae

Bombardier beetle shoots hot, noxious fluid from the abdomen that vaporizes and can blind a predator

Tiger beetle
Cicindela chinensis,
family Cicindelidae

Long head can search crevices for prey

Flattened body allows beetle to live in soil cracks and under bark

Java fiddle beetle
Mormolyce phylloides, family Carabidae

European ground beetle
Calosoma sycophanta, family Carabidae

European splendor beetle
Anthaxia hungarica, family Buprestidae

Vivid color warns predators of lady beetle's foul taste

Seven-spotted lady beetle
Coccinella septempunctata, family Coccinellidae

Larva of *Coccinella septempunctata*

Golden rove beetle
Emus hirtus, family Staphylinidae

Golden rove beetle is covered in fine hairs

Flesh-eating beetle
Phosphuga atrata, family Silphidae

Common carpet beetle
Anthrenus scrophulariae, family Dermestidae

Feeds on carpet, wool, and other animal products

Water scavenger beetle
Sphaeridium scarabaeoides, family Hydrophilidae

Glow worm
Lampyris noctiluca, family Lampyridae

Winged male glow worms are attracted by the strong light emitted by wingless females.

Larva of *Lampyris noctiluca*

European burying beetle
Necrophorus vespillo, family Silphidae

Buries corpses of small vertebrates as food for its young

Fuscous soldier beetle
Cantharis fusca, family Cantharidae

Beneficial insect that feeds on aphids and caterpillars

Bee beetle
Trichodes apiarius, family Cleridae

Parasitizes bee hives

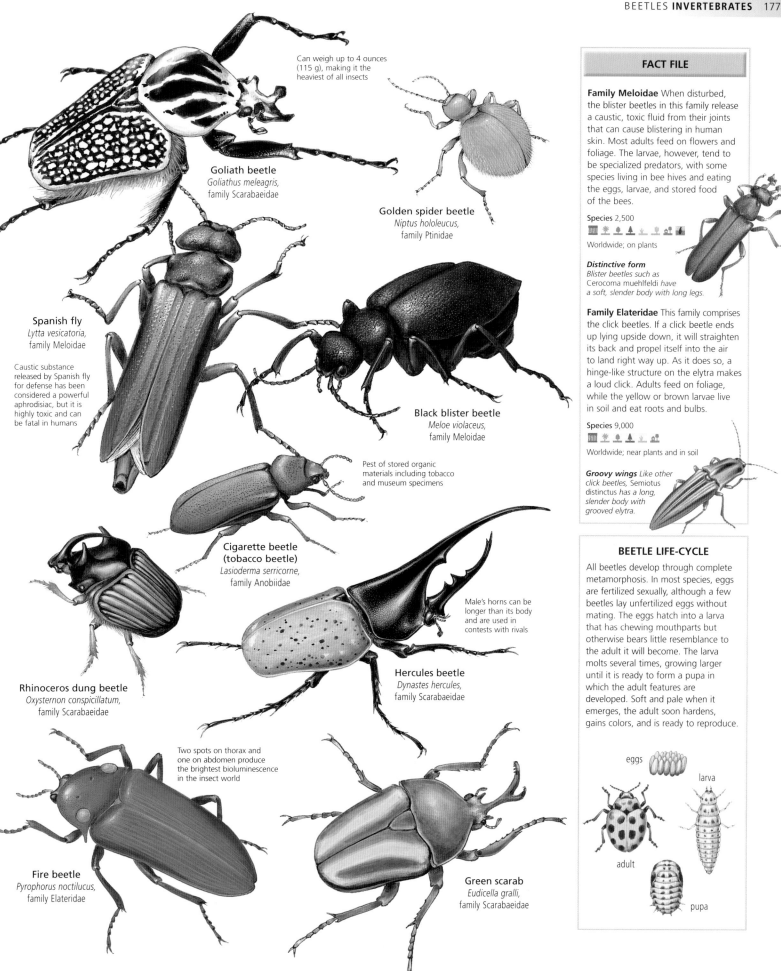

Can weigh up to 4 ounces (115 g), making it the heaviest of all insects

Goliath beetle
Goliathus meleagris,
family Scarabaeidae

Golden spider beetle
Niptus hololeucus,
family Ptinidae

Spanish fly
Lytta vesicatoria,
family Meloidae

Caustic substance released by Spanish fly for defense has been considered a powerful aphrodisiac, but it is highly toxic and can be fatal in humans

Black blister beetle
Meloe violaceus,
family Meloidae

Pest of stored organic materials including tobacco and museum specimens

Cigarette beetle (tobacco beetle)
Lasioderma serricorne,
family Anobiidae

Male's horns can be longer than its body and are used in contests with rivals

Hercules beetle
Dynastes hercules,
family Scarabaeidae

Rhinoceros dung beetle
Oxysternon conspicillatum,
family Scarabaeidae

Two spots on thorax and one on abdomen produce the brightest bioluminescence in the insect world

Fire beetle
Pyrophorus noctilucus,
family Elateridae

Green scarab
Eudicella gralli,
family Scarabaeidae

FACT FILE

Family Meloidae When disturbed, the blister beetles in this family release a caustic, toxic fluid from their joints that can cause blistering in human skin. Most adults feed on flowers and foliage. The larvae, however, tend to be specialized predators, with some species living in bee hives and eating the eggs, larvae, and stored food of the bees.

Species 2,500

Worldwide; on plants

Distinctive form
Blister beetles such as Cerocoma muehlfeldi *have a soft, slender body with long legs.*

Family Elateridae This family comprises the click beetles. If a click beetle ends up lying upside down, it will straighten its back and propel itself into the air to land right way up. As it does so, a hinge-like structure on the elytra makes a loud click. Adults feed on foliage, while the yellow or brown larvae live in soil and eat roots and bulbs.

Species 9,000

Worldwide; near plants and in soil

Groovy wings *Like other click beetles,* Semiotus distinctus *has a long, slender body with grooved elytra.*

BEETLE LIFE-CYCLE

All beetles develop through complete metamorphosis. In most species, eggs are fertilized sexually, although a few beetles lay unfertilized eggs without mating. The eggs hatch into a larva that has chewing mouthparts but otherwise bears little resemblance to the adult it will become. The larva molts several times, growing larger until it is ready to form a pupa in which the adult features are developed. Soft and pale when it emerges, the adult soon hardens, gains colors, and is ready to reproduce.

eggs

larva

adult

pupa

FACT FILE

Family Lucanidae This family contains the stag beetles. Much larger than the females, male stag beetles are further distinguished by their huge mandibles. Rival males will use their mandibles in mating contests. Larvae feed on dead or rotting wood and may take several years to mature. Some adults eat leaves, but most feed on nectar.

Species 1,300

Worldwide; in trees

South American stag Common in Chile and Argentina, Darwin's stag beetle (Chiasognathus grantii) often reaches 3½ inches (9 cm) in length.

Family Curculionidae Sometimes called snout beetles, weevils constitute Curculionidae, the largest of all families in the animal kingdom. A prominent snout carries biting mouthparts and is used for feeding on soft plants and boring holes in plants, seeds, fruit, or soil for its eggs. Usually longest on females, the snout can be much longer than the body in some species. Some weevil species are serious agricultural pests.

Species 50,000

Worldwide; near plants

Shimmering weevil The neotropical weevil Entimus splendidus has iridescent scales. The snout is less pronounced than in many other weevil species.

Family Cerambycidae Known as longhorn or longicorn beetles, the members of this family have long, narrow bodies, which reach a length of 6½ inches (16 cm) in the largest species. Their impressive antennae, however, can be many times as long as the body. The antennae are used for finding food such as pollen, nectar, sap, or leaves. Larvae feed on living and dead trees.

Species 30,000

Worldwide; near flowers and sap

Longhorn in danger The South American sawyer beetle (Macrodontia cervicornis) is threatened by the loss of its tropical forest habitat.

Larva of *Leptinotarsa decemlineata*

Serious pest of potato crops

Colorado potato beetle
Leptinotarsa decemlineata, family Chrysomelidae

Female acorn weevil bores into acorns and nuts to lay eggs

Acorn weevil
Curculio nucum, family Curculionidae

Stag beetle
Cyclommatus imperator, family Lucanidae

Bess beetle
Proculus goryi, family Passalidae

Bess beetle larvae and adults produce squeaking sound by rubbing body parts together

Male's hindlegs much larger than female's

Frog-legged leaf beetle
Sagra buqueti, family Chrysomelidae

Harlequin beetle
Acrocinus longimanus, family Cerambycidae

Male harlequin beetle uses his extremely long legs to attract mates

Large elm bark beetle
Scolytus scolytus, family Scolitidae

Beetle's galleries produce distinctive pattern on bark of elm trees

Large elm bark beetle spreads the fungus that causes Dutch elm disease

Great capricorn beetle
Cerambyx cerdo, family Cerambycidae

Declining in Europe as its oak-tree habitat disappears

Turnip flea beetle
Phyllotreta nemorum, family Chrysomelidae

King weevil
Gymnopholus weiskei, family Curculionidae

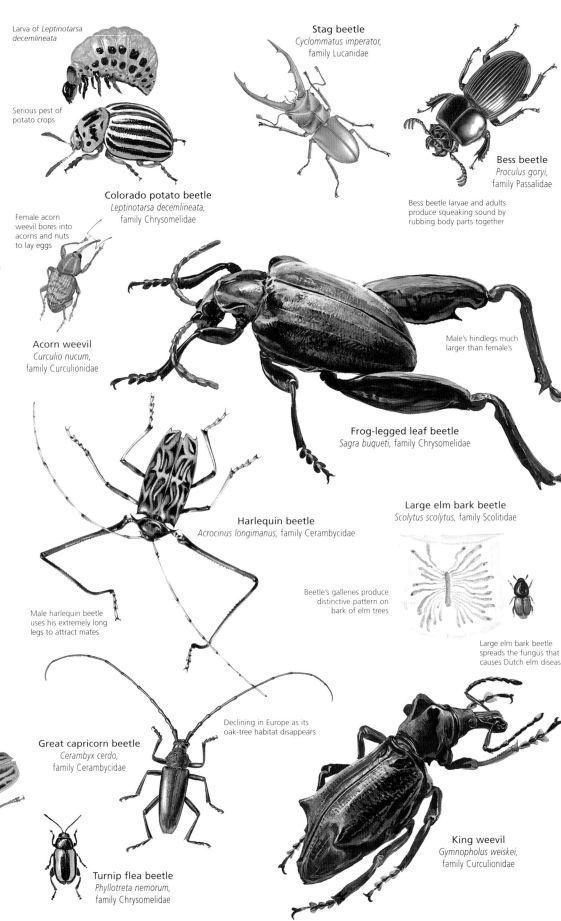

FLIES

Houseflies and mosquitoes are the most ubiquitous members of the order Diptera, which also includes gnats, midges, blowflies, fruit flies, crane flies, horseflies, hover flies, and other true flies. While most insects fly with four wings, dipterans are generally distinguished by their single pair of functional wings. The hindwings are reduced to halteres, tiny clubbed stalks that vibrate up and down in time with the forewings, helping the fly to balance during flight. Some species have lost their wings altogether and are flightless. Although often associated with moist environments and decaying matter, flies live almost everywhere in the world except Antarctica.

PHYLUM	Arthropoda
SUBPHYLUM	Hexapoda
CLASS	Insecta
ORDER	Diptera
FAMILIES	130
SPECIES	120,000

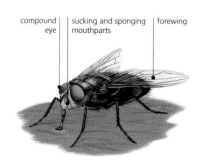

compound eye | sucking and sponging mouthparts | forewing

Eyes and wings Mostly active by day, flies rely on their large compound eyes, each with up to 4,000 lenses. The first segment of the thorax is enlarged to hold the huge muscles that propel the forewings.

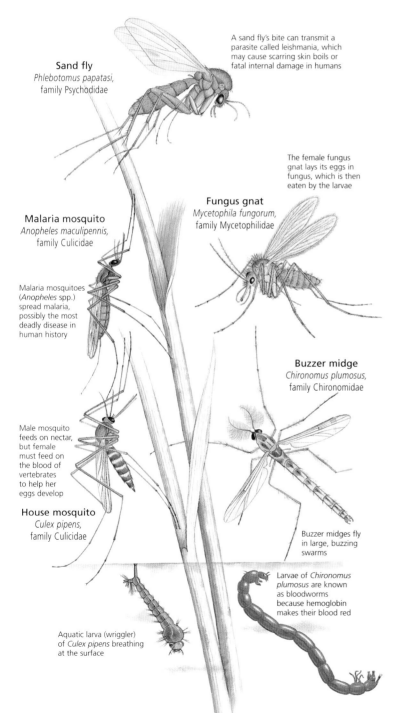

A sand fly's bite can transmit a parasite called leishmania, which may cause scarring skin boils or fatal internal damage in humans

Sand fly
Phlebotomus papatasi,
family Psychodidae

The female fungus gnat lays its eggs in fungus, which is then eaten by the larvae

Fungus gnat
Mycetophila fungorum,
family Mycetophilidae

Malaria mosquito
Anopheles maculipennis,
family Culicidae

Malaria mosquitoes (*Anopheles* spp.) spread malaria, possibly the most deadly disease in human history

Male mosquito feeds on nectar, but female must feed on the blood of vertebrates to help her eggs develop

Buzzer midge
Chironomus plumosus,
family Chironomidae

House mosquito
Culex pipens,
family Culicidae

Buzzer midges fly in large, buzzing swarms

Larvae of *Chironomus plumosus* are known as bloodworms because hemoglobin makes their blood red

Aquatic larva (wriggler) of *Culex pipens* breathing at the surface

Daddy long legs Crane flies make up Tipulidae, the largest family of flies. Adults have mosquito-like bodies with very long legs. They often feed on nectar in humid forests. Larvae live in moist soil or water.

STICKY SUCKERS

Flies are small insects, ranging from midges ⅟₂₅ inch (1 mm) in length, to robber flies about 3 inches (7 cm) long. Their feet have sticky pads with tiny claws, allowing the insects to walk on smooth surfaces, even upside down along a ceiling.

With mouthparts designed for sucking, flies can consume only liquid food. Houseflies have fleshy pads on their mouth that can sponge up a meal. Mosquitoes have piercing mouthparts for feeding on nectar and blood. Robber flies use their mouthparts to stab insect prey.

Flies begin life as eggs, from which larvae hatch. Often known as maggots, the larvae usually have pale, soft bodies and lack true legs. After several molts, they pupate into the adult form.

Their feeding habits, abundance, and wide distribution have made flies responsible for the spread of deadly diseases such as malaria and sleeping sickness. They also play key ecological roles—as pollinators, as decomposers of organic matter, and as links in the food chain.

FACT FILE

Family Syrphidae The hover flies of this family will hover in one spot, then dart forward or sideways before hovering again. With their black and yellow abdomen and habit of feeding on nectar, they resemble bees or wasps, but do not bite or sting. The larvae of many hover-fly species are welcome in gardens because they eat aphids.

Species 6,000

Worldwide; on flowers

Pollinating pest
The narcissus fly (Merodon equestris) is considered a pest because its larvae eat plant bulbs, but, like other hover flies, the adults are important pollinators.

Family Tabanidae The stout flies in this family are known as horseflies or deerflies. While the males feed on nectar, honeydew, and sap, the females are bloodsuckers because they need protein to develop their eggs. Females use their blade-like mouthparts to slice through the skin of mammals so they can suck up the blood.

Species 4,000

Worldwide; near mammals

Common names
Like other species in its genus, Chrysops caecutiens is usually known as a deerfly. Species in the genus Tabanus tend to be called horseflies.

FLIGHTLESS FLIES

In several families of flies, some species have lost their wings and do not fly. The family Tipulidae (crane flies) includes the flightless snow fly (Chionea sp.), which remains active throughout the winter in its snow-covered habitat. Able to tolerate temperatures of 20°F (–6°C), it avoids the many predators that appear in warmer months. Since flight requires warmer muscles than possible in this environment, the snow fly has discarded its wings. The halteres, however, have been retained.

Wingless parasite The bee louse (Braula caeca) from the family Chamaemyiidae is a wingless fly that lays its eggs in beehives so that the larvae can feed on the honey.

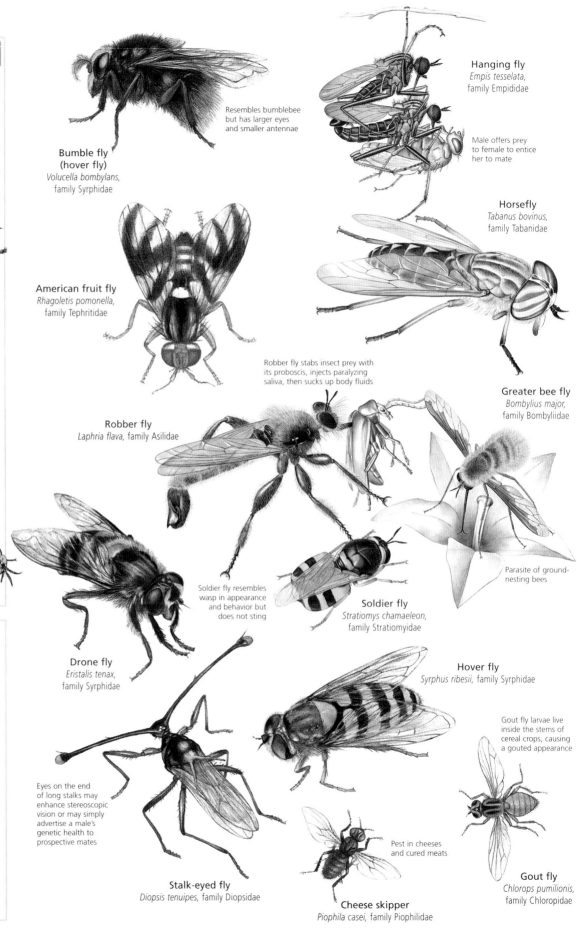

Resembles bumblebee but has larger eyes and smaller antennae

Bumble fly (hover fly)
Volucella bombylans, family Syrphidae

Hanging fly
Empis tesselata, family Empididae

Male offers prey to female to entice her to mate

American fruit fly
Rhagoletis pomonella, family Tephritidae

Horsefly
Tabanus bovinus, family Tabanidae

Robber fly stabs insect prey with its proboscis, injects paralyzing saliva, then sucks up body fluids

Greater bee fly
Bombylius major, family Bombyliidae

Robber fly
Laphria flava, family Asilidae

Parasite of ground-nesting bees

Soldier fly resembles wasp in appearance and behavior but does not sting

Soldier fly
Stratiomys chamaeleon, family Stratiomyidae

Drone fly
Eristalis tenax, family Syrphidae

Hover fly
Syrphus ribesii, family Syrphidae

Gout fly larvae live inside the stems of cereal crops, causing a gouted appearance

Eyes on the end of long stalks may enhance stereoscopic vision or may simply advertise a male's genetic health to prospective mates

Pest in cheeses and cured meats

Stalk-eyed fly
Diopsis tenuipes, family Diopsidae

Cheese skipper
Piophila casei, family Piophilidae

Gout fly
Chlorops pumilionis, family Chloropidae

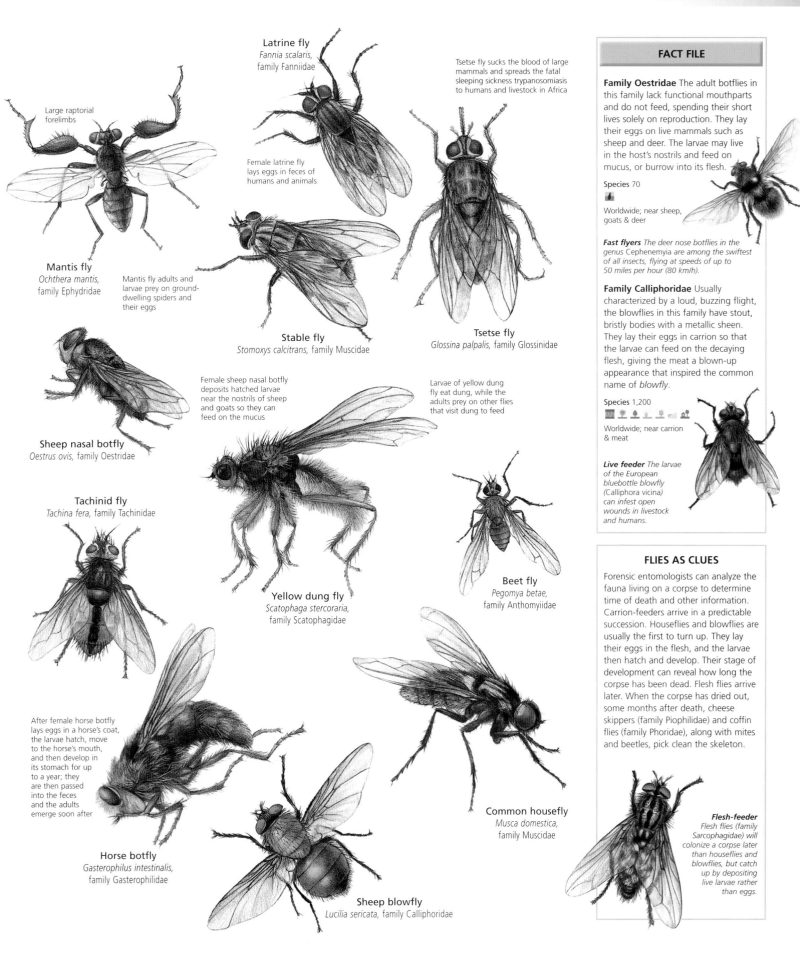

Large raptorial
forelimbs

Mantis fly
Ochthera mantis,
family Ephydridae

Mantis fly adults and
larvae prey on ground-
dwelling spiders and
their eggs

Latrine fly
Fannia scalaris,
family Fanniidae

Female latrine fly
lays eggs in feces of
humans and animals

Tsetse fly sucks the blood of large
mammals and spreads the fatal
sleeping sickness trypanosomiasis
to humans and livestock in Africa

Stable fly
Stomoxys calcitrans, family Muscidae

Tsetse fly
Glossina palpalis, family Glossinidae

Sheep nasal botfly
Oestrus ovis, family Oestridae

Female sheep nasal botfly
deposits hatched larvae
near the nostrils of sheep
and goats so they can
feed on the mucus

Larvae of yellow dung
fly eat dung, while the
adults prey on other flies
that visit dung to feed

Tachinid fly
Tachina fera, family Tachinidae

Yellow dung fly
Scatophaga stercoraria,
family Scatophagidae

Beet fly
Pegomya betae,
family Anthomyiidae

After female horse botfly
lays eggs in a horse's coat,
the larvae hatch, move
to the horse's mouth,
and then develop in
its stomach for up
to a year; they
are then passed
into the feces
and the adults
emerge soon after

Common housefly
Musca domestica,
family Muscidae

Horse botfly
Gasterophilus intestinalis,
family Gasterophilidae

Sheep blowfly
Lucilia sericata, family Calliphoridae

FACT FILE

Family Oestridae The adult botflies in
this family lack functional mouthparts
and do not feed, spending their short
lives solely on reproduction. They lay
their eggs on live mammals such as
sheep and deer. The larvae may live
in the host's nostrils and feed on
mucus, or burrow into its flesh.

Species 70

Worldwide; near sheep,
goats & deer

*Fast flyers The deer nose botflies in the
genus Cephenemyia are among the swiftest
of all insects, flying at speeds of up to
50 miles per hour (80 km/h).*

Family Calliphoridae Usually
characterized by a loud, buzzing flight,
the blowflies in this family have stout,
bristly bodies with a metallic sheen.
They lay their eggs in carrion so that
the larvae can feed on the decaying
flesh, giving the meat a blown-up
appearance that inspired the common
name of *blowfly.*

Species 1,200

Worldwide; near carrion
& meat

*Live feeder The larvae
of the European
bluebottle blowfly
(Calliphora vicina)
can infest open
wounds in livestock
and humans.*

FLIES AS CLUES

Forensic entomologists can analyze the
fauna living on a corpse to determine
time of death and other information.
Carrion-feeders arrive in a predictable
succession. Houseflies and blowflies are
usually the first to turn up. They lay
their eggs in the flesh, and the larvae
then hatch and develop. Their stage of
development can reveal how long the
corpse has been dead. Flesh flies arrive
later. When the corpse has dried out,
some months after death, cheese
skippers (family Piophilidae) and coffin
flies (family Phoridae), along with mites
and beetles, pick clean the skeleton.

*Flesh-feeder
Flesh flies (family
Sarcophagidae) will
colonize a corpse later
than houseflies and
blowflies, but catch
up by depositing
live larvae rather
than eggs.*

BUTTERFLIES AND MOTHS

PHYLUM	Arthropoda
SUBPHYLUM	Hexapoda
CLASS	Insecta
ORDER	Lepidoptera
FAMILIES	131
SPECIES	165,000

With their delicate fluttering flight and often intricate wing patterns, butterflies and moths are the most studied and admired of all insects. They belong to the order Lepidoptera, which means "scale wing" in Greek. Their four broad wings are covered by tiny, overlapping scales—hollow, flattened hairs that create the bright colors and iridescence of diurnal species. Almost all butterflies and moths are plant-feeders. Their larvae, known as caterpillars, have biting mouthparts for chewing plants, which can make them pests. Most adults have a long proboscis for sucking flower nectar and are important pollinators, though a few lack mouthparts and do not feed at all.

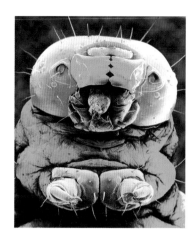

Plant muncher A caterpillar is an eating machine, with biting mouthparts for munching through foliage or other plant food. Many species are brightly colored to warn predators that they are unpalatable.

Nectar-feeder To drink nectar from flowers, butterflies and moths extend a long proboscis, which sits coiled like a watchspring when not in use. Many flowering plants evolved with colors and shapes to attract these pollinating insects.

European pine shoot moth
Rhyacionia buoliana, family Tortricidae

Larvae of European pine shoot moth feed on pine shoots, causing considerable damage in pine forests

DAY AND NIGHT FLYERS
Absent only from the polar ice caps and the oceans, butterflies and moths are most abundant in the tropics but are found virtually anywhere that land plants grow. Most are highly specialized for feeding on particular flowering species.

As adults, butterflies and moths have slim bodies, broad wings, long antennae, and two large compound eyes. Their wingspans range from about 3/16 inch to 12 inches (4 mm to 30 cm). More than 85 percent of species in Lepidoptera are moths, most of which fly at night and have dull wings that are coupled by a spine-like structure known as a frenulum. Butterflies fly by day, display vibrant colors, have clubbed antennae, and lack the frenulum. Some moth species, however, are also diurnal and brightly colored.

Caterpillars are covered in hairs, and walk using three pairs of true legs and several false legs. When ready to pupate, they often enclose themselves in a cocoon using silk from modified salivary glands. The entire life-cycle takes from a few weeks to a few years.

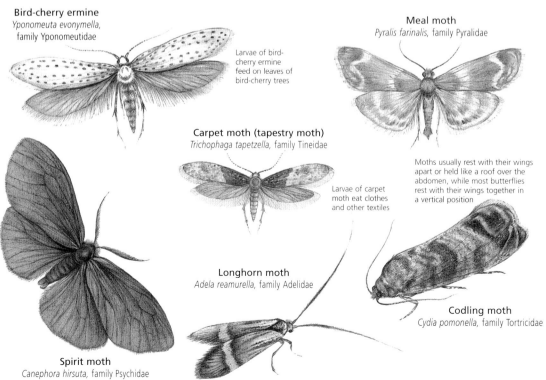

Bird-cherry ermine
Yponomeuta evonymella, family Yponomeutidae

Larvae of bird-cherry ermine feed on leaves of bird-cherry trees

Meal moth
Pyralis farinalis, family Pyralidae

Carpet moth (tapestry moth)
Trichophaga tapetzella, family Tineidae

Larvae of carpet moth eat clothes and other textiles

Moths usually rest with their wings apart or held like a roof over the abdomen, while most butterflies rest with their wings together in a vertical position

Longhorn moth
Adela reamurella, family Adelidae

Codling moth
Cydia pomonella, family Tortricidae

Spirit moth
Canephora hirsuta, family Psychidae

⚡ CONSERVATION WATCH

Deadly trade Only 303 lepidopterids have been assessed by the IUCN, but of these, 94 percent are on the Red List and 37 are extinct. Habitat loss is the major cause of the decline, but over-collecting has also had a major impact on attractive species such as the birdwing butterflies.

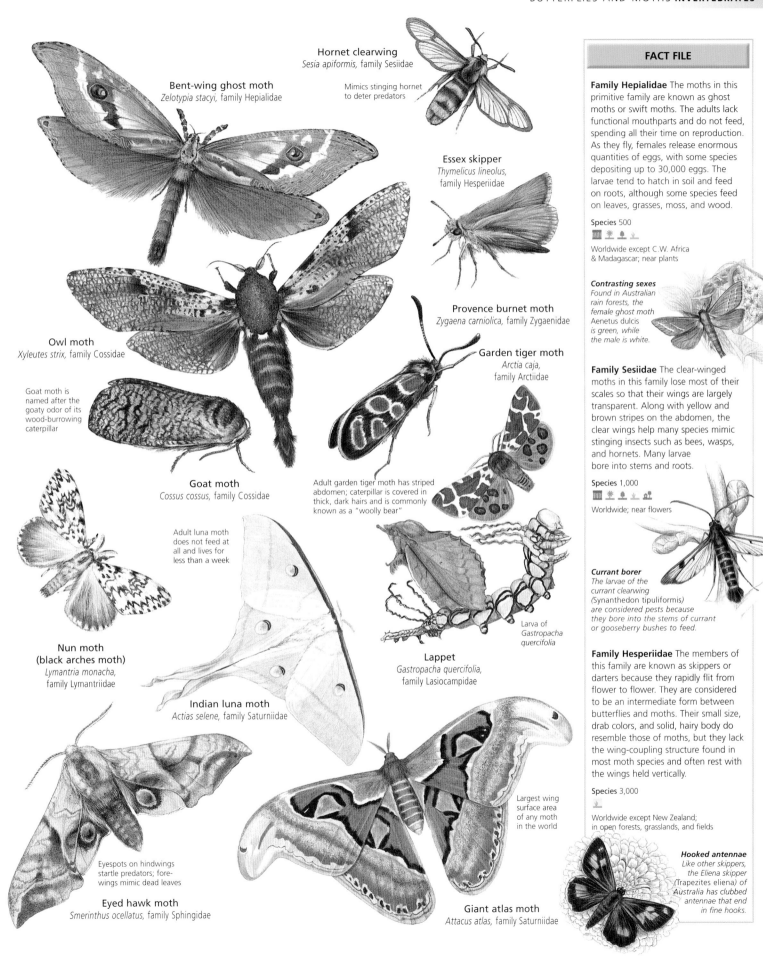

Hornet clearwing
Sesia apiformis, family Sesiidae

Mimics stinging hornet
to deter predators

Bent-wing ghost moth
Zelotypia stacyi, family Hepialidae

Essex skipper
Thymelicus lineolus,
family Hesperiidae

Provence burnet moth
Zygaena carniolica, family Zygaenidae

Owl moth
Xyleutes strix, family Cossidae

Garden tiger moth
Arctia caja,
family Arctiidae

Goat moth is
named after the
goaty odor of its
wood-burrowing
caterpillar

Goat moth
Cossus cossus, family Cossidae

Adult garden tiger moth has striped
abdomen; caterpillar is covered in
thick, dark hairs and is commonly
known as a "woolly bear"

Adult luna moth
does not feed at
all and lives for
less than a week

Larva of
*Gastropacha
quercifolia*

**Nun moth
(black arches moth)**
Lymantria monacha,
family Lymantriidae

Lappet
Gastropacha quercifolia,
family Lasiocampidae

Indian luna moth
Actias selene, family Saturniidae

Largest wing
surface area
of any moth
in the world

Eyespots on hindwings
startle predators; fore-
wings mimic dead leaves

Eyed hawk moth
Smerinthus ocellatus, family Sphingidae

Giant atlas moth
Attacus atlas, family Saturniidae

FACT FILE

Family Hepialidae The moths in this primitive family are known as ghost moths or swift moths. The adults lack functional mouthparts and do not feed, spending all their time on reproduction. As they fly, females release enormous quantities of eggs, with some species depositing up to 30,000 eggs. The larvae tend to hatch in soil and feed on roots, although some species feed on leaves, grasses, moss, and wood.

Species 500

Worldwide except C.W. Africa
& Madagascar; near plants

Contrasting sexes
Found in Australian
rain forests, the
female ghost moth
Aenetus dulcis
is green, while
the male is white.

Family Sesiidae The clear-winged moths in this family lose most of their scales so that their wings are largely transparent. Along with yellow and brown stripes on the abdomen, the clear wings help many species mimic stinging insects such as bees, wasps, and hornets. Many larvae bore into stems and roots.

Species 1,000

Worldwide; near flowers

Currant borer
The larvae of the
currant clearwing
*(*Synanthedon tipuliformis*)*
are considered pests because
they bore into the stems of currant
or gooseberry bushes to feed.

Family Hesperiidae The members of this family are known as skippers or darters because they rapidly flit from flower to flower. They are considered to be an intermediate form between butterflies and moths. Their small size, drab colors, and solid, hairy body do resemble those of moths, but they lack the wing-coupling structure found in most moth species and often rest with the wings held vertically.

Species 3,000

Worldwide except New Zealand;
in open forests, grasslands, and fields

Hooked antennae
Like other skippers,
the Eliena skipper
*(*Trapezites eliena*) of*
Australia has clubbed
antennae that end
in fine hooks.

FACT FILE

Family Papilionidae Often large and brightly colored, the swallowtails of this family are named after the tail-like extensions on the hindwings of most species. All swallowtail caterpillars have an osmetrium, a fork-shaped organ on their head that can release a foul odor to deter a predator. In some species, the caterpillars feed on poisonous plants, absorbing enough toxins to make both themselves and their adult form unpalatable.

Species 600

Worldwide; near flowers

Vivid warning
*The bright wing markings of the crimson rose (*Pachliopta hector*) and many other swallow-tails warn predators that they have an unpleasant taste.*

Family Noctuidae Noctuid or owlet moths make up the largest family in the order Lepidoptera. These night flyers have hearing organs on their thorax that can pick up echolocation signals emitted by bats, their main predators. Adults feed on nectar, sap, rotting fruit, tears, or dung, while the larvae may eat foliage or seeds, or bore into stems and fruit, with some being serious crop pests.

Species 35,000

Worldwide; on plants

Background colors
Like many noctuid moths, Moma alpium has cryptic coloration, the mottled wings blending in with its woodland habitat.

Family Geometridae Known as geometer, looper, or inchworm moths, the members of this family tend to be small with slender bodies. The larvae, which often resemble twigs when resting, lack at least one middle pair of false legs. They move by stretching out the front part of the body, then bringing the tail forward to meet it, creating a "looping" or "inching" gait.

Species 20,000

Worldwide; on foliage

*Leaf mimic The wings of the Southeast Asian geometer moth (*Sarcinodes restitutaria*) resemble leaves.*

Moth butterfly
Liphyra brassolis, family Lycaenidae

Caterpillars of moth butterfly feed on larvae of citrus ants and have tough skin that protects them from the ants' bites

African giant swallowtail
Papilio antimachus, family Papilonidae

Cabbage butterfly
Pieris brassicae,
family Pieridae

Orange-barred sulphur
Phoebis philea,
family Pieridae

African giant swallowtail is the largest of all African butterflies, with a wingspan of 10 inches (25 cm) or more

Scarce copper
Lycaena virgaureae,
family Lycaenidae

Giant agrippa
Thysania agrippina,
family Noctuidae

Large blue
Maculinea arion, family Lycaenidae

Union Jack butterfly
Delias mysis, family Pieridae

Giant agrippa has wingspan of up to 12 inches (30 cm), the largest of any butterfly or moth

Bogong moth
Agrotis infusa, family Noctuidae

Bhutan glory butterfly
Bhutanitis lidderdalii,
family Papilionidae

Newly emerged adult bogong moths avoid the summer heat by migrating to mountain caves and becoming dormant until autumn, when they return to the plains to breed

Apollo butterfly
Parnassius apollo,
family Papilionidae

Only male mottled umbers fly; females are wingless

Red underwing moth
Catocala nupta, family Noctuidae

Mottled umber
Erannis defoliaria,
family Geometridae

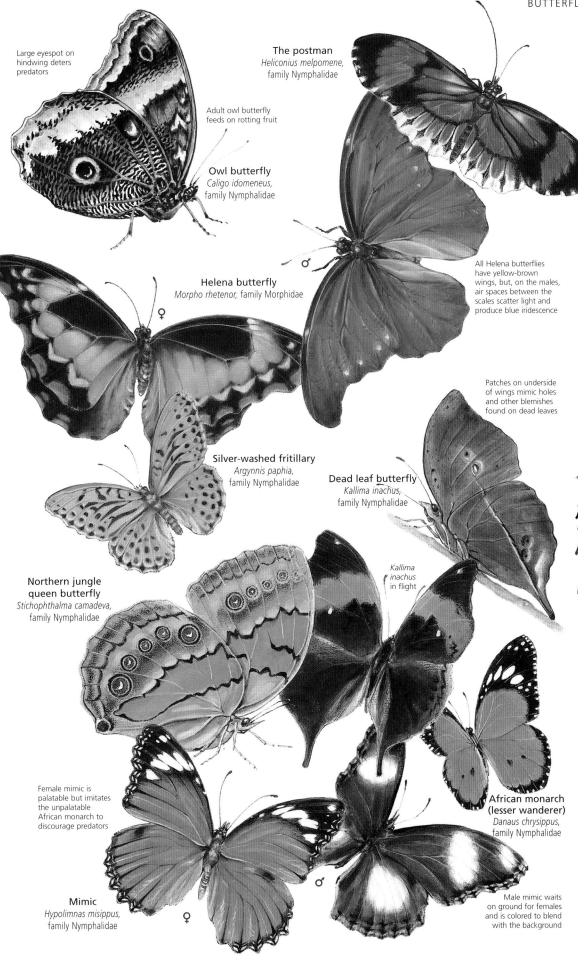

Large eyespot on hindwing deters predators

Adult owl butterfly feeds on rotting fruit

Owl butterfly
Caligo idomeneus,
family Nymphalidae

The postman
Heliconius melpomene,
family Nymphalidae

All Helena butterflies have yellow-brown wings, but, on the males, air spaces between the scales scatter light and produce blue iridescence

Helena butterfly
Morpho rhetenor, family Morphidae

Silver-washed fritillary
Argynnis paphia,
family Nymphalidae

Patches on underside of wings mimic holes and other blemishes found on dead leaves

Dead leaf butterfly
Kallima inachus,
family Nymphalidae

Kallima inachus in flight

Northern jungle queen butterfly
Stichophthalma camadeva,
family Nymphalidae

Female mimic is palatable but imitates the unpalatable African monarch to discourage predators

Mimic
Hypolimnas misippus,
family Nymphalidae

African monarch (lesser wanderer)
Danaus chrysippus,
family Nymphalidae

Male mimic waits on ground for females and is colored to blend with the background

FACT FILE

Family Nymphalidae Known as brush-footed butterflies, the species in this family have very small and hairy forelegs, and walk using only the middle and back legs. The underside of the wings tends to be drab, while the upperside usually features strongly contrasting colors.

Species 5,200

Worldwide; near flowers

Seasonal variation *The map butterflies (Araschnia levana) that emerge in spring have orange-marked wings, while those that emerge in summer are black and white.*

COCOONS AND CHRYSALISES

When they are ready to transform into adults, caterpillars stop eating and find a safe spot. Some pupate underground without any further protection, but most moths spin a cocoon of silk, while almost all butterflies create a chrysalis, a hard shell formed from the caterpillar's skin and secured by silk to a branch.

Sticky cocoon *The larvae of bagworm moths (Thyridopteryx ephemeraeformis) live in cases of silk and plant debris, which harden into cocoons when they are ready to pupate.*

Transforming chrysalis
The pale green chrysalis of the monarch butterfly becomes transparent when the adult is ready to emerge.

BUTTERFLY MIGRATION

A monarch butterfly (*Danaus plexippus*) may travel more than 1,800 miles (2,900 km) in the 9 months of its life. Every autumn, millions of monarchs migrate south to their wintering sites in California and Mexico. Here, they shelter in great clusters on trees. In autumn, they begin the return journey north, during which they lay eggs and die. The new generation completes the trip to the summer feeding grounds.

BEES, WASPS, ANTS, AND SAWFLIES

PHYLUM	Arthropoda
SUBPHYLUM	Hexapoda
CLASS	Insecta
ORDER	Hymenoptera
FAMILIES	91
SPECIES	198,000

The order Hymenoptera is named after the Greek words for "membrane wing," and most of its species have two pairs of transparent wings. Although many bees, wasps, and sawflies are solitary creatures, some species of bees and all species of ants live in highly structured societies, whose thousands or millions of members belong to different castes and perform specific tasks. Many of the world's most beneficial insects are hymenopterids. Bees and some wasps are the chief pollinators of both crops and wild plants, while many parasitic wasps play a crucial role in controlling the populations of other insects. Honeybees have been domesticated for their honey and wax.

Bite and sting Despite their formidable jaws, adult bull ants mainly eat nectar and plant juices, but they do capture insect prey to feed their young. They use an abdominal stinger to subdue prey and deter predators.

ANATOMY AND LIFE-CYCLE

Generally small to medium-sized, hymenopterans include the parasitic *Megaphragma caribea*, which, at just $\frac{1}{500}$ inch (0.17 mm) long, is one of the smallest insects. Hymenopterids' hindwings are attached to the larger forewings by tiny hooks so that they beat together. The more primitive sawflies and their kin lack the slim waist that separates the thorax and abdomen of bees, wasps, and ants.

Hymenopterans have mouthparts designed for biting or for biting and sucking. Sawflies, gall wasps, and some ants and bees are herbivorous, while most other species in the order are predatory or parasitic. In many species, the female's ovipositor (egg-laying organ) has become modified—sawflies use it for sawing into plant stems, where they lay their eggs; while bees, wasps, and ants often use it for piercing or stinging predators or prey.

Female hymenopterans may lay their eggs in soil, in plants, in nests or hives, or in living insect hosts. In many species, the female determines whether the eggs are fertilized, with unfertilized eggs producing male larvae, and fertilized eggs producing females. In solitary species, the larvae hatch near a food source and develop independently, but in social species they rely on constant care from the adults. Development is by complete metamorphosis, and larvae usually pupate in a cocoon.

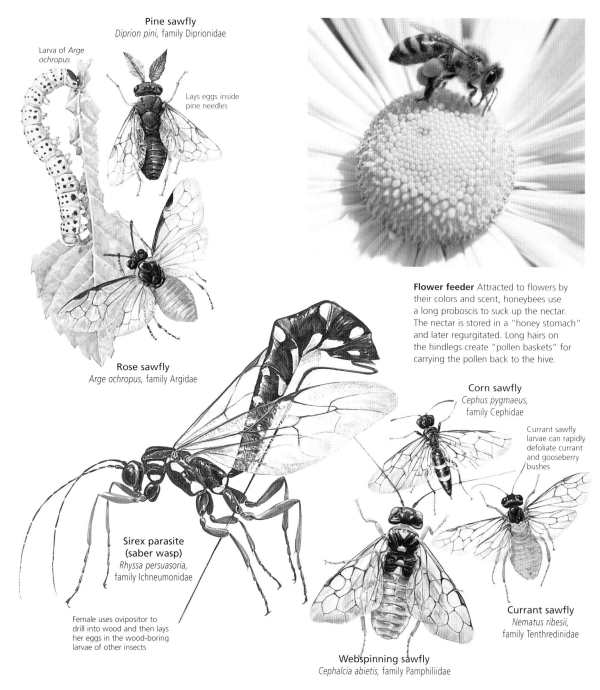

Pine sawfly
Diprion pini, family Diprionidae

Larva of *Arge ochropus*

Lays eggs inside pine needles

Rose sawfly
Arge ochropus, family Argidae

Flower feeder Attracted to flowers by their colors and scent, honeybees use a long proboscis to suck up the nectar. The nectar is stored in a "honey stomach" and later regurgitated. Long hairs on the hindlegs create "pollen baskets" for carrying the pollen back to the hive.

Corn sawfly
Cephus pygmaeus, family Cephidae

Currant sawfly larvae can rapidly defoliate currant and gooseberry bushes

Sirex parasite (saber wasp)
Rhyssa persuasoria, family Ichneumonidae

Female uses ovipositor to drill into wood and then lays her eggs in the wood-boring larvae of other insects

Currant sawfly
Nematus ribesii, family Tenthredinidae

Webspinning sawfly
Cephalcia abietis, family Pamphiliidae

Ruby-tailed wasp
(common cuckoo wasp)
Chrysis ignita, family Chrysididae

American
pelecinid wasp
Pelecinus polyturator,
family Pelecinidae

Oak apple gall wasp
Biorrhiza pallida, family Cynipidae

Velvet wasp
Megascolia maculata,
family Scoliidae

Alternates an all-female
generation with a generation
of males and females

Clover seed chalcid
Bruchophagus gibbus,
family Eurytomidae

Woolly aphid parasite
Aphelinus mali, family Aphelinidae

Rose cynipid
(rose bedeguar gall)
Diplolepis rosae,
family Cynipidae

Torymid wasp
Torymus bedeguaris,
family Torymidae

Torymid wasp
parasitizes
gall-forming
insects

Yellow ophion (red wasp)
Ophion luteus, family Ichneumonidae

Eucharitid wasp
Eucharis adscendens,
family Eucharitidae

Ensign wasp
Evania appendigaster,
family Evaniidae

FACT FILE

Family Chrysididae Known as cuckoo wasps, ruby-tailed wasps, or jewel wasps, the species in this family lay their eggs in the nests of bees, wasps, or other insects. The cuckoo wasp larvae then feed on the nest's larvae or the food that has been provided for them. To resist the stings of the host insects, adult cuckoo wasps have a tough exoskeleton as well as a flexible body that can roll up into a ball.

Species 3,000

Worldwide; near flowers & insect hosts

Peer parasites
Most cuckoo wasps lay their eggs in the nests of other wasps and bees, but some species parasitize sawflies, silk moths, or stick insects.

Family Scoliidae Adult scoliid wasps feed on flower nectar and pollen, but the larvae are parasites. The adult female will burrow into soil to find the grubs of scarab beetles. She then paralyzes each grub with a sting to the neck and lays an egg into it. When the wasp larva hatches, it will feed on the paralyzed grub, which dies once the larva pupates.

Species 8,000

Worldwide; near scarab beetles

Striped body *Scoliid wasps such as Scolia procera are relatively large and robust insects. Their hairy bodies often have bright markings.*

Family Cynipidae This family contains the gall wasps, most of which are inconspicuous insects less than ¼ inch (5 mm) long. Females lay their eggs on oaks and other trees, where the larvae hatch and secrete saliva that forces the plant to form a protective gall around them. The larvae feed on the gall until they emerge through small holes as adults. Each cynipid species creates a characteristic gall.

Species 1,400

Mainly Northern Hemisphere; on trees

Rose galls *The larvae of the rose cynipid develop from unfertilized eggs laid in rose bushes. About 50 larvae share the mass of red filaments that make up each gall.*

HIVE OF ACTIVITY

The social life of the honeybee (genus *Apis*) is among the most complex in the animal world. A queen bee can lay up to 1,500 eggs a day. Fertilized eggs develop into workers or queens, and unfertilized eggs become drones. The workers feed the hatched larvae before they are capped inside cells to pupate. When a hive reaches its optimum size, the old queen flies off to found a new colony, followed by thousands of workers. The first new queen to emerge will rule the old nest.

Close view This electron micrograph shows a honeybee's large compound eyes, each made up of more than 4,000 lenses. Two sensitive antennae emerge between the eyes.

Inside a beehive All the drones and workers in a hive (below) are the offspring of the queen, whose only task is to lay eggs. Drones are male bees, and their only job is to mate with new queens. Worker bees gather food, maintain the hive, and feed the queen and her young. Glands in their head produce royal jelly for the larvae. Workers also make honey by regurgitating nectar and spreading it in cells to dehydrate, then capping it with wax.

Being queen *A queen bee is the largest bee in the hive. She can live for up to 5 years.*

Hard workers *Workers are females that cannot breed. They live for only a few weeks.*

Bee young Worker bees bring food to the larvae as they mature inside water-resistant waxen cells. These larvae (above) are transforming into pupae, and will emerge as adults.

Honeybee swarm A swarm of bees gathers when an old queen, along with up to 70,000 workers, leaves an established hive to establish a new colony. The swarm waits while scouts find a good location for the nest.

sun

angle

food

waggle

hive

Dance of the bees A worker bee uses a figure-eight dance to convey information about a new food source. The rate of tail-wagging indicates the distance to the food source, while the direction is signaled by the angle of the dance to the sun.

Larva cells Most larvae become workers. They are first fed royal jelly, and later pollen and honey. Queen larvae are fed only royal jelly. Drones develop from unfertilized eggs.

queen bee

worker

nectar store

honey store

pollen store

empty cell

drone

drone cell

queen cell

open larva cell

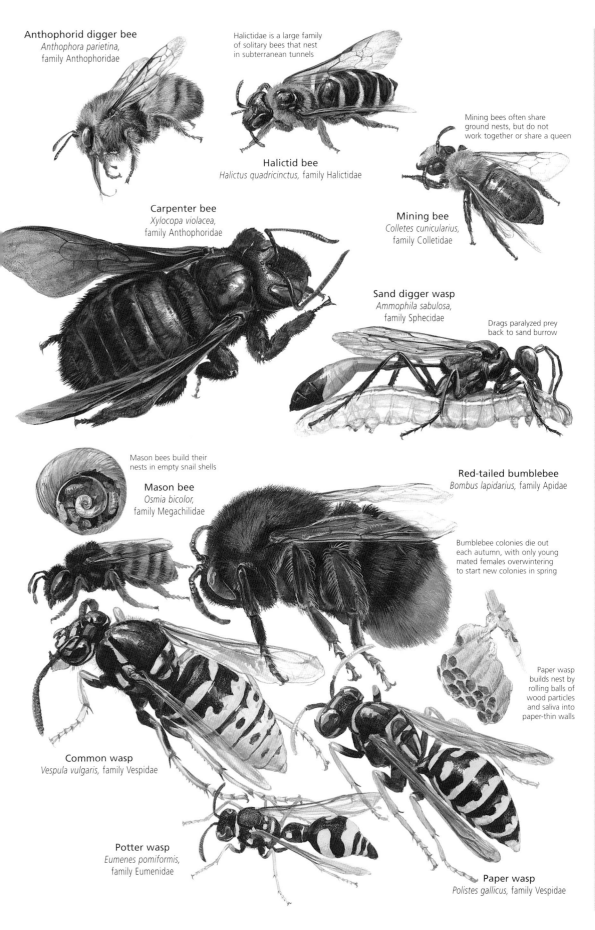

Anthophorid digger bee
Anthophora parietina,
family Anthophoridae

Halictidae is a large family
of solitary bees that nest
in subterranean tunnels

Halictid bee
Halictus quadricinctus, family Halictidae

Mining bees often share
ground nests, but do not
work together or share a queen

Carpenter bee
Xylocopa violacea,
family Anthophoridae

Mining bee
Colletes cunicularius,
family Colletidae

Sand digger wasp
Ammophila sabulosa,
family Sphecidae

Drags paralyzed prey
back to sand burrow

Mason bees build their
nests in empty snail shells

Mason bee
Osmia bicolor,
family Megachilidae

Red-tailed bumblebee
Bombus lapidarius, family Apidae

Bumblebee colonies die out
each autumn, with only young
mated females overwintering
to start new colonies in spring

Paper wasp
builds nest by
rolling balls of
wood particles
and saliva into
paper-thin walls

Common wasp
Vespula vulgaris, family Vespidae

Potter wasp
Eumenes pomiformis,
family Eumenidae

Paper wasp
Polistes gallicus, family Vespidae

FACT FILE

Family Sphecidae This family includes
species known as digger wasps, sand
wasps, mud-dauber wasps, and thread-
waisted wasps. A female sphecid wasp
paralyzes arthropod prey with her sting
and deposits it in her nest, where her
larvae later feed on its body. Most
species have their nests underground
in burrows, but some use plant stems
or rotten wood, and mud daubers
build rows of cells from pellets of mud.

Species 8,000

Worldwide; often in sandy soil

Solitary hunter *The female bee wolf
(Philanthus triangulum) will carry paralyzed
honeybees back to its sandy burrow.*

Family Apidae The honeybees,
bumblebees, and stingless bees in this
family live in communal nests centered
on a queen. Worker bees forage for
nectar and pollen, which they bring
back to the nest to feed the queen
and her larvae. While honeybees often
attach their hives to trees, bumblebees
usually create their nests in the soil.

Species 1,000

Worldwide; near flowers

Fierce bee
*When provoked, a colony of Southeast
Asia's giant honeybees (Apis dorsata) is
capable of stinging a person to death.*

Family Vespidae This family contains
all the social wasps, as well as some
solitary ones. Hornets, yellowjackets,
and paper wasps all use chewed wood
and saliva to build their papery nests.
In most species, the colony dies out in
late autumn, leaving only a few mated
queens to overwinter and establish
new colonies in spring.

Species 4,000

Worldwide

Self-sacrifice *To defend its
colony, a worker of the social
wasp species Brachygastra
lecheguana will sting an attacker
and may well die when the sting
detaches from its abdomen.*

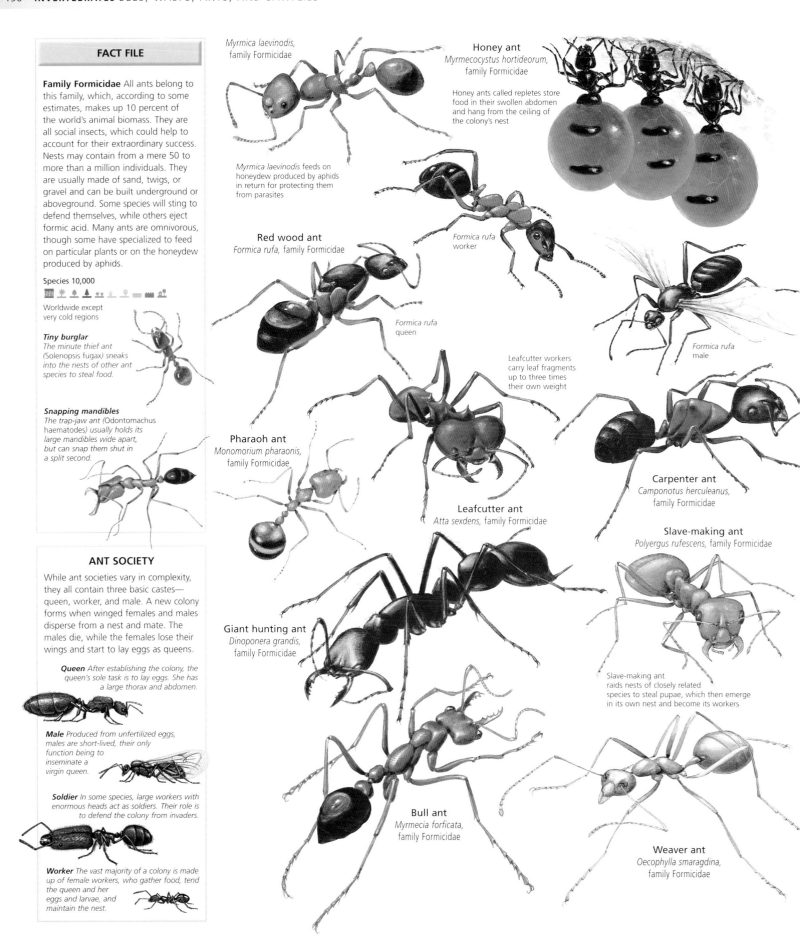

FACT FILE

Family Formicidae All ants belong to this family, which, according to some estimates, makes up 10 percent of the world's animal biomass. They are all social insects, which could help to account for their extraordinary success. Nests may contain from a mere 50 to more than a million individuals. They are usually made of sand, twigs, or gravel and can be built underground or aboveground. Some species will sting to defend themselves, while others eject formic acid. Many ants are omnivorous, though some have specialized to feed on particular plants or on the honeydew produced by aphids.

Species 10,000

Worldwide except very cold regions

Tiny burglar
The minute thief ant (Solenopsis fugax) sneaks into the nests of other ant species to steal food.

Snapping mandibles
The trap-jaw ant (Odontomachus haematodes) usually holds its large mandibles wide apart, but can snap them shut in a split second.

ANT SOCIETY

While ant societies vary in complexity, they all contain three basic castes—queen, worker, and male. A new colony forms when winged females and males disperse from a nest and mate. The males die, while the females lose their wings and start to lay eggs as queens.

Queen After establishing the colony, the queen's sole task is to lay eggs. She has a large thorax and abdomen.

Male Produced from unfertilized eggs, males are short-lived, their only function being to inseminate a virgin queen.

Soldier In some species, large workers with enormous heads act as soldiers. Their role is to defend the colony from invaders.

Worker The vast majority of a colony is made up of female workers, who gather food, tend the queen and her eggs and larvae, and maintain the nest.

Myrmica laevinodis, family Formicidae

Myrmica laevinodis feeds on honeydew produced by aphids in return for protecting them from parasites

Honey ant
Myrmecocystus hortideorum, family Formicidae

Honey ants called repletes store food in their swollen abdomen and hang from the ceiling of the colony's nest

Red wood ant
Formica rufa, family Formicidae

Formica rufa worker

Formica rufa queen

Formica rufa male

Pharaoh ant
Monomorium pharaonis, family Formicidae

Leafcutter workers carry leaf fragments up to three times their own weight

Leafcutter ant
Atta sexdens, family Formicidae

Carpenter ant
Camponotus herculeanus, family Formicidae

Slave-making ant
Polyergus rufescens, family Formicidae

Slave-making ant raids nests of closely related species to steal pupae, which then emerge in its own nest and become its workers

Giant hunting ant
Dinoponera grandis, family Formicidae

Bull ant
Myrmecia forficata, family Formicidae

Weaver ant
Oecophylla smaragdina, family Formicidae

OTHER INSECTS

PHYLUM	Arthropoda
SUBPHYLUM	Hexapoda
CLASSES	Insecta
ORDERS	19*
FAMILIES	218*
SPECIES	> 3,000*

Totals refer only to the 19 orders that make up "Other insects."

Of the remaining 19 orders of Insecta, 16 are illustrated here. They are a diverse assortment, which include primitive, wingless forms such as silverfish and bristletails; parasites of mammals and birds such as fleas and lice; parasites of insects such as strepsipterans; and crop pests such as thrips. Also included are insects that spend most of their lives in water, such as mayflies, caddisflies, dobsonflies, and stoneflies. Stick and leaf insects are plant-feeders; angel insects, snakeflies, antlions, lacewings, and hanging flies prey on other invertebrates; while rock crawlers, webspinners, earwigs, booklice; and scorpionflies recycle detritus.

Earwigs The order Dermaptera contains the earwigs, small flattened insects that feed on detritus. The large "forceps" extending from the abdomen are used in defense and courtship. Females guard their eggs and newly hatched larvae.

Webspinners The only insects other than danceflies with silk-producing glands in the legs, webspinners (order Embioptera) use their silk to create a shared network of nests and tunnels. They develop by incomplete metamorphosis, with nymphs resembling their parents.

Elongated thorax allows head to be lifted in a snake-like fashion

Snakefly
Raphidia notata,
order Raphidioptera

Spines on hindlegs used for defense and battles with rivals

Spiny devil walking stick
Eurycantha horrida, order Phasmatodea

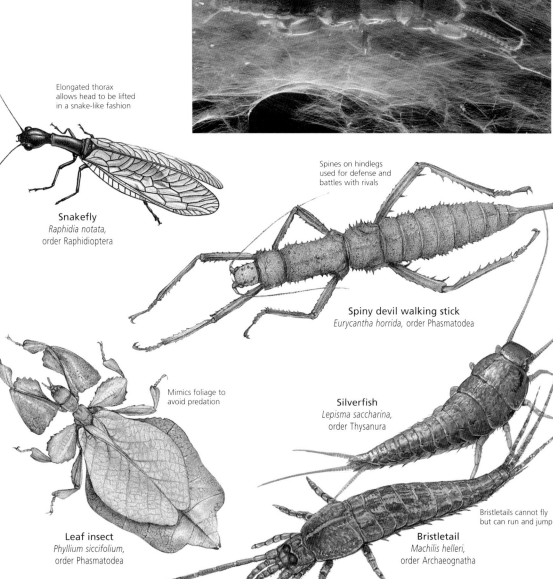

Mimics foliage to avoid predation

Silverfish
Lepisma saccharina,
order Thysanura

Bristletails cannot fly but can run and jump

Leaf insect
Phyllium siccifolium,
order Phasmatodea

Bristletail
Machilis helleri,
order Archaeognatha

FACT FILE

Order Thysanura This order contains the silverfish, flightless insects that may closely resemble the earliest insects. They have long antennae on their head, and three "tails" extending from the abdomen. Silverfish hatch from eggs laid in crevices near food sources.

Species 370

Worldwide; in trees, caves & buildings

House guest *This silverfish (Lepismodes iniquilinus) is often found in houses, where it feeds on paper, glue in book bindings, starched clothing, and dry foods.*

Order Phasmatodea The supreme mimics in this order are known as stick insects and leaf insects. They feed on foliage. Most species are wingless, and, when wings are present, they usually are fully developed and functional only in the males. Many females can produce offspring from unfertilized eggs.

Species 3,000

Worldwide, esp. in the tropics; near plants

Stick mimic
When disturbed, stick insects such as Bacillus rossii may freeze for hours or they may sway as if blowing in the wind.

Order Ephemeroptera The mayflies in this order live very short lives as adults, often lasting only a day. The males form great swarms from which females select mates. Eggs are deposited in or near water, and the nymphs are aquatic. Nymphs leave the water to molt into winged forms, which soon molt again into the adults. Mayflies are the only insects to molt once they have wings.

Species 2,500

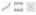

Worldwide; in fresh or brackish water

Flying romance
Mayflies mate in flight, with the male using his long forelegs to grasp the female.

Order Megaloptera The dobsonflies and alderflies in this order spend most of their lives as predatory aquatic larvae. They leave the water to pupate, emerging as winged adults that usually do not feed and only live long enough to breed. Eggs are usually laid on rocks or plants beside ponds or streams, and the larvae crawl or fall into the water.

Species 300

Worldwide; in fresh water

Toebiter *The larva of the dobsonfly* Archichauliodes *is known as the "toebiter." It breathes through the leg-like gills along its abdomen.*

Order Phthiraptera The parasitic lice in this order are tiny wingless insects that evolved from winged ancestors. They feed on birds and mammals and cannot survive long away from their host. Lice can travel to a new host only when two members of the host species come into contact, which restricts most lice to particular host species. Some lice have sucking mouthparts, while others have chewing mouthparts.

Species 5,500

Worldwide; on bird or mammal hosts

Louse bites dog *The dog-biting louse (Trichodectes canis) uses its chewing mouthparts to feed on the hair, skin, and blood of domestic dogs and other canids. Gripping claws on its legs make it difficult to dislodge.*

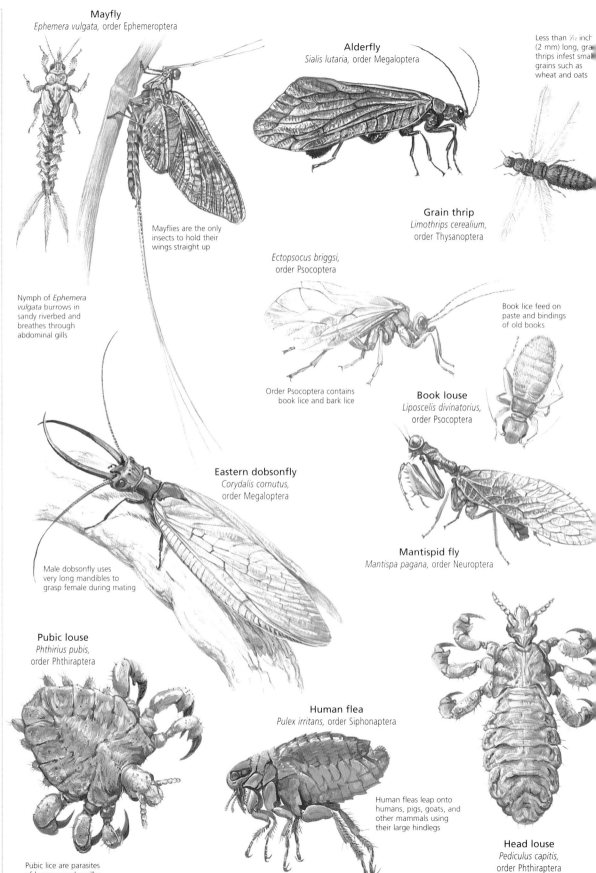

Mayfly
Ephemera vulgata, order Ephemeroptera

Mayflies are the only insects to hold their wings straight up

Nymph of *Ephemera vulgata* burrows in sandy riverbed and breathes through abdominal gills

Alderfly
Sialis lutaria, order Megaloptera

Less than 1/12 inch (2 mm) long, grain thrips infest small grains such as wheat and oats

Grain thrip
Limothrips cerealium, order Thysanoptera

Ectopsocus briggsi, order Psocoptera

Order Psocoptera contains book lice and bark lice

Book lice feed on paste and bindings of old books

Book louse
Liposcelis divinatorius, order Psocoptera

Eastern dobsonfly
Corydalis cornutus, order Megaloptera

Male dobsonfly uses very long mandibles to grasp female during mating

Mantispid fly
Mantispa pagana, order Neuroptera

Pubic louse
Phthirius pubis, order Phthiraptera

Pubic lice are parasites of humans and gorillas

Human flea
Pulex irritans, order Siphonaptera

Human fleas leap onto humans, pigs, goats, and other mammals using their large hindlegs

Head louse
Pediculus capitis, order Phthiraptera

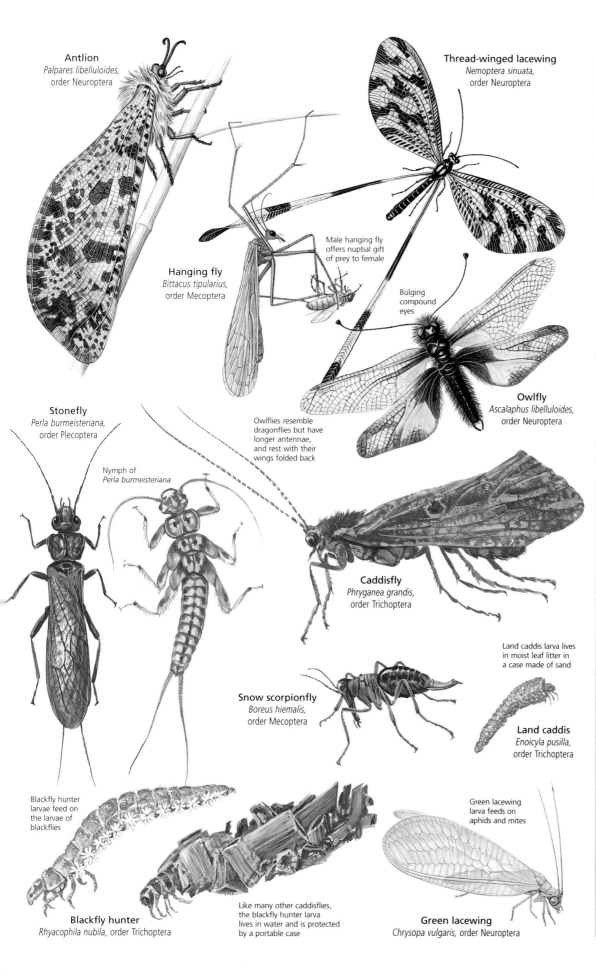

Antlion
Palpares libelluloides,
order Neuroptera

Thread-winged lacewing
Nemoptera sinuata,
order Neuroptera

Hanging fly
Bittacus tipularius,
order Mecoptera

Male hanging fly
offers nuptial gift
of prey to female

Bulging
compound
eyes

Owlfly
Ascalaphus libelluloides,
order Neuroptera

Owlflies resemble
dragonflies but have
longer antennae,
and rest with their
wings folded back

Stonefly
Perla burmeisteriana,
order Plecoptera

Nymph of
Perla burmeisteriana

Caddisfly
Phryganea grandis,
order Trichoptera

Land caddis larva lives
in moist leaf litter in
a case made of sand

Snow scorpionfly
Boreus hiemalis,
order Mecoptera

Land caddis
Enoicyla pusilla,
order Trichoptera

Blackfly hunter
larvae feed on
the larvae of
blackflies

Green lacewing
larva feeds on
aphids and mites

Like many other caddisflies,
the blackfly hunter larva
lives in water and is protected
by a portable case

Blackfly hunter
Rhyacophila nubila, order Trichoptera

Green lacewing
Chrysopa vulgaris, order Neuroptera

FACT FILE

Order Neuroptera The members of this order all have complex branching veins on their wings. Most are predators as both larvae and adults. Lacewing larvae are welcome in gardens because they devour aphids, mites, and scale insects. Antlion larvae live in sand and feed mainly on ants. Owlfly larvae live in leaf litter near stones, and prey on invertebrates. Spongefly larvae live in fresh water and eat only sponges.

Species 4,000

Worldwide; often near vegetation

Pit trap Antlion larvae, known as doodlebugs in North America, dig pits in loose sand to trap ants and other prey.

Order Mecoptera This order includes scorpionflies, named after the large tail the male uses to hold onto the female during mating, and hanging flies, which hang from leaves to hunt and mate. Males often offer their mates a nuptial gift of a prey item or a pellet of saliva that the female eats during copulation. Most species feed on detritus, insects, and plants.

Species 500

Worldwide; near damp vegetation

Stingless scorpion
Like other males in its genus, the male common scorpionfly (Panorpa communis) is harmless but has an enlarged "tail" that resembles the stinger of a scorpion.

Order Plecoptera The nymphs of the stoneflies in this order can indicate the environmental health of streams. They are entirely aquatic and can survive only in cool, clean, flowing water with high concentrations of oxygen. After going through up to 30 molts, nymphs crawl from the water and emerge as adults, which are usually winged.

Species 3,000

Worldwide except Australia;
near running water

Feeding strategies
While adult stoneflies of the genus Perla may not feed at all, the aquatic nymphs are carnivorous and feed on other larvae.

INSECT ALLIES

PHYLUM	Arthropoda
SUBPHYLUM	Hexapoda
CLASSES	3
ORDERS	5
FAMILIES	31
SPECIES	8,300

Hexapods are arthropods with six legs and a body divided into three parts—head, thorax, and abdomen. The vast majority of hexapods are insects, but there are also three classes of non-insect hexapods—the springtails (class Collembola), proturans (Protura), and diplurans (Diplura). Found in soil and leaf litter, these tiny creatures range from ½₀ inch to 1¼ inches (0.5 mm to 3 cm) in length. They are distinguished from insects by their mouthparts, which are fully tucked into the head. As in the most primitive of insects, the silverfish and the bristletails, these tiny soil-dwellers evolved from a wingless ancestor and they continue to molt throughout their life.

Ready to leap Springtails are ubiquitous, occurring in freshwater, coastal marine, and most terrestrial habitats, including deserts and polar zones. They feed mainly on microorganisms. Surface-dwellers tend to be covered in hairs (above) or scales.

PRIMITIVE HEXAPODS

The springtails that make up the class Collembola are named after a forked organ on the abdomen that can propel them up to 100 times their own body length—a quick way to escape danger. They are among the most abundant animals, with populations of 300 million individuals per acre (750 million per ha) in some grassland habitats.

With a length of less than ½₂ inch (2 mm), proturans are rarely seen and were not even discovered until 1907. They live in soil and leaf litter, where they feed on fungi and decaying matter. They are the most primitive of all hexapods and lack eyes and antennae. Instead, the forelegs perform a sensory function and are held out in front of the animal rather than being used for walking. With each molt, proturans gain another segment of abdomen.

Diplurans lack eyes but feel their way around in soil or leaf litter with their long antennae and two tail-like structures known as cerci. In some carnivorous species, the cerci have become powerful pincers that can capture other soil-dwellers. Other species are herbivorous and feed on soil fungi and detritus. Diplurans are able to regenerate some of their body parts.

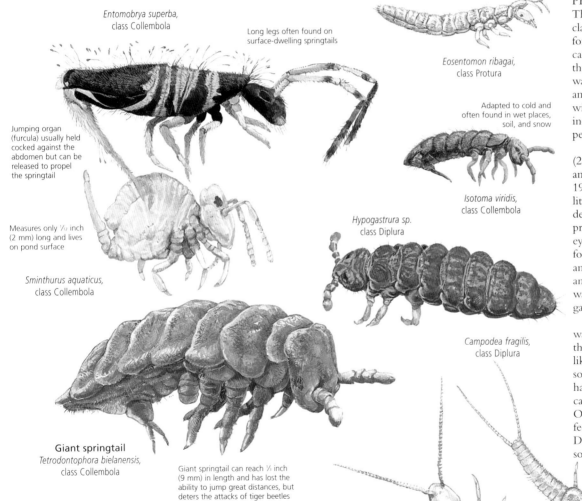

Entomobrya superba, class Collembola

Long legs often found on surface-dwelling springtails

Jumping organ (furcula) usually held cocked against the abdomen but can be released to propel the springtail

Measures only ½₂ inch (2 mm) long and lives on pond surface

Sminthurus aquaticus, class Collembola

Giant springtail
Tetrodontophora bielanensis, class Collembola

Giant springtail can reach ⅓ inch (9 mm) in length and has lost the ability to jump great distances, but deters the attacks of tiger beetles by releasing chemicals

Eosentomon ribagai, class Protura

Adapted to cold and often found in wet places, soil, and snow

Isotoma viridis, class Collembola

Hypogastrura sp. class Diplura

Campodea fragilis, class Diplura

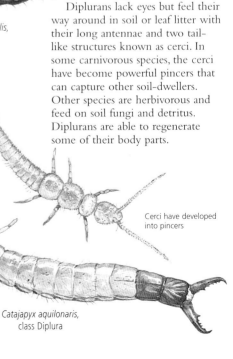

Proturans hold their forelegs out in front of the body

A dipluran can regrow a lost leg, antenna, or cerci over several molts

Cerci have developed into pincers

Baculentulus breviunguis, class Protura

Catajapyx aquilonaris, class Diplura

ECHINODERMS

PHYLUM	Echinodermata
CLASSES	5
ORDERS	36
FAMILIES	145
SPECIES	6,000

The sea stars, sea urchins, brittle stars, feather stars, and sea cucumbers that belong to the phylum Echinodermata display diverse body forms, but share some defining characteristics. Adults usually have pentamerous symmetry, with the body arranged into a five-part radial pattern around a central axis. Most internal organs are also arranged in this pattern. An internal skeleton of calcareous plates provides protection and support. The plates often bear spines or small lumps—the name echinoderm means "spiny skin." The body cavity includes a water-vascular system, a network of water vessels that controls the tube feet used for locomotion, feeding, respiration, and sensory functions.

Sticky defense In sea cucumbers, the five-part symmetry is internal and the skeleton is reduced. This leopard sea cucumber (*Bohadschia argus*) has ejected a mass of sticky white threads, known as Cuvierian tubules, to confuse or entangle a predator.

Sea apple
Pseudocolochirus violaceus, class Holothuroidea

Stalked young All members of the class Crinoidea are initially attached to the substrate by a slender stalk, but feather stars such as this *Comanthus* sp. then become free-living. The branched arms hold tube feet that catch plankton from the water and transfer it to the mouth.

Sea apples release a toxin called holothurin that is lethal to many marine animals

Synapta maculata can grow to a length of 16½ feet (5 m)

Synaptid sea cucumber
Synapta maculata, class Holothuroidea

Common starfish
Asterias rubens, class Asteroidea

Pelagic sea cucumber
Pelagothuria natatrix, class Holothuroidea

Feather star
Tropiometra afra, class Crinoidea

Pencil urchin often associates with the striped bumblebee shrimp (*Gnathophyllum americanum*)

Red pencil urchin
Heterocentrotus mammillatus, class Echinoidea

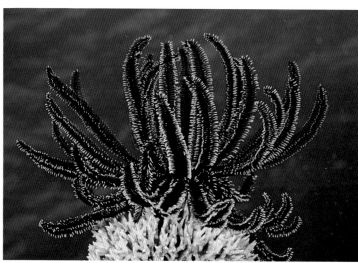

SPINY BOTTOM-DWELLERS

All echinoderms are marine and most are mobile bottom-dwellers, although sea lilies are fixed to the seafloor by a long stalk, and a few sea cucumbers float in the open ocean. Echinoderms are found throughout the world at all depths. Sea urchins and sea stars are very commonly seen along the seashore.

The phylum Echinodermata is divided into five classes. Members of the class Crinoidea include the sessile sea lilies as well as the mobile feather stars. They are filter-feeders and, unlike other echinoderms, have their mouth facing away from the substrate. The other echinoderm classes include predators, grazers of algae, and deposit-feeders. The sea stars of class Asteroidea and brittle stars of class Ophiuroidea have arms radiating from their body. Their skeletal plates are held together by muscles, which allows flexibility. In the class Echinoidea, sea urchins and sand dollars have a rigid skeleton of fused plates that supports a globular or flattened form, usually featuring

Spiky gathering Many echinoderms, such as these sea urchins, gather in large groups, influenced by the availability of food. The strategy may also provide some protection from predators and enhance reproduction.

prominent spines. Sea cucumbers (class Holothuroidea) are generally soft-bodied, with their skeletons reduced to minute spicules.

Although a few echinoderms can reproduce asexually, most have separate sexes that release eggs and sperm into the water for fertilization. The larvae are often free-swimming and metamorphose into bottom-dwelling adults. In some species, the larval stage is omitted and the newly hatched young resemble small adults.

Class Asteroidea Also known as starfish, the sea stars in this class move and feed using the suckered tube feet along their arms. Most are predators that evert their stomach over sessile or slow-moving prey to begin digesting it. Some use their tube feet to prise open the shells of bivalves such as clams. Sea stars are usually vibrant colors such as red, orange, or purple and may have a smooth, spiny, or ridged surface.

Species 1,500

Worldwide; on the seafloor

Many arms The common sun star (Crossaster papposus) can have as many as 40 arms and grow to about 1 foot (30 cm) in diameter.

Class Ophiuroidea In contrast to sea stars, in which the arms grade into the central disk, the brittle stars and basket stars of Ophiuroidea have sharply demarcated arms. Rather than using their tube feet to crawl, they move by using any two of their flexible, jointed arms in a breast-stroke action. The class includes predators, scavengers, and filter-feeders.

Surface star The brittle star (Ophiura ophiura) usually lives on the surface of sandy or muddy sediment but may also burrow shallowly.

Species 2,000

Worldwide; on the seafloor

Class Echinoidea The sea urchins in this class have a spherical body protected by a skeletal case called a test, and long, movable spines. Sand dollars are flattened and covered in smaller spines. Many echinoids have a system of plates, muscles, and teeth known as the Aristotle's lantern, with which they scrape algae from rocks.

Species 950

Worldwide; on or in the seafloor

Rock burrower A coastal species, the purple sea urchin (Paracentrotus lividus) uses its spines and teeth to burrow into soft rocks where it is protected from waves.

Spiny starfish
Marthasterias glacialis, class Asteroidea

The spiny starfish can reach a diameter of 28 inches (70 cm)

Sand dollar (sea biscuit)
Clypeaster humilis, class Echinoidea

Reef sea urchin
Diadema setosum, class Echinoidea

Black brittle star
Ophiocomina nigra, class Ophiuroidea

The arms of brittle stars are easily broken off, hence the common name

Sea urchins move slowly using their tube feet and spines

Gorgon's head
Astrospartus mediterraneus, class Ophiuroidea

Goose-foot starfish
Anseropoda placenta, class Asteroidea

Heart urchin (sea potato)
Echinocardium cordatum, class Echinoidea

Sea pancake
Echinodiscus auritus, class Echinoidea

Edible sea urchin
Echinus esculentus, class Echinoidea

Cushion star
Culcita novaeguineae, class Asteroidea

An increase in the numbers of this coral predator has devastated large areas of the Great Barrier Reef

Crown-of-thorns starfish
Acanthaster planci, class Asteroidea

African red knob sea star
Protoreaster linckii, class Asteroidea

OTHER INVERTEBRATES

The preceding pages have covered eight major invertebrate phyla, as well as two subphyla of invertebrate chordates. There are, however, another 25 phyla of invertebrates, many of which are profiled in this chapter. Although the phylum Bryozoa contains 5,000 species, most of these minor groups are small—Phoronida (horseshoe worms), for example, contains a mere 20 species. The members of these phyla also tend to be physically small and are often microscopic. Most are marine, although many are found in fresh water and some occur on land. Often overlooked, the minor invertebrate phyla all display fascinating solutions to the challenges presented by their environment.

Ribbon worms Roughly 1,000 species of long ribbon worms make up the phylum Nemertea. The majority are marine, but some live in fresh water or moist soil. They trap or stab their invertebrate prey using a unique projectile proboscis.

Invading comb jelly Native to America's Atlantic coast, the sea walnut (*Mnemiopsis leidyi*) was accidentally introduced into the Black Sea in the early 1980s. Explosive population growth followed, and soon this predator of zooplankton and fish eggs and larvae had devastated the ecosystem and triggered fishery crashes.

Extreme survivors Water bears such as *Echiniscus testudo* (shown here magnified) are able to survive environmental stress by entering cryptobiosis, a death-like state. They can survive for years before reviving when conditions become favorable.

FACT FILE

Phylum Entoprocta Attached by a stalk to the substrate, goblet worms use a ring of mucus-secreting tentacles to filter particles from the water. Many species form colonies by budding.

Species 150

Worldwide; mostly on the seafloor

Phylum Tardigrada Unknown until 1773, following the invention of the microscope, water bears crawl over ocean sediment, soil, or plants with a slow, bear-like gait. These minute creatures occur in almost all aquatic and moist terrestrial environments.

Species 600

Worldwide; aquatic & moist land habitats

Phylum Ctenophora The marine comb jellies that make up this phylum swim by beating the fused cilia (tiny hairs) arranged in eight comb rows along their body. They engulf their prey directly or capture it with a pair of sticky, retractable tentacles.

Species 100

Worldwide; mostly planktonic

Water bear
Macrobiotus hufelandi, phylum Tardigrada

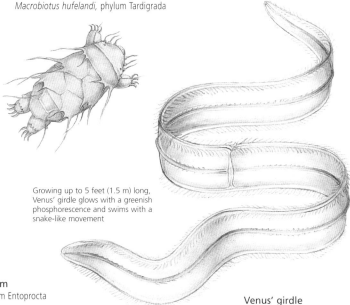

This solitary species can move about on its suckered stalk

Goblet worm
Loxosoma harmeri, phylum Entoprocta

Growing up to 5 feet (1.5 m) long, Venus' girdle glows with a greenish phosphorescence and swims with a snake-like movement

Venus' girdle
Cestus veneris, phylum Ctenophora

Melon jellyfish
Beroe cucumis, phylum Ctenophora

Can engulf prey (such as other comb jellies) that are as large as itself

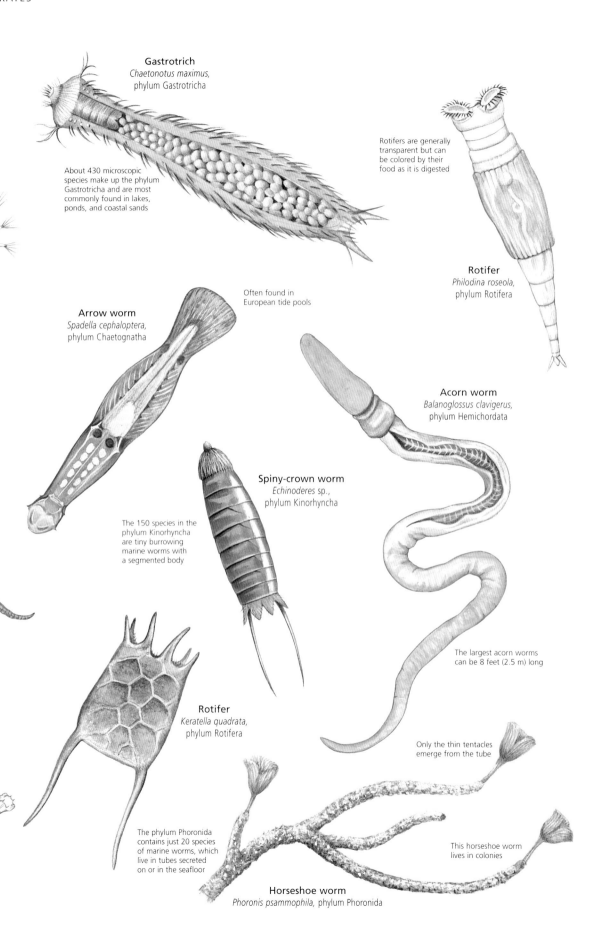

Gastrotrich
Chaetonotus maximus,
phylum Gastrotricha

About 430 microscopic species make up the phylum Gastrotricha and are most commonly found in lakes, ponds, and coastal sands

Rotifers are generally transparent but can be colored by their food as it is digested

Rotifer
Philodina roseola,
phylum Rotifera

Often found in European tide pools

Arrow worm
Spadella cephaloptera,
phylum Chaetognatha

Acorn worm
Balanoglossus clavigerus,
phylum Hemichordata

Spiny-crown worm
Echinoderes sp.,
phylum Kinorhyncha

The 150 species in the phylum Kinorhyncha are tiny burrowing marine worms with a segmented body

The largest acorn worms can be 8 feet (2.5 m) long

Rotifer
Keratella quadrata,
phylum Rotifera

Only the thin tentacles emerge from the tube

This horseshoe worm lives in colonies

The phylum Phoronida contains just 20 species of marine worms, which live in tubes secreted on or in the seafloor

Horseshoe worm
Phoronis psammophila, phylum Phoronida

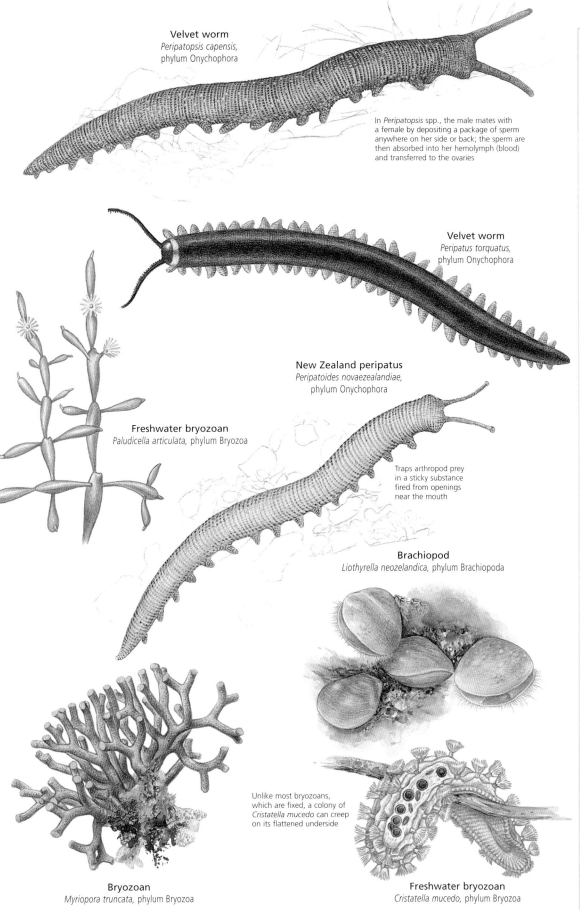

Velvet worm
Peripatopsis capensis,
phylum Onychophora

In *Peripatopsis* spp., the male mates with
a female by depositing a package of sperm
anywhere on her side or back; the sperm are
then absorbed into her hemolymph (blood)
and transferred to the ovaries

Velvet worm
Peripatus torquatus,
phylum Onychophora

New Zealand peripatus
Peripatoides novaezealandiae,
phylum Onychophora

Freshwater bryozoan
Paludicella articulata, phylum Bryozoa

Traps arthropod prey
in a sticky substance
fired from openings
near the mouth

Brachiopod
Liothyrella neozelandica, phylum Brachiopoda

Unlike most bryozoans,
which are fixed, a colony of
Cristatella mucedo can creep
on its flattened underside

Bryozoan
Myriopora truncata, phylum Bryozoa

Freshwater bryozoan
Cristatella mucedo, phylum Bryozoa

FACT FILE

Phylum Onychophora Since their thin,
non-waxy cuticle does little to prevent
water loss, the velvet worms of this
phylum are restricted to moist land
habitats. They are found in leaf litter
and soil and under stones and rotting
logs. To entangle insects and other
prey, velvet worms squirt out
sticky threads from slime glands
near the mouth, a technique that
can also be used in defense.

Species 70

Tropical & southern
temperate zones

Like velvet *Like other velvet
worms,* Peripatus trinitatis *is
covered in tiny projections that
give it a velvety appearance.
The cylindrical body can have
13 to 43 pairs of stumpy legs.*

Phylum Brachiopoda With their
bivalved shells, brachiopods look like
clams or mussels, but are in fact much
more closely related to bryozoans.
Both brachiopods and bryozoans filter
food particles from the water with
a lophophore, a crown of hollow
tentacles around the mouth.

Species 350

Worldwide; on the
seafloor at all levels
of the ocean

Burrowing stalk
The brachiopod Lingula
anatina *uses it fleshy stalk, or
pedicle, to burrow into sediment.
Most brachiopods, however,
attach themselves to rocks.*

Phylum Bryozoa Sometimes called
moss animals, bryozoans are tiny,
aquatic, and colonial. Most secrete a
protective covering around the body
with an opening for the lophophore
(feeding tentacles). Created by
budding, the colonies usually
grow as encrustations on
rocks or seaweed, or have
a branching form, but
a few are free-living.

Species 5,000

Worldwide; on the
bottom of aquatic
habitats

Fixed in place *The
bryozoan* Bowerbankia
imbricata *has an erect
branching form rising
from an attached stolon.*

GLOSSARY

abdomen The part of the body containing the digestive system and the reproductive organs. In insects and spiders, the abdomen makes up the rear of the body.

adaptation A change in an animal's behavior or body that allows it to survive and breed in new conditions.

amphibious Able to live on land and in water.

amplexus A breeding position of frogs and toads, in which the male holds the female with his front legs.

annulus (pl. annuli) A marking resembling a ring, as in turtle scutes, that is used in estimating age.

antenna (pl. antennae) A slender organ on an animal's head, used to sense smells and vibrations around it. Insects have two antennae.

aquatic Living all or most of the time in water.

arachnid An arthropod with four pairs of walking legs; includes spiders, scorpions, ticks, and mites.

arboreal Living all or most of the time in trees.

arthropod An animal with jointed legs and a hard exoskeleton.

biodiversity The total number of species of plants and animals in a particular location.

book lungs Lungs found in primitive insects and arachnids, consisting of "pages" of tissue forming the respiratory surface through which blood and oxygen circulate

camouflage The colors and patterns of an animal that enable it to blend in with the background. Camouflage conceals the animal from predators and helps it to ambush prey.

cephalic Of, relating to, or situated on or near the head.

cephalothorax In arachnids and crustaceans, a region of the body that combines the head and thorax. It is covered by a hard body case.

chelicera (pl. chelicerae) A pincer-like, biting mouthpart, such as a fang, as in spiders, ticks, scorpions, and mites.

chitin A hard, plastic-like substance that gives an exoskeleton its strength.

chrysalis The form taken by a butterfly in the pupal stage of its metamorphosis, or the case in which it undergoes this stage.

cloaca An internal chamber in amphibians and reptiles into which the contents of the reproductive ducts and the waste ducts empty before being passed from the body.

clutch The full and completed set of eggs laid by a female reptile or amphibian in a single nesting attempt.

cocoon In insects and spiders, a case made of silk used to protect themselves or their eggs. In amphibians, a protective case made of mud, mucus, or a similar material, in which the animal rests during estivation.

complete metamorphosis A form of development in which a young insect changes shape from an egg to a larva, to a pupa, to an adult. Insects such as beetles and butterflies develop by complete metamorphosis.

compound eye An eye that is made up from many smaller eyes, each with its own lens; found in most insects, but not in spiders.

crest In lizards, a line of large, scaly spines on the center of the neck and back. Some lizards can raise or lower the crest as a means of communication with others.

crocodilians Crocodiles, caimans, alligators, and gavials. Members of the order Crocodilia.

crustacean A mostly aquatic animal, such as a lobster, crab, or prawn, that has a hard external skeleton.

dewlap In a lizard, a flap of skin, sometimes brightly colored, on the throat. A dewlap usually lies close to the neck and can be extended to communicate with other lizards.

dimorphic Having two distinct forms within a species. Sexual dimorphism is the situation in which the male and female of a species differ in size and/or appearance.

dinosaurs A group of reptiles that dominated Earth from the Triassic to the Cretaceous Period (245–65 million years ago). The largest land animals that ever lived, dinosaurs are more closely related to today's birds and crocodilians than they are to other living reptiles.

dioecious Born either male or female and remaining that way through life.

display Behavior used by an animal to communicate with its own species, or with other animals.

Displays can include postures, actions, or showing brightly colored parts of the body, and may signal threat, defense, or readiness to mate.

diurnal Active during the day. Most reptiles are diurnal because they rely on the Sun's heat to provide energy for hunting and other activities.

dragline A strand of silk that spiders leave behind them as they move about.

drone A male honeybee. Drones mate with young queens but, unlike worker bees, they do not help in collecting food or maintaining the hive.

ecosystem A community of plants and animals and the environment to which they are adapted.

ectothermic Unable to internally regulate the body temperature, instead relying on external means such as the Sun, as in cold-blooded animals such as reptiles.

egg sac A silk bag that some spiders spin around their eggs. Some egg sacs are portable, so the eggs can be carried from place to place. Others are more like a blanket, and are attached to leaves or suspended from twigs.

egg tooth A special scale on the tip of the upper lip of a hatchling lizard or snake. It is used to break a hole in the egg so that the newborn animal can escape. The egg tooth falls off within a few days of hatching.

elytra The thickened front wings of beetles that cover and protect the back wings.

embryo An unborn animal in the earliest stages of development. An embryo may grow inside its mother's body, or in an egg outside her body.

endothermic Able to regulate the body temperature internally, as in warm-blooded animals.

estivate To spend a period of time in a state of inactivity to avoid unfavorable conditions. During times of drought, many frogs greatly reduce their overall metabolic rate and estivate underground until rain falls.

evolution Gradual change in plants and animals, over many generations, in response to their environment.

exoskeleton A hard external skeleton or body case. All arthropods are protected by an exoskeleton.

food chain A system in which one organism forms food for another,

which in turn is eaten by another, and so on along the food chain.

fossorial Adapted to digging or burrowing underground.

frill In a lizard, a collar around the neck. Like a crest or dewlap, a frill can be raised to signal to other lizards or to surprise a predator.

gastroliths Stones swallowed by animals such animals as crocodilians, that stay in the stomach to crush food and help digestion.

gestation period The period of time during which a female animal is pregnant with her young.

gills Organs that collect oxygen from water and are used for breathing. Gills are found in many aquatic animals, including some insects and the larvae of amphibians.

global warming The increase in the temperature of Earth and its lower atmosphere due to human activity such as deforestation, land degradation, intensive farming, and the burning of fossil fuels.

gravid Full of eggs; pregnant.

grub An insect larva, usually that of a beetle.

habitat The area in which an animal naturally lives. Many different kinds of animals live in the same environment (for example, a rain forest), but each kind lives in a different habitat within that environment.

hatchling A young animal, such as a reptile, that has recently hatched from its egg.

heat-sensitive pit Sense organs in some snakes that detect tiny changes in temperature.

hibernate To remain completely inactive during the cold winter months. Insects may hibernate.

hybrid The offspring of parents of two different species.

incomplete metamorphosis A system of development in which a young insect gradually changes shape from an egg, to a nymph, to an adult.

insectivore An animal that eats only insects or invertebrates.

introduced An animal or plant species imported from another place by humans and deliberately or accidentally released into a habitat.

invertebrate An animal with no backbone. Many invertebrates are soft-bodied animals, such as worms, leeches, or octopuses, but most have an exoskeleton, or hard external skeleton, such as insects.

Jacobson's organ Two small sensory pits on the top part of the mouth of snakes and lizards. They use this organ to analyze small molecules picked up from the air or ground with their tongue.

keratin A protein found in horns, hair, scales, feathers, and fingernails.

larva (pl. larvae) A young animal that looks completely different from its parents. An insect larva, sometimes called a grub, maggot, or caterpillar, changes into an adult by either complete or incomplete metamorphosis. In amphibians, the larval stage is the stage before metamorphosis that breathes with gills rather than lungs (for example, tadpoles).

live-bearing Giving birth to young that are fully formed.

maggot The larva of a fly.

mandibles Biting jaws of an insect.

metamorphosis A way of development in which an animal's body changes shape. Many invertebrates, including insects, and some vertebrates, such as amphibians, metamorphose as they mature.

migration A usually seasonal journey from one habitat to another. Many animals migrate vast distances to another location to find food, or to mate and lay eggs or give birth.

mollusk An animal, such as a snail or squid, with no backbone and a soft body that is often partly or fully enclosed by a shell.

molt To shed an outer layer of the body, such as hair, skin, scales, feathers, or the exoskeleton.

morph A color or other physical variation within, or a local population of, a species.

neoteny The retention of some immature or larval characteristics into adulthood. Some salamander species are usually or often neotenic.

niche The ecological role played by a species within an animal community.

nocturnal Active at night. Nocturnal animals have special adaptations, such as large, sensitive eyes or ears, to help them find their way in the dark.

nymph The young stage of an insect that develops by incomplete metamorphosis. Nymphs are often similar to adults, but do not have fully developed wings.

ocellus A kind of simple eye with a single lens. Insects usually have three ocelli on the top of their heads.

ovipositor A tubelike organ through which female insects lay their eggs. The stinger of bees and wasps is a modified ovipositor.

ovoviviparous Reproducing by giving birth to live young that have developed from eggs within the mother's body. The embryos may hatch as they are laid or soon after.

paleontology The scientific study of life in past geological periods.

parallel evolution The situation in which related groups living in isolation develop similar structures to cope with similar evolutionary pressures.

parasitism The situation in which an animal or plant lives and/or feeds on another living animal or plant, sometimes with harmful effects.

pedicel The narrow "waist" that connects an insect's head to its thorax, or a spider's cephalothorax to its abdomen.

pedipalp One of a pair of small, leglike organs on the head of insects and the cephalothorax of spiders and scorpions, used for feeling or for handling food. In spiders, they are also used for mating.

pheromone A chemical released by an animal that sends a signal and affects the behavior of others of the same species. Many animals use pheromones to attract mates, or to signal danger.

pollen A dustlike substance produced by male flowers, or by the male organs in a flower, and used in reproduction.

pollination The process by which the pollen produced by the male organs of a flower comes into contact with the female parts of the flower, thus fertilizing the flower and enabling seeds to form.

pore A minute opening, as in the skin of an animal or the leaf surface of a plant.

predator An animal that lives mainly by killing and eating other animals.

proboscis In insects, a long, tubular mouthpart used for feeding.

pupa (pl. pupae) The stage during which an insect transforms from a larva to an adult.

queen A female insect that begins a social insect colony. The queen is normally the only member of the colony that lays eggs.

rostrum A tubular, beak-like feeding organ on the head of some insects.

rudimentary Describes a simple, undeveloped, or underdeveloped part of an animal, such as an organ or wing.

scutes In a turtle or tortoise, the horny plates that cover the bony shell.

sedentary Having a lifestyle that involves little movement; also used to describe animals that do not migrate.

semi-aquatic Living some of the time in water, and some of the time on land.

silk A strong but elastic substance made by many insects and spiders. Silk is liquid until it leaves the animal's body.

social Living in groups. Social animals can live in breeding pairs, sometimes together with their young, or in a colony or herd of up to thousands of animals.

spawn To release eggs and sperm together directly into the water.

species A group of animals with very similar features that are able to breed together and produce fertile young.

spermatophore A container or package of sperm that is passed from male to female during mating.

spicule A minute, needle-like, siliceous or calcareous body, found in invertebrates.

spinnerets The finger-like appendages of spiders that are connected to silk glands, found near the tip of the abdomen.

spiracle A small opening that leads into the trachea, or breathing tube, of an insect or spider.

stereoscopic vision Vision in which both eyes face forward, giving an animal two overlapping fields of view and thus allowing it to judge depth.

stridulate To make a sound by scraping objects together. Many insects communicate in this way, some by scraping their legs against their body.

stylet A sharp mouthpart used for piercing plants or animals.

symbiosis An alliance between two species that is usually (but not always) beneficial to both. Animals form symbiotic relationships with plants, microorganisms, and other animals.

sympatric Of two or more species, occurring in the same area.

taxonomy The system of classifying living things into various groups and subgroups according to similarities in features and adaptations.

terrestrial Living all or most of the time on land.

tentacles On marine invertebrates, long, thin structures used to feel and grasp, or to inject venom. On caecilians, sensory organs located on the sides of the head, possibly used for tasting and smelling.

territory An area of land inhabited by an animal and defended against intruders. The area often contains all the living resources required by the animal, such as food and a nesting or roosting site.

thorax The middle part of an animal's body. In insects, the thorax is divided from the head with a narrow "waist," or pedicel. In spiders, the thorax and head make up a single unit.

torpid In a sleep-like state in which bodily processes are greatly slowed. Torpor helps animals to survive difficult conditions such as cold or lack of food. Estivation and hibernation are types of torpor.

trachea A breathing tube in an animal's body. Insects and some spiders have many small tracheae that spread throughout the body.

venom Poison injected by animals into a predator or prey through fangs, stingers, spines, or similar structures.

venomous Describes an animal that is able to inject venom into another. Venomous animals usually attack by biting or stinging.

vertebrate An animal with a backbone. All vertebrates have an internal skeleton of cartilage or bone. Fishes, reptiles, birds, amphibians, and mammals are vertebrates.

vertebral column The series of vertebrae running from head to tail along the back of vertebrates, and which encloses the spinal cord.

vestigial Relating to an organ that is non-functional or atrophied.

vibrissae Specialized hairs, or whiskers, that are extremely sensitive to touch.

worker A social insect that collects food and tends a colony's young, but which usually cannot reproduce.

INDEX

Page numbers in *italics* refer to illustrations, photographs, and to information in captions. Species are listed by both their common name/s and scientific name, although page references to scientific names often relate only to mentions in the text of common names.

ACKNOWLEDGMENTS

t=top; l=left; r=right; tl=top left; tcl=top center left; tr=top right; cl=center left; c=center; cr=center right; b=bottom; bl=bottom left; bcl=bottom center left; bc=bottom center; bcr=bottom center right; br=bottom right

AAP = Australian Associated Press; APL = Australian Picture Library; APL/CBT = Australian Picture Library/Corbis; APL/MP = Australian Picture Library/ Minden Pictures; AUS = Auscape International; AUST = Austral; BCC = Bruce Coleman Collection; GI = Getty Images; NHPA = Natural History Photographic Agency; NPL=Nature Picture Library; PL = photolibrary.com; SP=Seapics.com; WA = Wildlife Art Ltd.

PHOTOGRAPHS

Front cover GI

1b GI **2**l GI **4**c GI **8**l PL **10**cr APL/MP cr SP/Doug Perrine **12**c APL/MP **14**bl APL/CBT **15**bl, br, tl APL/CBT cl GI **17**tr APL/CBT **18**bl, tr APL/CBT br APL/MP **19**br APL/CBT tr GI **20**b, cr APL/CBT cl APL/MP **21**bcr, r APL/CBT **22**br, cr APL/CBT tr GI **23**b APL/CBT tr AAP **24**bc PL cl APL/ MP cr SP/Doug Perrine **32**bc, bl GI br APL/CBT tl PL **33**c, cl APL/MP **36**bc APL/CBT cr APL/MP **37**cr PL **38**bc APL/CBT cr GI tl APL/MP **44**bl, br, c, tr PL **52**c GI tr PL **60**bc APL/MP bl APL/CBT **61**br, cr PL t APL/MP **66**cl APL/MP tl AUS/Jean-Paul Ferrero **67**br AUS/Joe McDonald c GI tl PL tr APL/CBT **73**bc, cl GI bl APL/MP cr AUS/Paul de Oliveira/OSF tl AUS/Glen Threlfo tr APL/CBT **82**c GI **84**bc GI c APL/MP tl PL **85**tr APL/CBT **86**cl GI **87**br PL c GI tr APL/MP **88**b BCC tr GI **89**br APL/CBT tr GI **90**bc APL tr GI **91**br APL/CBT tr Esther Beaton **92**c, t APL/CBT **98**cr PL tl APL/CBT **99**cr PL **100**cl AUS/Satoshi Kuribayashi/OSF cr AUS/Kitchin & Hurst **101**c AUS/MichaelFogden/OSF r AUS/Stephen Dalton/OSF tl GI **107**b, c APL/CBT cl AUS/Kathie Atkinson tl AUS/Jean-Paul Ferrero **113**cl AUS/ Michael Fogden/OSF cr APL/CBT tl APL/MP **120**c PL **122**br AUS **123**bl AUS tr NPL **125**br APL/CBT tr PL **126**cl GI **127**bcl GI bcr APL/MP cr APL/CBT **128**bl APL/MP br APL/CBT cl, cr, tr APL/CBT **129**tr APL/CBT **130**tcl AUS tr APL/MP **131**c, tr APL/CBT **132**c APL/MP tr GI **135**l GI tc PL **136**c PL tr GI cl PL **144**c APL/CBT tr GI **145**cl, cr, tr APL/CBT tl PL **146**bc APL/MP c APL/CBT tr PL **147**c PL c GI tl APL/CBT **148**bc GI cl tr APL/CBT **152**bl AUS c PL **156**c, cr APL/CBT **157**c PL tr APL/CBT **158**c, cr APL/CBT **164**c PL tl AUS/Andrew Henely tr PL **165**bc APL/MP tc GI tl APL/CBT **166**c GI cl PL cl PL tr APL/MP **167**cl APL/CBT cr, tr PL **168**c AUS/Kathie Atkinson **169**cl PL tr GI **170**c GI tr APL/MP **171**c PL cl GI tr AUS/John Cancalosi **174**c AUST tl PL tr APL/CBT **175**cl PL tr APL/CBT **179**cr PL **182**c PL tr GI **186**c APL/MP tr GI **188**tl PL tr PL **191**c NHPA tr AUS/Pascal Goetgheluck **194**tr APL/CBT **195**cr, tr APL/MP cr GI **197**c GI cl PL tr AUS **358**bc PL

ILLUSTRATIONS

All illustrations © MagicGroup s.r.o. (Czech Republic) - www.magicgroup.cz; except for the following:

Susanna Addario 188bl; **Alistar Barnard/ Frank Knight/John Bull** 98bl, 124br cl, 151br; **Anne Bowman** 33bc, 170tl; **Simone End** 17bc, 124bl cl, 174cl; **Christer Eriksson** 31br, 34bl, 39br, 42cl; **Alan Ewart** 153cr; **Giuliano Fornari** 152cr, 179tr, 185cr, 37c, 169br; **John Francis/ Bernard Thornton Artists UK** 46bl, 61c cl; **Mike Golding** 142cl; **Ray Grinaway** 125tr, 164r; **Robert Hynes** 16br; **Ian Jackson** 168tr; **David Kirshner** 10bc, 85b, 86bcl cr, 165c; **David Kirshner/John Bull** 115bl, 108bl, 109br; **Frank Knight** 25br, 64cl, 138tcr; **James McKinnon** 36c; **Rob Mancini** 124cl, 152cr c cl tl, 153tr; **Tony Pyrzakowski** 17bcr, 163cr; **John Richards** 188cr; **Edwina Riddell** 188c, 25br, 30bl, 38cr tr, 40cl, 48bl, 59tr, 62bl cl; **Barbara Rodanska** 123cr; **Trevor Ruth** 78bl; **Peter Schouten** 51br; **Kevin Stead** 145c, 190bl, 24bl, 26bl, 29br, 35br, 36bl br, 37bl, 39cr, 41cr tr, 43br, 49cr, 50tl, 59br, 60c, 61tl, 65cr, 67cr, 75br, 79cr, 81cr, 98tr, 99cl, 113tr; **Guy Troughton** 52l, 66br; **WA/Robin Bouttell** 123cr; **WA/Sandra Doyle** 124tl, 148c, 150bcl bl, 153br; **WA/Ken Oliver** 46tl, 92bl, 100bl; **WA/Mick Posen** 16tr, 123br; **WA/Chris Shields** 92tl, 151tr cr, 173bl.

CAPTIONS

Page 1 The Amazon poison dart frog displays the kind of brilliant colors and bold patterns normally associated with butterflies. Skin secretions of these small frogs produce the most potent natural toxins known.

Page 2 Horns on the male Jackson's chameleon are not just ornamental. They are used in shoving contests with rivals for territory and mating rights.

Page 4–5 A bee balances on the petals of the cosmos flower, drinking its nectar. As the bee moves on, the dusting of pollen grains caught on its body will pollinate the next flower.

Page 6–7 The color, delicacy, and size of soft coral make it one of the most spectacular animals found on coral reefs.

Page 8–9 Ants are members of a highly social family of insects. The collaborative efforts of leaf-cutter ants ensure they have a constant source of food.

Page 12–13 The green iguana is the largest South American lizard. An agile climber, it is never far from trees.

Page 82–83 A green frog peeps from under a lily pad on Highbank Lake in Manistee National Forest, Michigan, United States.

Page 120–121 Gypsy moth caterpillars are able to consume as much as one square foot ($0.1m^2$) of leaves per day. They have become a serious pest to trees such as the oak in the United States.